Vincent E. Petrucci

McGRAW-HILL PUBLICATIONS IN THE
AGRICULTURAL SCIENCES
LEON J. COLE, Consulting Editor

# APPLIED ENTOMOLOGY

*This book is produced in full compliance
with the government's regulations for con-
serving paper and other essential materials.*

# APPLIED ENTOMOLOGY

An Introductory Textbook of Insects
in their Relations to Man

BY

## H. T. FERNALD, PH. D.

*Emeritus Professor of Entomology, Massachusetts State College,
and Onetime Entomologist of the Massachusetts Agricultural
Experiment Station*

AND

## HAROLD H. SHEPARD, PH. D.

*Assistant Professor of Entomology
University of Minnesota*

FOURTH EDITION
FOURTH IMPRESSION

McGRAW-HILL BOOK COMPANY, INC.
NEW YORK AND LONDON
1942

*To the memory of*

## PROFESSOR CHARLES H. FERNALD

one of the first teachers of Economic Entomology
to college students, in this country

# PREFACE

In the preface to the third edition of this book it was stated that the previous ten years had seen great advances in our knowledge of insects and how to control them. Now after seven years more the statement still holds true, especially in the field of insect control.

Although lead arsenate and petroleum oils remain the leading insecticides for use against chewing and sucking insects, respectively, other materials such as cryolite and rotenone-containing preparations have within a few years become standard for the control of numerous pests. Because the development of synthetic organic chemicals for use as insecticides has been made easier by important governmental and commercial researches, more and better materials seem likely to come into general use in this field.

New insecticides have been discussed in this book only if their use is accepted generally as an improvement over the previous control methods. The authors have preferred to give but slight reference to methods and materials of very recent development which need further trial to prove them practical.

Special attention has been paid to bringing the control methods up to date wherever any changes have become general; to adding new insects of importance as well as new facts about the insects discussed in the previous editions; and to changing the sequence of the orders to express their relationship better. Chapters V to IX, dealing with the economic importance of insects and with insecticides and other methods of insect control, have been rewritten, and the chapters on the Hymenoptera and on Animals Other Than Insects have been rearranged. Nearly one third of the book has been rewritten in order to include an adequate treatment of the new information in this field. New illustrations have been substituted in many cases for less satisfactory ones and worn-out figures have been replaced through the kindness of their owners and publishers. Reference to the sources of the illustrations is made in connection with the individual figures. Those not otherwise credited are original.

As in the last edition the common names of insects approved by the American Association of Economic Entomologists have been used. Scientific names, however, are still being changed for one reason or another, in some cases being changed back to a former name after several

years.   How much or how soon this unsettled condition can be improved
is a question.   The names used here must be considered only as the
accepted ones at the present moment.

In the preparation of this text many entomologists have been con-
sulted about those parts related to their special fields.   Their hearty
cooperation, together with the kindness of the persons who have in so
many ways aided the authors in their work, is gratefully acknowledged
here.

Every text of this kind must certainly contain errors.   The authors
would be glad to have their attention called to any found, or to changes
that would improve the book for its intended use.

H. T. Fernald,
Harold H. Shepard.

Winter Park, Florida,
St. Paul, Minnesota,
   *May*, 1942.

# CONTENTS

ix

# APPLIED ENTOMOLOGY

## CHAPTER I

### INSECTS AND OTHER ANIMALS

Among the larger groups of animals now recognized by science, the one known as the Chordata is naturally the most familiar, including the mammals, birds, reptiles and fishes, besides numerous forms less well known. Another group, also familiar, called the Mollusca, includes the snails, clams, etc. The starfish and sea urchins, often seen at the seashore, belong with other similar animals to a third group called the Echinodermata, and a multitude of tiny beings, almost all too small to be seen without the aid of a microscope, are included in the group Protozoa. A fifth large group is composed mainly of soft, jelly-like animals, the more common larger members being called jellyfish, and to this group the name Coelenterata is applied. Several other groups including various kinds of worms and less familiar forms are also known.

The largest group of all, however, is the Arthropoda, its members found in the seas, in fresh water, on land or even flying freely; a group with remarkable differences of structure, and so abundant that all the other animals taken together are less than one-sixth as many as the arthropods. Well-known members of this group are the lobsters, crayfish and crabs; scorpions, spiders, mites, ticks and "daddy longlegs"; the centipedes and millipedes; and last, and most abundant of all, the insects.

No one feature will serve to separate the arthropods from all other animals, but the possession by an animal of several of those here described will enable the observer to determine in each case whether he is examining one of this group. In arthropods the body is composed of a series of more or less similar pieces or segments, placed one behind another, the line of attachment of these to each other being usually somewhat evident on parts of the body at least. This character is also shown, and indeed more clearly, in some worms, such as the common earthworm. Another character of the arthropods is the presence of jointed legs (or appendages of some kind), as is indicated by the name of the group, and these are not possessed by worms. The surface of the body is covered by a secretion

1

which hardens on exposure to the air, forming an outside shell or external skeleton (exoskeleton), there being practically no internal structures supporting the soft organs within this shell except as ingrowths from the outside.

In the possession of this external skeleton these animals have a seeming resemblance to the shells (Mollusca), but the materials of which

the skeleton is composed are quite different, being largely calcium carbonate in the Mollusca, and chitin which somewhat resembles horn in its nature, sometimes with calcareous salts deposited in it, in the Arthropoda. In its simplest members the arthropod body is also practically bilaterally symmetrical, though this condition is concealed somewhat by secondary changes in many of the group. The possession of a bilaterally symmetrical body consisting of a series of segments, an exoskeleton of chitin and the presence of jointed legs are, then, distinctive features of the arthropods.

FIG. 1.—Crayfish (*Crustacea*); about one-half natural size.

To separate the various groups of arthropods, other characters must be used. Aside from several small sections not often seen, there are five large and important divisions which call for recognition. These are the Crustacea, including the lobster, crab, beach flea, sowbug and many others; the Diplopoda or millipedes; the Chilopoda or centipedes; the Hexapoda or insects; and the Arachnida, including the scorpions, pseudo-scorpions, spiders, mites, ticks, etc.

The Crustacea (Fig. 1) are mainly water-inhabiting animals which breathe either by gills or, in the smaller forms, through the surface of the body. In those cases where its members live on land (Fig. 2) the gills are still present, though in a somewhat modified condition. They have numerous pairs of legs and generally two pairs of antennae (jointed "feelers"). Often some of the body segments are fused with the head to form a cephalothorax.

FIG. 2.—Sowbug; slightly enlarged. A crustacean living on land.

The Diplopoda (Fig. 3) are land animals breathing by air tubes opening on the sides of the body, these tubes carrying the air into all the internal parts of the animal. The head bears a pair of antennae and is followed by a series of segments all practically alike and each, except the first three, with two pairs of legs. The reproductive organs open

far forward on the body. In most of the more common members of
this group the body is quite cylindrical, and when disturbed the animal
usually curls up in a sort of close spiral. Small diplopods about the

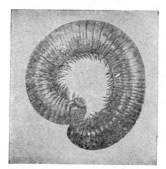

Fig. 3.—Millipede (*Diplopoda*);
natural size. (*From Folsom.*)

Fig. 4.—Centipede (*Chilopoda*);
about three-quarters natural size.

diameter of the lead of a pencil and gray in color are often found boring
into potatoes and roots in the ground in the fall and are sometimes
wrongly called wireworms. The common name, millipede, refers to
the large number of legs possessed by these animals.

Fig. 5.—Hairy
spider (*Arachnida*);
about natural size.

Fig. 6.—Large-bodied
spider (*Arachnida*); about
natural size.

The Chilopoda are also land animals (Fig. 4). Like the diplopods
they have antennae and breathe by air tubes, and the body segments are
practically all alike. The general form, however, is rather flattened;
each segment bears only one pair of legs, and the reproductive organs
open at the hinder end of the body. The front leg on each side is modified to serve as a poison claw. The numerous legs present in these
animals have resulted in their receiving the common name, centipede.

The Arachnida (Figs. 5, 6, 7 and 8) generally have the segments of the body grouped into two sections called the cephalothorax and abdomen. No antennae are present and the eight legs are all attached to the first-

Fig. 7.— Adult female castor-bean tick (*Arachnida*); natural size. (*From U.S. Dept. Agr. Farmers' Bull.* 1057.)

Fig. 8.—Adult female European dog tick (*Arachnida*); natural size. (*From U.S. Dept. Agr. Farmers' Bull.* 1057.)

named section. They breathe by air tubes somewhat similar to those of the other groups; by sacs containing many thin plates resembling leaves of a book, whence these structures take the name of book lungs; or, in the smallest forms, directly through the body surface. In the mites there is no evident division of the body into sections. Though most of the group are land forms, a few are aquatic.

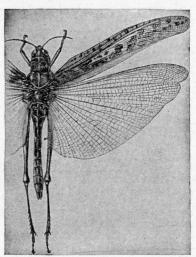

Fig. 9.—Grasshopper (*Hexapoda*); with wings spread. (*From Folsom.*)

In the Hexapoda or insects (Fig. 9) the segments of the body are grouped in three distinct sections: the head, thorax and abdomen. A pair of antennae is (with rare exceptions) present on the head; the six legs are attached to the thorax, as are the four wings usually present; the animals breathe by air tubes; and, although living under a great diversity of conditions, the group as a whole is emphatically a terrestrial one, though in many cases their early life is spent in water.

### DISTINCTIVE CHARACTERS OF THE MAIN ARTHROPOD GROUPS

| | Where found | Body divisions | Antennae | Legs | Breathe by | Reproductive organs open |
|---|---|---|---|---|---|---|
| Crustacea | Mainly in water | Head and body: often a cephalothorax | Two pairs generally | Numerous: may be built for swimming | Gills or through body surface (rarely by air tubes) | Well forward |
| Diplopoda | On land | Head and body | One pair | Many : two pairs on most body segments | Air tubes | Near head |
| Chilopoda | On land | Head and body | One pair | Numerous: one pair on each body segment | Air tubes | Next to last body segment |
| Arachnida | Mainly on land | Cephalothorax and abdomen (no divisions in a few cases) | None | Eight: joined to cephalothorax | Air tubes, book lungs or body surface | Front part of abdomen (a few exceptions) |
| Hexapoda | Mainly on land | Head, thorax, abdomen | One pair | Six: joined to thorax | Air tubes | Near hind end of abdomen |

# CHAPTER II

## THE INSECT: ITS EXTERNAL STRUCTURE

Bringing together the facts already stated about insects we find that an adult insect is (1) a bilaterally symmetrical animal; (2) consisting of a series of segments one behind another; (3) that these segments are grouped into three regions, the head in front, followed in order by the thorax and the abdomen as shown in Fig. 10; (4) that the animal is covered by a skeleton, shell-like in that it is on the outside of the body, but horny in its nature; (5) that attached to the thorax are three pairs of jointed

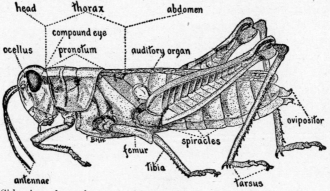

Fig. 10.—Side view of grasshopper with parts named. (*From Walden, Conn. Geol. & Nat. Hist. Surv., Bull.* 16.)

legs; (6) that a pair of antennae, (7) mouth parts (8) and usually two pairs of wings are present; (9) that it breathes through air tubes; and (10) that the reproductive organs open near the hinder end of the body.

In the body of the adult insect there are apparently from 7 to 15 segments; 1 in the head, 3 in the thorax and from 3 to 11 in the abdomen. In the egg, however, the embryo shows the presence of 6 (some investigators think 7) segments in the head, 3 in the thorax and 11 or 12 in the abdomen, indicating that the original total number was 21 (or 22). This change to the adult has been brought about in the head by an extreme amount of fusion and condensation and in the abdomen partly by fusion, partly by a sort of telescoping or gradual shifting of one segment within another until it has been partly or entirely concealed.

The skeleton of the body, or cuticula as it is called, supports and protects the soft, living tissues within. It rests on the outer surface of

6

a layer of living cells, the hypodermis. It seems to be formed in part from a fluid poured out from the hypodermis and in part by a transformation of a portion of the hypodermis cells themselves. The cuticula hardens quickly after its production and consists quite largely, at least, of a nitrogenous substance called chitin (pronounced ky'-tin). It varies in thickness and is flexible where movement is needed, but thicker, more rigid and usually darker colored elsewhere. The hypodermis along certain lines forms folds which project inward, carrying its cuticular secretion along with it. Where these infoldings occur at places that need to be movable the cuticula remains flexible, thus forming the movable joints; along the other infoldings it hardens (becomes sclerotized) and becomes rigid and such places show on the surface only as slight grooves or scratches called sutures. These sutures and the joint lines divide the cuticula into areas called plates or sclerites. The sutures and joint lines are

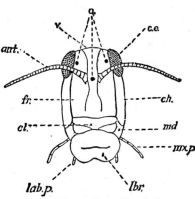

Fig. 11.—Front view of head of a grasshopper showing a hypognathous head: *ant.*, antenna; *c. e.*, compound eye; *ch.*, cheek; *cl.*, clypeus; *fr.*, frons; *lab. p.*, labial palpus; *lbr.*, labrum; *md.*, mandible; *mx. p.*, maxillary palpus; *o.*, ocelli; *v.*, vertex.

sufficiently regular in position in most insects to make them convenient landmarks in descriptions. The sclerites on the back of each segment are usually together termed the notum or tergum; those on each side, the pleuron; and those below, the sternum.

In the head (Figs. 10 and 11) the sutures are few in number, so only a few plates or sclerites are generally in evidence. In the thorax they are more numerous, and in the abdomen often only a dorsal and a ventral sclerite for each segment are found. Occasionally weakly sclerotized areas are quite large (queen white ant, Fig. 46a) and elastic. Usually the elasticity of these places, as, for example, the portions connect-

Fig. 12.—Side view of beetle (*Lucanus dama* Fab.) showing a prognathous head.

ing the segments, is rather slight. Spines, hairs, scales or other structures are often present on the cuticula, sometimes entirely concealing its surface and its sutures.

The heads of different insects vary much in form and in the location of the mouth. In some cases this is on the underside (Fig. 10); in others

(Fig. 12) it is practically on the front. Heads with the mouth beneath are called hypognathous; those with it in front are prognathous. Structures found on the head are a pair of antennae, the two compound eyes, ocelli and the mouth parts. On the thorax are the wings and legs; on the abdomen are various organs such as the ovipositor, sting, cerci and styli, present in some cases, absent in others.

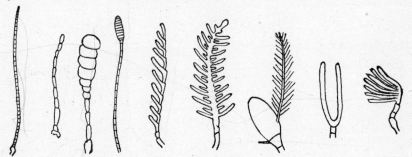

FIG. 13.—Different forms of insect antennae.

Antennae are nearly always present. They are usually slender, jointed and therefore more or less flexible organs, varying greatly in the number of segments composing them. They are sometimes very short; sometimes long; often thread-like; sometimes enlarged near the tip; in many cases with fine branches either on one or both sides, so that they resemble feathers or plumes; rarely they fork; in fact they are of many forms (Figs. 13 and 14). Sense organs are present on them for the sense of touch, and probably also for smell and hearing, at least in some cases.

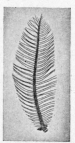

FIG. 14.— Antenna of cecropia moth. (*Samia cecropia* L.) About twice natural size.

The eyes are of two kinds. There is a pair of compound eyes, each of which is a group of similar structures which usually are like tall, slender pyramids in form. Only the bases of these pyramids show on the surface, the remainder being within the head. The bases, closely pressed together, are usually more or less hexagonal, and their outlines can often be easily seen with a magnifying glass. They are called facets, and the eyes themselves are sometimes termed the faceted eyes.

The other kind of eyes, called ocelli, may be absent or, if present, may vary in number in different insects, three being perhaps the most usual. Each, as seen from the surface, is a nearly circular, convex spot about the size of one of the facets of a compound eye. It may be larger than this but is never equal to an entire compound eye in size. The cuticula of the surface of the body is transparent where it covers the surface of an eye, permitting access of light to the sensory structures within; elsewhere it is usually pigmented and rather opaque.

The mouth parts of insects vary extremely in their structure. Apparently the original mouth parts were for biting and chewing, and this type is very common. In some groups, however, they have been transformed into a sucking apparatus. Biting mouth parts, being the more primitive and simple, are described here, while sucking mouth parts

FIG. 15.—Three types of insect mandibles, greatly enlarged. Somewhat diagrammatic.

having been differently transformed in different groups will be taken up in connection with those groups.

In front of (in hypognathous heads) or above the mouth opening (prognathous heads) is the front lip or labrum. It is a thin flap, hinged to the skeleton of the head, and moves forward and backward. It is often more or less divided by a central notch at the middle of its free edge. Its inner surface, forming the roof of the mouth, is often called the epipharynx.

At the sides of the mouth opening, immediately behind the labrum, is a pair of jaws, the mandibles. These differ greatly in form in different insects (Fig. 15). They are often stout, heavy structures with crushing faces bearing blunt projections or teeth; sometimes they are long, curved and rather slender. In general their form is adapted to the feeding habits of the insect.

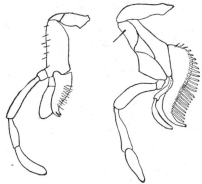

FIG. 16.—Two types of insect maxilla greatly enlarged. Somewhat diagrammatic.

Immediately behind each mandible at the side of the mouth is a second appendage, the maxilla. This differs markedly from the mandible, being much weaker and composed of a number of pieces (Fig. 16). The tips and outer internal margins of the maxillae usually bear numerous spines or hairs, but this condition varies according to the nature of the food of the insect. Attached on the outer side of each maxilla, not far from where the latter articulates with the head, is a sort of tiny antenna-like structure consisting of from one to six (usually five) segments, which is called the maxillary palpus.  The function of the maxillae appears to be to hold and retain the food in the mouth while it is being worked upon by the mandibles, and also to aid these in breaking it up.  The presence of sense organs on the maxillary palpi suggests that these are possibly concerned with the sense of smell.  Both mandibles and maxillae move sideways.

Behind the maxillae and closing the mouth opening behind, is the hinder lip or labium (Fig. 17).  This was evidently once a pair of jaws somewhat similar to the maxillae, but with no mouth cavity between to separate them, their inner edges have grown together to varying degrees in different insects.  In some, only one or two of the pieces nearest the head have fused; in others, fusion all the way to the tip has been accomplished; and all intermediate stages also occur, thus producing a structure which now moves forward and backward like the front lip, but which may be complete, or partly or almost entirely cleft in the middle line.

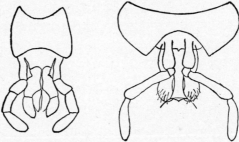

Fig. 17.—Two types of insect labium much enlarged.  Somewhat diagrammatic.

Like the maxilla the labium has a palpus on each side arising from near its base, and composed of three (rarely four) segments.  The function of these labial palpi appears to be similar to that of the maxillary palpi.

Near the base of the labium on its inner or mouth side there is frequently a fleshy swelling more or less covered by bristles or hairs, which is called the hypopharynx, lingua or tongue.  It varies greatly in size and form.

The thorax has its three segments usually quite clearly marked.  Each segment bears a pair of legs, but the prothorax, or first of the three behind the head, bears no wings.  On the second, or mesothorax, and on the third, or metathorax, both wings and legs occur in the majority of insects.  There is a tendency in some groups, carried farthest in the higher Hymenoptera, for the first segment of the abdomen to consolidate more closely with the metathorax than with the second abdominal segment, which in such cases is often slender (Figs. 364, 376) and gives thereby a semidetached appearance to the rest of the abdomen, as though the line of division between thorax and abdomen were at that place instead of farther forward. The first abdominal segment, when seemingly more a part of the thorax than of the abdomen, is called the median segment or propodeum.

The three pairs of legs may be quite similar or differ widely, according to the uses to which they are put. In running and walking insects they are usually most similar; but when, for example, the forelegs are used for capturing other insects, their form will depart greatly from that of the others. The jumping power of the grasshopper is due to the great development of its hind legs as compared with its others. Different types of legs are shown in Fig. 18.

Whatever may be the variations in form and details of the legs, all are composed of a definite number of pieces or segments, connected by hinge joints so arranged that, by combining the motions of these, a leg can be placed in nearly any position desired.

The leg (Fig. 19) is composed of a coxa, a trochanter (two in a few cases), a femur, a tibia and a tarsus. The last is really not a single segment but a row of from one to five, small, and on the whole rather resembling each other.

The coxa is the segment that articulates with the body, frequently partly lying in a more or less cup-shaped hollow of the latter. It may be short or long and is generally freely movable on the body and powerful. The trochanter is usually small and may not be visible on all sides of the leg. It is followed by the femur, generally the largest and stoutest, but not often the longest leg segment. The tibia is in most cases quite long, more slender than the femur and often provided with downwardly projecting spines or other structures which are of assistance to the insect in climbing plant stems and other objects, to help prevent slipping. The tarsal segments are generally rather small, short, tend to be broadest at their outer ends and vary greatly in details of structure. At the end of the last a pair of claws is generally found, and between them a sort of pad or cushion, the pulvillus. Sometimes there are three of these, in which case the outer ones are called the pulvilli and the middle one the empodium. Where the tarsi are reduced to a small number of segments, only one claw may be present.

The wings are chitinous outgrowths from the body which vary much in size and form in different insects. Each consists of two delicate membranes in contact with each other except along certain lines (Fig. 20). Along these lines each membrane thickens and also rises above the general surface, so that if the two membranes could be separated and examined from the inner surface, they would appear uniform except for grooves with thickened sides and bottoms, running here and there. When the membranes are brought together again, these grooves combining form hollow rods which, being stronger than the rest of the membrane, serve as its support and hold it stiff.   These hollow rods are usually called veins or nerves, though they are nothing of the sort.   The main

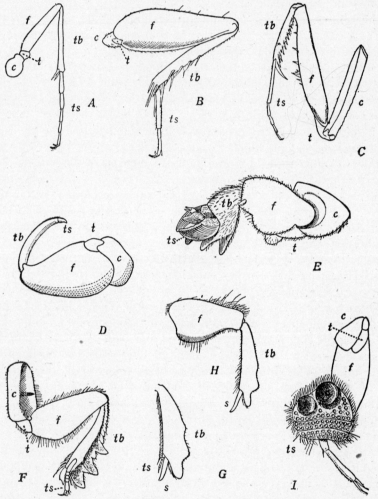

Fig. 18.—Different forms of insect legs: *A, Cicindela sexguttata* Fab. (beetle); *B, Nemobius fasciatus* De G. (cricket) hind leg; *C, Stagmomantis carolina* L. (mantis) foreleg; *D, Pelocoris femoratus* P. B. (carnivorous bug) foreleg; *E, Gryllotalpa hexadactyla* Perty (mole cricket) foreleg; *F, Canthon lævis* Dru. (a digging beetle) foreleg; *G, Phanœus carnifex* L. (a digging beetle) fore tibia and tarsus of female; *H,* same, fore tibia of male; *I, Dytiscus fasciventris* Say, male (water beetle) foreleg.   *c,* coxa; *f,* femur; *s,* spine; *t,* trochanter; *tb,* tibia; *ts,* tarsus.   (*From Folsom.*)

and largest veins arise at the base of the wing and extend outward, branching as they go, and some branch several times before they reach the wing margin (Fig. 21).   Cross veins also occur, connecting the radiating main veins or their branches. Areas of membrane between veins are termed cells and where entirely surrounded by veins are called closed cells. These may be relatively few or many, according to the number of veins and their branches present. The arrangement and number of the chief veins and their branches are of importance in identifying insects.

There is usually a point or tip called the apex, somewhere along the margin of the wing, though frequently the outline is so rounded that the exact apex is uncertain. The front margin of the wing from where it joins the body to where the edge begins to turn backward (in an extended wing) is called the costa.

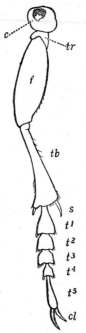

Wings are entirely absent in some groups of insects. It is probable that some of these are direct descendants of the earliest forms before wings were developed. In other cases where wings are absent this condition is associated with a parasitic life where they might be a distinct disadvantage, or with peculiar habits which would render them useless or even inconvenient; in such cases they appear gradually to have become lost. In the flies the hinder pair is modified, forming small structures called halteres.

The abdomen does not usually show great differences in its segments except in those near the hinder end, which may be modified for various purposes. Generally a dorsal plate (notum or tergum) and a ventral plate (sternum) are the only two skeletal plates evident in a segment. Small openings, usually a pair in each, or at least in some of the segments, are the openings of the breathing organs, and these also occur on some of the thoracic segments where they are ordinarily less noticeable than on the abdomen.

Fig. 19.—Leg of a beetle showing parts: *c*, coxa; *cl*, claws; *f*, femur; *s*, spine or spur; $t^1 - t^5$, tarsal segments; *tb*, tibia; *tr*, trochanter. (*From Folsom.*)

Legs are very rarely present on the abdomen in adult insects but are often found in the earlier stages (Fig. 22). At the end of the abdomen

Fig. 20.—Diagram of cross section of an insect wing showing the two membranes somewhat separated and the ways in which the veins are formed. (*Modified from Woodworth.*)

in the females of those insects which lay their eggs within objects is a combination of pieces known as an ovipositor. It usually consists of about three pairs of parts, long or short, slender or stout, as the case may be, for the purpose of making a hole or sawing a slit in the object in which the eggs are placed and in guiding the eggs into the hole thus made.　In one group which has apparently changed its habits and no longer needs

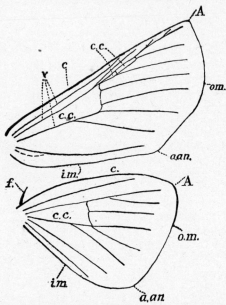

Fig. 21.—Diagram of the margins and veins in the wings of moths: *A*, apex; *a. an.*, anal angle; *c.*, costa; *c.c.*, closed cell; *f.*, frenulum; *i.m.*, inner margin; *o.m.*, outer margin; *v.*, veins.

to make holes for egg laying, the ovipositor being unnecessary for this purpose has been transformed into a sting.

Fig. 22.—Larva of cecropia moth showing abdominal legs.　Two-thirds natural size.

A pair of many-segmented, antenna-like structures, sometimes short, sometimes long, may occur at the end of the abdomen (Fig. 40), and these are called cerci.　They probably serve as organs of touch and possibly also of smell in some cases.

# CHAPTER III

## THE INSECT: ITS INTERNAL STRUCTURE

Few of the internal structures of insects are of any great importance from the standpoint of control methods, but some knowledge of them and their arrangement is desirable.

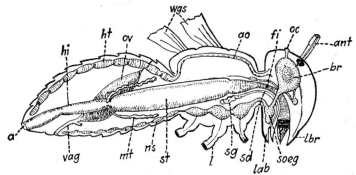

FIG. 23.—Diagrammatic longitudinal section of an insect to show the arrangement of the internal organs: *a*, anus; *ant*, antenna; *ao*, aorta; *br*, brain; *fi*, fore intestine; *hi*, hind intestine; *ht*, heart; *l*, leg; *lab*, labium; *lbr*, labrum; *mt*, Malpighian tube; *ns*, nervous system; *oc*, ocellus; *ov*, ovary; *sd*, salivary duct; *sg*, salivary gland; *soeg*, subesophageal ganglion; *st*, stomach (mid intestine); *vag*, vagina; *wgs*, wings. (*After Berlese.*)

**Digestive organs** (Fig. 23).—The alimentary canal extends from the mouth through about the center of the body to the anus at the hinder end. In those insects whose food is most concentrated (Fig. 24), it is in its simplest form and is but little, if any, longer than the body. In those which feed on less concentrated food (Fig. 25), the necessity for a greater digestive and absorptive surface has resulted in an increase of its length and the accommodation of this within the body by the production of loops and coils.

In the embryo the alimentary canal forms as three separate sections which connect later. One of these is an ingrowth from the surface where the mouth is to be; another and similar ingrowth occurs where the anus forms; and a third, forming earlier than the other two, arises as two masses of cells, one near each end of the embryo, which move inward and toward each other, unite, and surround the yolk. Later, when this has been absorbed, a space is left with which the two ingrowths already mentioned connect, the hollow centers of all three joining to form the tube through which the food travels. The ingrowth from the mouth is

15

usually called the fore intestine, the central portion the mid intestine, and the ingrowth from the anus the hind intestine. The first and last of these begin to grow inward from the surface of the body after that surface has begun the formation of its chitinous exoskeleton, and accordingly they also have this power, and line the inside of the parts of the canal which they form, with chitin. In that portion of the canal termed the mid intestine, however, this power does not appear to be present, and the mid intestine is without this lining.

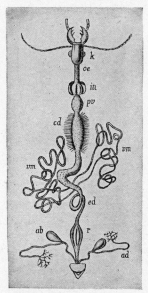

The mid intestine forms the stomach of the adult insect; the fore intestine forms those parts of the alimentary canal from the mouth to the stomach; and the hind intestine those from the stomach to the anus. Each of these sections may sometimes have portions differing in structure, producing a greater or lesser number of subdivisions. Thus the fore intestine, by differences of structure, may sometimes consist of a mouth cavity, esophagus, crop and proventriculus; the stomach may develop side pouches or gastric caeca; and the hind intestine is often separable by differences of structure into an ileum, colon and rectum.

FIG. 24.—Alimentary canal of a carnivorous beetle: *ad,* anal glands; *cd,* stomach; *ed,* hind intestine; *in,* crop; *k,* head and mouth-parts; *oe,* esophagus; *pv,* proventriculus; *r,* rectum; *vm,* Malpighian tubes. (*Modified from Lang's Lehrbuch.*)

Lined as these parts are by chitin which often bears rough, tooth-like projections and spines, some persons have suggested that in insects where these structures are present in the fore intestine, the food is masticated more thoroughly and mixed with digestive juices before it reaches the stomach. In the stomach, digestion is probably completed and absorption at least begun, but the length of the hind intestine in many insects suggests the idea that absorption in those cases has not been completed when the food leaves the stomach but continues in the hind intestine.

Opening into the mouth is a tube leading to the salivary glands, which generally lie in the front of the thorax and appear to have a similar function to those in man. In some cases other glands for different purposes are also present in the head or front of the thorax and open into the mouth.

Some of the poisons used in control measures are swallowed by the insect, passing to the stomach and there are dissolved by the digestive juices. Thus dissolved, they set up inflammation of the stomach walls and finally cause death.    Poisons acting in this way are called stomach poisons.

**Breathing organs.**—Respiration in insects is accomplished by a method which is nearly unique.    The oxygen needed, instead of being drawn into lungs and there being taken up by the blood and carried to

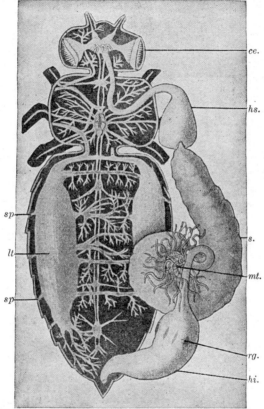

Fig. 25.—Internal anatomy of the honeybee showing alimentary canal, tracheal and nervous systems; *ce.*, compound eye; *hi.*, hind intestine; *hs.*, honey stomach; *lt*, lateral trachea (enlarged); *mt.*, Malpighian tubes; *rg.*, rectal glands; *s*, stomach; *sp*, spiracles. (*Modified from Leuckart's Wandtafeln.*)

the parts of the body where it is needed, as in man, is carried directly to those parts by a system of air tubes which open along the sides of the body (Fig. 26).    Here the air enters the tubes and proceeds through them to where it is utilized.    The openings by which the air enters are called spiracles, and these occur in pairs on some of the thoracic and most of the abdominal segments, varying somewhat in number and in position on the segment in different insects.    The spiracles often have valves by which they can be more or less completely closed at will.

Each spiracle opens into a short tube or trachea which, with the others of that side, soon joins a similar tube running along the side of the body and quite close to its surface. From these longitudinal tracheae, branches pass off in various directions and in turn branch again and again until every part of the body is reached by its air supply. The tracheae frequently enlarge here and there, forming so-called air sacs.

The tracheae are lined by chitin connected with that of the surface of the body. In these tubes, however, it is formed with spiral thickenings which act like a spring, keeping the tracheae open when not under pressure. There is probably considerable pressure on them in different places by the movements of various parts of the body in walking and other activities, as well as by regular respiratory movements, and the resulting temporary variations in diameter aid in the circulation of air in these tubes.

Not only are the tracheae of use in carrying oxygen to all parts of the body, but they also receive much of the carbon dioxide gas produced by the activities of the cells and permit it to escape through the spiracles from the body, thus performing both of the functions which the blood, so far as gases are concerned, accomplishes in man. Blood then, in insects, does not have an important respiratory function.

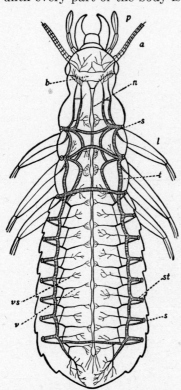

FIG. 26.—Diagram showing arrangement of the main tracheal tubes in an insect; *a*, antenna; *b*, brain; *l*, leg; *n*, nerve cord; *p*, palpus; *s*, spiracle; *st*, branch from main lateral trunk; *t*, to spiracle; *v*, ventral branch; *vs*, visceral branch. (*After Kolbe, from Folsom.*)

The destruction of insects by fumigation is accomplished by the substitution of a gas, destructive to life, for the air. This gas enters the spiracles and follows along the tracheae to the living tissues, which take it in place of the oxygen usually received in this way, and the insects are killed.

It was formerly supposed that certain materials called contact insecticides, which kill insects by contact with their bodies, caused death by entering the spiracles and closing them up, thus producing suffocation. This has now been proved to be incorrect in most cases.

Insects which in their early stages live in water cannot, of course, breathe air into their bodies through spiracles during that period of their lives. These are closed in such cases and the animal obtains air usually through special structures called tracheal gills. These will be described in connection with the insects that possess them. In a few small water-inhabiting forms, the chitin covering the surface of the body is so thin that oxygen present in the water can pass directly through it into the body and to the parts there that need it, and carbon dioxide passes in the reverse direction.

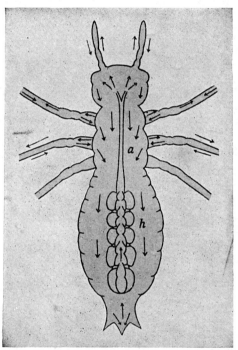

FIG. 27.—Diagram showing by the direction of the arrows the general course of the blood flow in a dragonfly nymph; *a*, aorta; *h*, heart. (*Modified from Kolbe.*)

**Circulatory organs.**—Insects have only an incomplete system of blood vessels. A tube lies in the middle of the body close beneath the back, beginning near the hinder end of the animal and extending forward into the head (Fig. 27). In the abdomen this tube is constricted, forming chambers, and the chambered portion is called the heart. There is a pair of openings on the sides of each chamber through which blood can enter, and valves there which prevent its going out again. The walls of the heart contain muscles which contract one after another, forming a sort of wave of contraction which begins at the hinder end and travels forward. Blood in the heart, being unable because of the valves to pass out at the sides, is pressed forward by this contraction wave and at the front end of the heart finds itself in a tube without chambers or valves, called the aorta, through which it is led to the head where the aorta may divide into a few short branches or may be unbranched. In either case, at this point the blood pours out of it into the body, the system of blood vessels coming to an end.  There is now no definite and particular path for the blood to follow, but it would, in theory at least, remain near where it escaped from the aorta or gradually pass into any spaces it might find unoccupied between the different structures in the head. With each heartbeat, however, more blood is poured out of the aorta, increasing the pressure upon that already in the head.  It therefore is gradually forced backward and to other parts of the body, each particle probably taking the path where there is least resistance to its passage.  In this way a general backward direction is given to the flow.

As it approaches the heart, another influence appears.  During each contraction, the heart occupies less space, which leads to less than normal pressure near it, and blood close by naturally flows closer to it.  Upon its expansion again and the opening of its valves, the direction of least resistance is now through the valves and into the heart.

As the blood passes back through the body, a given particle may at one circuit go over certain organs, and at the next over entirely different ones.  All the internal organs, however, have their surfaces bathed by blood and this as it passes over the stomach or other parts of the alimentary canal will pick up any food which having been digested has passed through the canal walls.  Likewise in passing over any organ needing this food, it is given up to those organs.  The blood therefore serves as a distributor of food from the place where it is digested to all the parts that need it.

We have already seen that the living parts of the body—the cells—need oxygen and as the result of their activities give off carbon dioxide gas, but that this exchange is accomplished by the aid of the tracheae.  In a somewhat parallel way, the cells that need food obtain it from the blood.  The cells by their activities produce not only carbon dioxide gas but also waste material nitrogenous in nature which must be removed, like all wastes, from the body.  This nitrogenous waste is picked up at the cells by the blood and carried along, perhaps for some time, before a place to dispose of it can be found.  Sooner or later, however, a particle of blood containing this waste material will wash over certain structures called Malpighian tubes, to be described in the next section, and the cells which form these tubes have the power to collect this waste material from the blood as it flows over them, thus purifying it.

The blood itself is usually a colorless, yellowish, reddish or greenish fluid, in which are corpuscles resembling the white corpuscles of human blood.  It appears to serve to carry food to the tissues and waste matter from them, and therefore has no need of structures in it like the red blood corpuscles of man, the work of which in insects is done mainly by the tracheae.

**Excretory organs.**—The organs that eliminate the nitrogenous wastes from the body and correspond in function to the human kidneys are known as Malpighian tubes (Fig. 28).  These are blind-ended tubes, the walls of which consist of a single layer of cells surrounding a central channel which at one end opens into the hind intestine, usually near its front, just behind the stomach (Fig. 23). When blood containing nitrogenous waste matter washes over the outer surface of a Malpighian tube, the cells of which it is composed have the power of taking this matter out of the blood into their own substance and passing it through themselves into the channel between them, down which it moves until it enters the hind intestine, from which it is finally expelled at the anus.

The Malpighian tubes may be few or many, long or short (see Figs. 23–25). They show a tendency to collect in groups and to unite near the hind intestine, so that their outlets into this are much fewer than the number of tubes. It seems possible that a certain amount of poison entering the body by way of the stomach can be eliminated by the Malpighian tubes, which may explain the varying degree of resistance to such poisons by different insects.

**Nervous system.**—The nervous system of insects is located along the middle line of the body quite near its under surface (Fig. 23). As in animals generally, it is composed of cells and fibers. The former are for the most part gathered together in clusters which are called ganglia, and from each of the cells in a ganglion one or more nerve fibers pass out, to connect either with some other nerve cell or with some structure of the body. The larger nerves are really bundles of the fibers running side by side like the wires of a telephone cable.

FIG. 28.—Portion of the Malpighian tube of a fly, greatly enlarged: *k*, cell nucleus; *l*, lumen of the central canal; *tr*, tracheae. (*Modified from Gegenbaur.*)

Apparently each segment of the insect body once had a nerve ganglion, but with the fusion of the segments many of these have also fused, reducing the separate ganglia in adult insects to a smaller number, which varies in different kinds. This fusion has been produced by the hinder ganglia moving forward until in some cases none is found in the abdomen. Different degrees of this are shown in Fig. 29.

Each ganglion is connected to the one in front and the one behind by one or two bundles of nerve fibers which are called commissures. Each consists of numerous fibers which taken together form the means of communication between the different parts of the system.

In the head, in front of or above the esophagus, is the largest ganglion of the body, called the brain, produced by the fusion of several ganglia. In addition to its two commissures, which connect it with the ganglion next behind, it has nerves which lead to the eyes, to the antennae and to other parts of the front of the head.

Below or behind the esophagus is a second ganglion, also in the head, called from its position the subesophageal ganglion. As the esophagus lies directly between this and the brain, the commissures connecting the two do not lie close together but separate far enough to permit the esophagus to pass between them. The subesophageal ganglion, besides being connected with the brain in front and the first thoracic ganglion behind it, by commissures, sends nerves to the mouth parts and other near-by regions of the head.

The thoracic ganglia may be more or less separate or fused and may have fewer or more of the abdominal ganglia added. Commissures, however, connect all separate ganglia, and these also send out nerves to all the parts of the segments to which they belong, no matter what their final location may be. In this way, the wings, legs, muscles and other parts receive their nerve supply. A small "sympathetic nerve system," also present, appears to be concerned chiefly with the nerve supply of the alimentary canal and tracheae.

**Sense organs.**—All the more evident senses possessed by men appear to be present in insects, except possibly taste, but not in all cases in the same individual. Thus some cave-inhabiting insects have no eyes. It is almost certain also that insects have other senses not possessed by man.

**Reproductive organs.**—Insects are of distinct sexes, male and female. In many cases, however, individuals occur incapable of reproduction, their sexual organs not having become fully developed; such insects

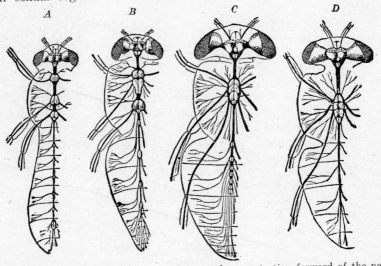

Fig. 29.—Diagram showing various degrees of concentration forward of the nervous system of four species of flies: *A, Chironomus plumosus*, little concentrated; *B, Empis stercorea; C, Tabanus bovinus; D, Sarcophaga carnaria*, most concentrated. (*After Brandt, from Lang's Lehrbuch.*)

may be termed neuters. Most of these appear to be really undeveloped females, though undeveloped males are also known. They are found in colonial insects where division of labor occurs, as in the honeybee, ants and termites, and are known according to their duties, as workers or soldiers or by other names. Conventional signs for the various forms of insects, as a convenience, are ♂ male; ♀ female; ♀ or ☿ worker.

In the female (Fig. 30) the eggs are produced in a pair of ovaries located in the upper front part of the abdomen. Each is a cluster of ovarian tubes whose walls are cells. Some of these cells grow and separate from the others to lie in the central cavity of the tube and then pass downward, growing till they reach its hinder end, which connects with the similar ends of all the ovarian tubes of that side to form a single tube called the oviduct. This extends downward and back-ward around the side of the alimentary canal, below which it joins with a similar oviduct from the other side of the body to form a single duct, the vagina, which lies below the alimentary canal and extends backward to its outer opening which is located, in most cases, in front of the next to the last abdominal segment. Surrounding this opening may be external structures (an ovipositor) for the purpose of together making holes in some object (the ground, wood, etc.) in which to deposit the eggs. A side pouch (seminal receptacle) connected with the vagina is for the storage of the sperms which fertilize the eggs; a gland-producing material, which forms the egg shell and is known as the shell gland, also opens into this portion; and other glands similarly connected with the vagina may also be present.

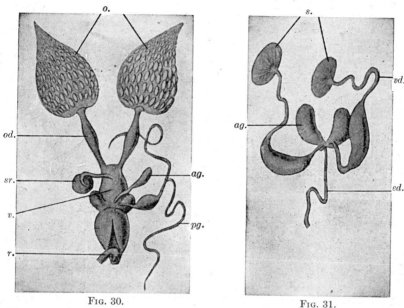

Fig. 30.        Fig. 31.

Fig. 30.—Female reproductive organs of honeybee (*Apis mellifera* L.): *ag.*, accessory gland; *o.*, ovaries; *od.*, oviduct; *pg.*, poison gland; *r.*, rectum, cut off and end bent back; *sr.*, seminal receptacle; *v.*, vagina. (*Modified from Leuckart's Wandtafeln.*)

Fig. 31.—Male reproductive organs of honeybee (*Apis mellifera* L.): *ag.*, accessory gland; *ed.*, ejaculatory duct; *s.*, spermaries; *vd.*, vasa deferentia. (*Modified from Leuckart's Wandtafeln.*)

In the male (Fig. 31) the arrangement of the organs closely corresponds to that in the female. A pair of spermaries or testes is present in the upper front part of the abdomen, each consisting of a rather closely coiled mass of tubes in which the sperms are produced. The tubes on each side unite to form a single tube, the vas deferens (plural, vasa deferentia). These differ from the oviducts usually, in being much longer and coiled or twisted. They pass downward and backward, however, and unite on the middle line of the body below the alimentary canal, forming a single tube, the ejaculatory duct, corresponding to the vagina in position, which leads backward to an opening in front of the last segment. An enlarged portion of the vas deferens is often present, for the temporary storage of the sperms, and is termed the seminal vesicle. Accessory pouches opening into the ejaculatory duct appear to be, in part at least, for the production of mucus and secretions to mix with the seminal fluid.

# CHAPTER IV

## THE DEVELOPMENT OF INSECTS

Most insects lay eggs from which the young hatch after a longer or shorter time, though in some cases the egg appears to be retained within the body of the parent until after it has hatched, the young then being produced in an active stage. Those which lay eggs hatching later are termed oviparous; those having eggs that remain in the body of the

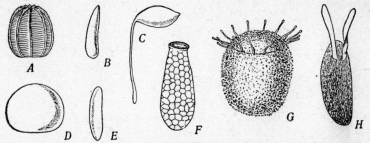

FIG. 32.—Eggs of various insects: A, butterfly; B, housefly; C, chalcid (*Bruchophagus*); D, butterfly; E, midge; F, bug (*Triphleps*); G, bug (*Podisus*); H, pomace fly. All much enlarged. (*From Folsom.*)

parent for a time after hatching are termed ovoviviparous. A few insects that supply nourishment to the young before its birth are termed viviparous.

Insect eggs are usually very small, vary greatly in form and may be laid singly or in clusters (Fig. 32). They are covered by a chitinous shell, the chorion, which often bears markings in the form of ridges, reticulations, etc., and frequently they are also colored. At one place on the surface is a minute opening or group of openings through the shell, called the micropyle, believed to be for the entrance of the fertilizing sperm. The length of time spent in the egg differs in different insects from a few hours to many months, and in some cases the eggs do not hatch until the second season after they are laid.

In hatching, the shell breaks and out of it crawls the young insect, in the majority of cases quite unlike the adult it is to become. In order to reach maturity it must now grow and undergo changes in structure and appearance. These together are expressed by saying that most insects in order to become adult undergo a metamorphosis. In some of the simpler insects, a few changes and growth only are needed to make them

24

mature, and these are therefore usually grouped together as the Ametabola, or insects having practically no metamorphosis.

The remaining insects, from this standpoint, form two groups: those which on hatching generally show some resemblance to the adults and reach maturity by a series of gradual changes; and those which on hatching are totally unlike the adults and become adults by a somewhat different process. These groups are known as the Hemimetabola, or Paurometabola, and the Holometabola, respectively, these names suggesting the amount of metamorphosis required for members of each group to become adult.

A member of the group Ametabola, upon hatching, will begin to feed and grow. Growth, however, is restricted because the insect is enclosed by a cuticula which, while elastic, to some extent, at least at its thinner places, has its limitations in this regard. Thus the insect is unable to reach its adult size within its cuticula, and a process called molting takes place. This is begun by a pouring out of fluid by the outside layer of living cells, the hypodermis, between it and the cuticula, separating the two. Next a split appears somewhere in the cuticula, usually along the back, and the insect crawls out of its skin, *i.e.*, molts. Until the fluid poured out has had time to harden, the insect is able to grow, but in a short time it hardens to become a new cuticula and thereafter only such growth occurs as the elasticity of the new shell will permit. In theory there should be some Ametabola that do not molt, the cuticula being so elastic it will stretch enough to permit growth to the adult (Fig. 33*A*). In fact, however, they all appear to molt at least two or three times (Fig. 33*B*); in a few cases it seems to occur at intervals throughout life. In any case the reproductive organs appear not to be mature at the time of hatching and only gradually become so during the period following.

In the Hemimetabola (or Paurometabola) the young insect on escaping from the egg, though resembling its parent to some extent, must, nevertheless, undergo many changes in structure and a considerable increase in size as well before reaching maturity. Thus a young short-horned grasshopper, on hatching, will need to grow to be about ten times as long before becoming adult; it is without wings, which will need to be developed; its reproductive organs are not mature and must become so; and other differences occur (Fig. 33*C*). All of these must be transformed into their condition in the adult; and to accomplish this, energy is necessary. In the egg the energy for development has been provided by the yolk; after hatching the young insect must provide it by gathering food.

The young insect, therefore, soon after hatching seeks for food and having found it begins feeding. The nourishment thus obtained results in growth so far as this is possible within a shell which is tightly fitting and only to some degree elastic. When no further growth in this way can occur and the body has stored within it all the materials needed for a greater increase in size, it proceeds to molt in the manner already described for the Ametabola. On escaping from its old skin or shell, however, besides a rapid increase in size, changes of structure also occur, so that a difference in appearance now becomes evident. These changes must be produced quickly, as the hypodermal cells of these parts, as well as of all the surface, are producing a new chitinous skin; when this has once hardened, no further changes and little further growth are possible. Molting, then, marks the beginning of a brief period—a day,

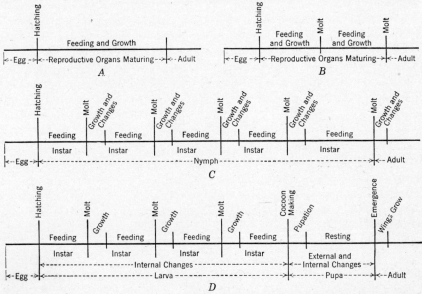

Fig. 33.—Diagram showing the development of: *A*, an Ametabolous insect which does not molt (not known to exist in nature); *B*, one which molts; *C*, a Hemimetabolous insect; *D*, a Holometabolous insect. Some of the Holometabola diverge from *D* at the point marked "Cocoon making." In *C* and *D* the spaces marked "Growth and Changes" and "Growth" are too great in proportion to the "Feeding" spaces which should be much longer.

more or less—of increase in size and of changes in appearance, these last all being in the direction of making the young insect more nearly like the adult it is to become. When the new shell has become hardened, the insect resumes its feeding.

After another feeding period the young insect is again confronted with the same difficulties as before, and it meets them in the same way, by molting, and immediately thereafter, before its new shell has hardened, it seizes the opportunity to grow and change its appearance further. Finally, after some molt, full adult size for the insect is attained and all its organs have also fully developed and matured, producing the adult insect itself (Figs. 33*C*, 34).

Thus the young insect becomes an adult by alternating periods of feeding, with brief periods of molting, following which growth and change take place, the total of which produces the adult.

The number of molts, and consequent opportunities for change that occur, vary in different Hemimetabola. There may be only two or three in some kinds; five is perhaps the average number though more are not uncommon; forty-five are known to occur in one species.

Certain names for these different conditions are convenient for use.

The feeding periods between the molts (or ecdyses) are called instars, so that the progress of an insect from hatching to adult is by an alterna-

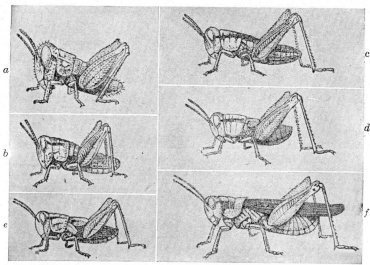

Fig. 34.—Incomplete metamorphosis of a grasshopper: *a*, first nymphal instar; *b*, second instar; *c*, third instar showing beginning of wings; *d*, fourth instar; *e*, fifth instar; *f*, adult. Figures not drawn to same scale. (*Modified from Packard's "Text-book of Entomology" by permission of The Macmillan Company.*)

tion of instars and molts. The insect itself, from hatching until maturity, is generally called a nymph. Figure 34 shows the changes in appearance of a grasshopper after each molt.

The term Hemimetabola was used for many years to include all those orders in which the insects underwent incomplete metamorphosis in the course of their development. In three of the orders, Ephemerida, Odonata and Plecoptera, however, the young live and develop in water and differ greatly from their adults in appearance. In recent years this has led some entomologists to divide the Hemimetabola into two groups; the three just named were left under the Hemimetabola and the others were given the group name Paurometabola which means a gradual metamorphosis. The young in the Hemimetabola thus limited are called naiads; those in the Paurometabola, nymphs. This is by no means a classification of the insects themselves, but only of the different types of development that occur. This classification has not been adopted in this book.

With the remaining group of insects, the Holometabola, although there is a little similarity in the metamorphosis to that in the Hemimetabola, there are also many differences.

When a young holometabolous insect hatches, it in no way resembles its adult. A caterpillar is totally different in appearance from the butterfly it finally becomes; the white grub in the earth is in no way suggestive of the June bug (May beetle) into which it transforms. Nevertheless, this young insect—called a larva—has to meet the same problems of growth and transformation to the adult condition as do the Hemimetabola and uses the same means for accomplishing the needed results, *viz.*, the utilization of the energy derived from its food.

Accordingly, upon hatching, in the Holometabola, a feeding period or instar comes first, followed by a molt and growth. At this point the story of the metamorphosis differs from that of the Hemimetabola, for after the molt no change in appearance to make the young insect more nearly like the adult takes place. It may be different in some regards, besides size, from what it was before the molt, but these differences do not increase its resemblance to what it finally becomes. This holds throughout the feeding period of its existence, so that after three, four or more molts a caterpillar is still a caterpillar, a grub is still a grub, and this is equally true for all holometabolous insects. Within the insect during this period, however, changes not perceptible on the surface are taking place, by the construction of portions of the adult which are forming as buds or ingrowths from various parts of the body and are termed imaginal buds (from "imago," the adult). They are closely compacted and many at least are infolded somewhat like buds, becoming finally ready to open when the proper time comes. And during its feeding instars, the larva is storing energy from its food not only for its growth at each molt but also to carry it on through a period yet to be described, during which it must transform into the adult condition while unable to feed and obtain the energy needed for this purpose (Fig. 33D).

After a varying number of feeding instars and molts, the young insect or larva has grown sufficiently and has stored within it energy enough to carry it through the remainder of its changes, and internally the essential parts for the adult condition have been formed as far as possible under existing conditions. As the next change will produce an animal practically helpless in most cases and unable to protect itself from its enemies, its next step is to find as much protection as possible. Accordingly, the full-grown larva usually, though not always, leaves the place where it has been feeding and elsewhere prepares for its next change.

Many larvae begin this by spinning around themselves a thread of silk, produced by glands within the body and opening to the surface on the lower lip. This thread is spun backward and forward and around the body until it sometimes forms a complete outer covering, entirely concealing the larva within from view. This case or cocoon appears to be protective in its function (Fig. 33D).

Some larvae go underground for this change. Here a cocoon, as such, seems unnecessary; but after digging into the earth a few inches, the insect forms a little earthen chamber or cell in which to lie and generally lines this more or less densely with silk, probably to keep the earthen walls from falling in and crushing it. A larva transforming in tunnels in wood where it has fed may make a partial cocoon with more or less of the chewed wood fragments mixed in. One staying above ground but not in tunnels or otherwise protected will spin more or less of a cocoon as already described.

The completeness of the cocoon, however, varies greatly with different insects. Instead of being a thick, dense wrapping which entirely conceals the insect, it may be so scanty that the animal within can be seen to some extent. In other cases it is merely a sort of network, in no degree giving concealment; and in still others, a few scattered threads to hold the insect in place are all that represent it. Sometimes hairs from the body of the larva, held together by silk, form most of the cocoon. In the case of butterflies only threads enough to attach the hinder end of the body at the place where it is to transform and usually to form a supporting loop around its middle, the ends of the loop also being fastened to what it rests on, are produced. In some flies the larva shrinks within its larval skin and transforms, this skin, now called a puparium, functioning like a cocoon (see Fig. 35c).

The reason for such variations in a structure, presumably formed for the purpose of protection, can only be guessed at. Possibly in the course of generations some insects found less need of this than others and gradually reduced it, thereby saving the vital energy so much needed for transformation, which would otherwise be expended in cocoon making.

Whether the larva forms a dense or scanty cocoon, or none whatever, the next step in the process is a molt. When the insect escapes from this skin, however, a great change in its appearance is evident, and it is now called a pupa (Fig. 35a and b). In a general way it may be said that it has at this one molt changed more than halfway to its adult condition. This is due in part at least to the unfolding of the imaginal buds already referred to, which contribute largely to form the new surface of the body in which head, thorax and abdomen are evident, as are also the antennae, legs, stubs of wings and other adult structures. Many of the internal organs of the larva, though, were necessary for use till the last moment before it became a pupa.   Then, too, the arrangement of the muscles in the larva would not be that needed by the adult.   Accordingly, most of the internal organs now gradually break down, losing all their earlier form and structure, and new ones to meet the needs of the adult are constructed to take their place.

During this breaking down and the reconstruction period, the pupa is practically helpless in most cases; hence generally the need for the protecting cocoon or earthen cell it constructs.

When the structure of the adult insect has been completed, another molt takes place, the pupa skin splitting and setting free the insect.   If it was enclosed in a cocoon, it now produces a fluid which sufficiently softens the silken threads so that it can push its way out and it escapes or "emerges."   It is now soft, its wings are only partly expanded, as in

a                    b                    c

Fig. 35.—Different types of pupation: a, pupa obtecta of a moth; b, pupa libera of a beetle; c, puparium of a fly.  a and b about natural size; c much enlarged.

most cases there would be no room for full-sized wings in a pupa, and because of its reconstruction there is considerable waste matter in its body.   The insect crawls upon whatever it may find to hold on to, expels the waste matter, and its wings begin to grow rapidly.   Drying out also takes place and in a short time (a few hours) the adult thus produced is in every way fully matured.   In some cases maturity of the reproductive organs is not complete until a little later.

To summarize the differences in metamorphosis of the three groups it may be said that in the Ametabola the insect hatches from the egg practically in an adult condition; i.e., there is little or no metamorphosis.   In the Hemimetabola the insect hatches from the egg in a form somewhat resembling the adult (except in the Ephemerida, Odonata and Plecoptera) but much smaller.   It becomes adult by alternating periods of feeding with molts, at which times growth and changes bringing it nearer to the adult occur, the last molt completing the growth and adult structure. In this life history we have a change; but as there was a resemblance to the adult from the start, the change to it (metamorphosis) is only an incomplete or partial one.

In the Holometabola the insect hatches from the egg in a form totally unlike the adult, and, whereas feeding periods followed by molts and growth give increase in size, no external evidence of any changes making the insect more like the adult can be found. These changes are largely made after the end of the feeding and growing periods during a pupa (generally quiet) stage, in which the breaking down of the larval, and construction of the adult, structures is completed. The difference between the larva on hatching and the adult is so great that an entire change (complete metamorphosis) takes place.

It should be evident from the foregoing that, when the adult condition is once reached, little if any growth is possible (except in rare cases) and that the belief so common that "big flies grow from little flies" is without any basis of fact.

The nymphs of the Hemimetabola appear not to have attracted sufficient attention to receive any special common names. In the Holometabola the larvae of various groups differ greatly in appearance; many are large and noticeable and some of them have, as a result, received special names. Larvae of butterflies and moths are commonly called caterpillars; those of beetles are usually called grubs; those of flies are called maggots. Larvae found boring in wood, however, whether they will become moths, beetles or other insects, are uniformly called borers.

In the Hemimetabola, then, the stages of life are egg, nymph, adult; in the Holometabola they are egg, larva, pupa, adult. Whether or not the pupa is enclosed by a cocoon depends upon circumstances.

# CHAPTER V

## ECONOMIC IMPORTANCE OF INSECTS: NATURAL CONTROL

### INSECT DAMAGES

Of the many thousands of insect species known to man some affect him and his property only slightly; some are beneficial; others are injurious in various degrees. Only rough estimates can be made of the monetary losses and gains by insect activities and even these are made with difficulty. Although it is the general practice to express losses in terms of dollar valuation, it probably would be safer to give them in bushels, tons, etc., because the relative values of different crops and products change from year to year.

No crop of either vegetable or animal origin appears to be entirely free from insect injury. Field, truck and fruit crops, both growing and in storage, household goods and food products, forests and the wood products derived from them, domestic animals and animal products, all are more or less liable to insect attack. Because there never has been a season free from the ravages of insects which might serve as a standard for comparison, much of this loss is not appreciated. If there could once be such a year entirely insect free, the difference would be apparent at once.

It is the general conclusion that the loss to all sorts of crops by insect damage in an average year is about 10 per cent. This estimate covers field crops, forests and forest products, farm wood lots, domestic animals and their products, stored articles, shade trees and ornamental plants, household goods and foods. Generally the injury to fruit and truck crops is believed to be more than one tenth.

Hyslop estimated in 1938 that the annual loss to agricultural crops by insects, including the costs of control, amounts to somewhat over 1,600 million dollars. No estimate of injury to human health is included. To value this destruction we have as a criterion only the price for which crops sell. If the tenth of all crops destroyed had been saved, the price of the whole might have been no greater than it was for the nine-tenths actually produced.

The loss by insect injury usually far exceeds the actual quantity consumed. Insect-contaminated food products originally intended for human consumption often must be destroyed or used in stock feeds.

32

Blemishes in fruit caused by insect bites impair the sale value much more than is accounted for by the actual loss in substance.

The most obvious losses are those caused by the feeding of insects, but it is now known that some of the most serious plant diseases are carried by them. The organisms that cause these, whether they are filterable viruses, fungi or bacteria, may enter the plant through feeding injuries made by either the chewing or the sucking type of insect, through punctures made for egg laying and by way of the burrows and galleries of insects in wood. Particularly in the case of the filterable viruses, those little-known agents causing the so-called mosaics and related plant diseases, insects become carriers of the disease from plant to plant. In such cases the insect involved is usually of the piercing-sucking type. Often this insect is essential to the overwintering of the disease, sometimes even necessary to carry the disease from one plant to another.

Another field in which insects are highly injurious is that of human and animal health and comfort. Some insects, notably mosquitoes and flies, annoy man and other animals by their bites and stings. Other insects such as lice have become adapted to more or less continuous life upon animals and cause much discomfort and loss of vitality. Not only do insects live externally on animals but also internally in the skin tissues, and in a few cases within the flesh and in the alimentary tract. Besides the mental and bodily loss due to their presence, insects transmit disease organisms from one person or animal to another. Just as in the transmission of plant diseases the insect may be an accidental agent or an essential carrier. A few of the more important insect-borne disease organisms are those responsible for malaria, bubonic plague and typhoid, typhus and yellow fevers. Cases of allergy (hay fever, asthma, etc.) are frequently caused by exposure of susceptible persons to dried insect scales and hairs. Not only is the loss of life because of insect-borne diseases a very serious matter but the total loss of productive labor through illness is tremendous.

### INSECT BENEFITS

The benefits to man from their activities are frequently overlooked in summing up the economic importance of insects. Although in many cases it is impossible to say how much good is derived from insects, reliable statistics are easily obtained relative to the production of useful insect products.

Those insects which attack injurious species probably form the most important group. They are divided into two sections: the parasites that live in or on the different stages of other insects, then called hosts, and the predators that capture and devour other insects. Parasites usually, though not always, live in or on a single host insect during their entire development whereas a single predator may derive its nourishment from many victim insects. Parasites are of many species, frequently so specialized in their habits that one kind of parasite attacks only one or a few host species. In some cases the parasites work only in insect eggs and thus prevent any feeding loss by the host insect. Other parasites attack early stages of the pests, in some instances killing them soon, in others not until the pests have completed their feeding in spite of being parasitized. In the latter the benefit is less, but at least there are fewer adults to produce the next generation. All stages are known to be attacked in different species by one parasite or another.

Another highly important group of insects includes those which pollinate flowers during their visits for nectar and pollen, thus enabling the plants to produce seeds. Some plants, as the Smyrna fig, clovers, melons, tomatoes, beans, peas and most of the common fruits, require the visits of insects before the seeds or fruits can form. The value of these crops which require the services of insects in the United States amounts to over two billion dollars.

A third group of insects is responsible for a number of commercial products, silk, honey, beeswax, shellac and a few less important ones.

Insects provide the entire diet of certain birds, mammals, etc., and an important part of the diet for many others. Even man in some parts of the world consumes large quantities of grasshoppers, crickets, ants and other insects.

The great value of some insects and the great losses, sometimes enormous, caused by others make it obviously important to encourage the beneficial forms while striving to prevent or at least to reduce the losses caused by the injurious ones.

### NATURAL CONTROL

Under the heading of natural control fall those various factors which affect the distribution and welfare of insects but do not depend upon man for their success. They include (1) climate, as temperature, humidity, air movement; (2) topography, as land and water barriers, soil texture and composition; (3) parasites and predators (insects and other animals); and (4) diseases (fungi, bacteria, etc.). Where no disturbing influence is introduced by man or any other agency, the insect population tends to be more or less completely held in balance by these natural factors.

Climate, including temperature, moisture, etc., is probably the most important factor affecting the distribution of insects. No insect can live and develop at temperatures higher or lower than a certain range. The temperature at which development is most rapid, is about midway of this range; at other points either higher or lower the development is proportionately slower. The same statements hold true for air moisture although variation due to moisture differences is usually less marked. The favorable range of either temperature or moisture varies with different insect species, often even during the stages of development.

It is easy to understand from these facts why some insects are prevented by winter temperatures from living in the northern United States, and why some can live only there. After several favorable winters an insect pest may become very numerous, then disappear suddenly when a severe winter occurs. One combination of weather conditions in summer may favor one type of insect pest; another set of conditions may suppress the first pest but favor others equally serious.

Not only the annual temperature range but the fluctuations that occur within short periods are often important in limiting the range of an insect. Frequent small showers have a different effect from infrequent cloudbursts; the latter may produce the greater total rainfall but actually supply less air moisture. Winds may carry some insects for considerable distances, and they may also bring moisture from large bodies of water or in other localities have a drying effect. Sunshine has much to do with insect flight, hence with the spread of insects.

Mountain ranges and large bodies of water are more or less effective barriers to the spread of animals (including insects) and plants. Lowlands are barriers to the spread of mountain types, because any region unsuited to the development of an insect presents a barrier to the spread of that species if the area is extensive enough.

Because so many insects are dependent upon plant life for their food, either directly or indirectly, those factors which limit plant development may indirectly form barriers to insect spread. It must be understood that most insects are limited to certain plants, many to only one kind or a few closely related plant species. In seasons unfavorable to the growth of its food plant an insect will be reduced in numbers, either by starvation or by the inability of the adult females to find food plants upon which to lay their eggs. Sometimes such numbers of an insect occur that the food plant is consumed almost completely and many of the insects starve as a result.

Not only do mountains, oceans, climate and plant life control the size and distribution of insect populations but insect parasites, birds, various diseases, etc., are vital factors in limiting the numbers of insects. The more abundant an insect becomes, the more food is available for its parasites. Finally the parasites become so numerous that practically all the hosts will have been found and killed. The next generation of parasites consists, of course, of many more individuals, but most of these will die for lack of food. Under such conditions, a "balance of Nature" develops. Though the scales may tip first to one side and then to the other, this balance is preserved within certain limits of fluctuation.

# CHAPTER VI

## ARTIFICIAL CONTROL

In the course of the development of agriculture, man has increased the number and magnitude of his entomological problems. Before the settlement of this country there were, of course, native insects attacking the various plants growing here. New plants were introduced by the settlers and grown in greater abundance than the wild and scattered ones. An insect finding in any of these an acceptable food had at once a more abundant supply and rapid multiplication thus became possible and resulted in increase of the pest to injurious numbers.

A second factor has been the accidental introduction of many insect pests from foreign countries. In the United States such forms have often failed entirely to maintain themselves. Unfortunately on the other hand some others have frequently found conditions favorable to a rapid increase. These multiply unchecked by their natural enemies which in most cases have not accompanied them to this country. A third factor is that with the increasing occupation of the country, insectivorous birds have been destroyed or frightened away. Although some birds have adjusted themselves to the new conditions it is not likely that their increase makes up for the loss of other species.

Nature tends to reestablish a balance after some new influence has upset the old state of affairs, although the process may require many years. Even then there will be certain years when the population of a species will be large as the result of normal fluctuation. Man cannot wait a number of years for Nature to adjust matters, nor can he afford avoidable crop failures every few years. He requires artificial measures by which he can protect himself and his crops from the ravages of injurious insects.

Measures for the artificial control of insects may be divided into six groups: (1) mechanical control, (2) cultural control, (3) biological control, (4) legislative control, (5) physical control, (6) chemical control.

Whatever the method and its effectiveness, the cost of control must be a deciding factor. It is evident no financial profit to an individual owner will be gained by attempting control when the cost is greater than the probable loss. Sometimes, however, the profit to the community over a period of years may warrant treatment costing more than the loss for any one year. Often it is not profitable to use any known method of control for insects injuring crops of small value.

36

## MECHANICAL CONTROL

Under mechanical control are included those methods by which insects are controlled directly by hand, as in hand-picking from infested plants or by mechanical devices such as window screens, flytraps and bands on trees. Frequently egg masses or nests of larvae may be cut from plants and destroyed as an important aid in the small-scale control of an insect pest or where labor is cheap enough to make the method profitable over larger areas. Deep furrows, lines of creosote or low fences of sheet metal or paper are used as barriers against the migration of nonflying insects. Sticky bands on trees are utilized to capture climbing insects; burlap and paper bands serve as localized hiding places from which the insects may be taken and destroyed. Paper collars are sometimes placed as insect barriers around individual plants, and the trunks of trees may be wrapped to ward off insect attack. Besides hand methods, traps and barriers, machines are used sometimes for actually crushing or grinding the insects.

## CULTURAL CONTROL

Cultural control has been defined as including "regular farm operations performed so as to destroy insects or prevent their injuries." Frequently a vigorous, healthy plant is not only better able to withstand insect injury but also less liable to attack than one weakened by lack of proper nourishment or by disease. Intelligent cultivation and use of fertilizers as well as pruning to remove injured or diseased parts will aid in insect control.

The destruction of vegetable trash and weeds, frequently called clean culture, is also an important factor, especially in the control of hibernating insects. Weeds not only interfere with successful crop growth by crowding, but they may reduce the vigor of the crop by competing for plant food in the soil. In winter they provide hiding places for hibernating pests. A pest appearing in the spring before its crop food plant is available may find certain weeds palatable until the crop has appeared. Other pests move to late summer and fall weeds after their particular crops have been harvested. Decaying fruits and vegetables also harbor insects and should be disposed of in such a manner that the insects will be destroyed. Dead grass and leaves may be burned to kill insects that would find protection under them, but the loss of soil fertility should be weighed against the possible value in insect control. The destruction of weeds and brush along fences is of advantage in the reduction of insects but it results in the elimination of nesting and hiding places for insectivorous and game birds.

A third farm operation useful in insect control is the rotation of crops. Often an insect pest may be reduced to unimportance if the crop which it affects is alternated with other crops not eaten by it.  The various grains are related to, in fact actually are, grasses and are eaten by many of the same insects.  Only a few general grass feeders are also injurious to clovers and other legumes.  It is therefore common practice to rotate grasses and legumes, cultivated crops also often being added to the rotation.  How far this principle can be put into practice depends upon many factors besides the insect phase.

Time and method of plowing and cultivating form a fourth factor in the cultural control of insects.  Many insect pests overwinter in larval or pupal cells in the ground.  These cells can often be broken up by fall plowing so the insects will not survive the winter.  Cultivation in the summer frequently breaks up pupation cells, but plowing or cultivation to be effective must be timed according to the life history of the insect that is being controlled, otherwise it is useless.  For the control of some insects it is necessary to refrain from cultivation at certain times.  The depth of plowing varies sometimes according to the habits of the insect.

As in tillage practice the time of planting and of harvesting are also of importance in protecting crops against insect pests.  It is sometimes possible to avoid the time of egg laying, to push young plants to the stage where they are not likely to be badly injured or even to mature a crop before the insects appear in dangerous numbers.  The timing of wheat planting to avoid infestation by the hessian fly is the best example of the success of such practices.

Varieties or strains of some plants have been found more resistant to insect attack than others.  To develop resistant strains and to prove their value, however, frequently require long, expensive research in plant genetics.  Instances in which some success has been obtained will be mentioned under the insect pests concerned.

### BIOLOGICAL CONTROL

Parasitic and predaceous insects as well as diseases of insects have already been discussed as vital factors in the natural control of injurious insects.  It is possible, however, for man to encourage such beneficial forms by introducing them into new areas or by growing them artificially for liberation whenever they become scarce in nature.  Until recent years most of this work dealt with the introduction of parasites from abroad to combat those foreign insect pests brought to this country accidentally but without their natural enemies.  Certain native parasites and predators are now being reared in large numbers for liberation in areas badly infested with their host species.

Probably the first introduction attempted from a foreign country was the now classic case of a ladybeetle brought from Australia to attack the cottony cushion scale which had already reached California and was endangering the existence of the citrus industry. Following this successful attempt many other parasites and predators have been imported which in many instances have proved valuable in reducing the numbers of foreign pests.

Parasites should not be expected to kill off all their hosts; they will merely reduce the population to greater or less extent. Other control measures must also be used if the insect is to be exterminated.

The discovery and introduction of parasites are expensive. However, since a successful parasite perpetuates itself, the initial high cost of establishment may be spread over a period of many years.

Many dangers are involved in bringing parasites into a new country. These insects may attack not only the pest that is to be controlled but also other parasites of the pest. In such cases the introduction may be of little value. There is always the chance also that their own secondary parasites may be imported along with the primary ones. Only thoroughly trained entomologists, therefore, should be permitted to bring parasites and predators to this country if we are to avoid the introduction of undesirable insects along with the desirable ones.

The liberation of insect diseases is not so generally successful as variations in natural conditions limit the growth of the disease. Many of the disease organisms are widely distributed and appear spontaneously when suitable conditions prevail, even without any encouragement. The most systematic use of diseases in artificial insect control in the United States appears to be the annual distribution by the state of Florida of fungi that live on the whiteflies that attack citrus.

### LEGISLATIVE CONTROL

Various laws and regulations both Federal and state have been enacted to prevent the introduction of foreign pests, to prevent their spread within the United States, to enforce control and extermination and to ensure that chemicals used for controlling insects are neither adulterated nor misbranded.

These laws and regulations take the form of absolute quarantines, the inspection of plants to be shipped, the obligatory treatment of growing and harvested crops and the testing of insecticides. Plants entering the United States or crossing state boundaries must at least be inspected, and in some cases shipment is barred absolutely. If any pest in a state is the subject of a Federal quarantine, a limiting line may be fixed within that state by Federal authority to prevent shipment to points outside the quarantined area. Various regulations are in force controlling particular cases but in general, plants, especially nursery stock, carried from one region to another must be passed by an authorized state or Federal inspector as free from insect pests and plant diseases before shipment will be permitted.

Because insects will spread by flight and by wind carriage and because many escape discovery during inspection it is reasonably certain that in spite of quarantines these pests will gradually spread over such parts of this country as they are able to inhabit. The chief gains from legislation, then, are (1) to delay the spread of pests and protect uninfested localities from their attacks as long as possible and (2) to prevent new pests from entering this country. It is believed that the tremendous expense involved in thus delaying the spread of new insect pests is far outweighed by the crop losses avoided and the time gained for preparing the country to control those pests which will eventually spread over it.

## PHYSICAL CONTROL

The extremes of both temperature and humidity, either high or low, are not only effective barriers in the natural control of insects, but they are also useful in artificial control. Light and electricity are other factors that come under this heading.

**Heat.**—Most insects cease reproduction and soon die at temperatures from 100 to 110°F. The temperature of their surroundings should be raised to 120° or higher to kill them with heat artificially within a few hours. The length of period for effective treatment is more dependent upon the time to heat the grain, clothing or other material in which the insects are located than upon the heat resistance of the pests themselves, because no insect can survive more than an hour if actually exposed to a temperature of 120°F. Bales and bags are difficult to heat through. Even in superheating a house, usually easiest to accomplish in summer, a thermometer hung in the center of a room will not indicate the temperature of the floor or the outside walls which are usually slower to warm. High temperature is frequently used for killing insect infestations in soil and bulbs, in small lots of seeds and cereal products, in flour and feed sacks and in furniture, bedding and clothing. It is common commercial practice to fit a small tight room with steam pipes, often with automatic temperature control, as a place in which to treat bags and various products that may be infested. Most products may be injured if they are heated too long; this is particularly true of bulbs, seeds and flour.

**Cold.**—Although low temperatures are not so effective as high ones in killing insects, many insect pests of stored products such as furniture, rugs, clothing and seeds become inactive at 40 to 45°F. Under these conditions infested materials suffer no further damage or increase in infestation, and materials free from insects when put into cold storage will remain so. Those insects which hibernate outdoors withstand temperatures far below zero. Most insect pests of stored products, however, are unable to become dormant in the true sense and are killed in a relatively short time even at temperatures considerably above zero. The use of low temperatures in the artificial control of insects, therefore, is of two types. The more important is cold storage, as for furs, at temperatures just low enough to protect the stored materials from injury. The other use of cold actually to kill insects is feasible only on a large scale in zero weather in the north. Here as in the case of the heat-treatment much more time is required to chill grain, flour, clothing and other products than is usually realized.

**Moisture.**—A conspicuous example of the manipulation of moisture to control insects is the drying of grain to reduce the likelihood of weevil injury.

**Light.**—It is well known that many insects are attracted to bright lights. This fact has been used extensively to trap insects, sometimes for the purpose of studying their distribution, sometimes as a control measure. Although considerable research is still required in this field it is apparent that insects are attracted more by lights of some colors than by those of others.

**Electricity.**—Devices are available for electrocuting insects, some in the form of electrical window screens for flies, others as electric light traps for moths and beetles. These are so arranged that an insect striking parallel wires of the device completes an electrical circuit and is killed by the shock. A machine for the electrical treatment of insect-infested grain and cereal products has been used successfully for several years, in which the insects are killed when the product is passed through a field of high frequency between two electrodes.

## CHEMICAL CONTROL

The chemical control of insects includes-control not only with insecticides in the true sense as discussed in the following chapters but also with various materials used to attract and repel insects without actually killing them.

**Attractants** (sometimes called attrahents) are materials used to lure insects to traps and poisoned baits. The use of geraniol in Japanese beetle traps, sugar sirups for ant baits, and fermenting sirup solutions for trapping various moths are good examples.

**Repellents** are those materials used to keep insects away from crops, animals and man. Various coal-tar and pine products are rather general insect repellents. Naphthalene is a clothes moth repellent and oil of citronella is a common ingredient of preparations used to keep mosquitoes away from people.

# CHAPTER VII

## INSECTICIDES: STOMACH POISONS

The chemical control of insects by the use of insecticides (chemical control) must be depended upon for the protection of valuable plants, animals and their products when mechanical (cultural) or biological control methods are too slow. The reduction of an insect population on a practical scale by parasites or predators often requires more than one season or several insect generations. Mechanical control by rubbish disposal, crop rotation or other methods is often a valuable aid, but rarely does it alone produce practical control.

In order to kill an insect with a toxic material the poison must penetrate to vital tissues and organs. Penetration directly through the body wall of "soft-bodied" insects may be rapid. Other insects with the body wall thick, waxy or otherwise well protected are resistant to direct penetration. In the latter case the insecticide must be taken into the digestive tract with food or water, or absorbed through poorly protected points such as the spiracles.

Insecticides are classified into (1) stomach poisons, (2) contact insecticides and (3) fumigants, on the basis of the manner in which the insect takes up the poison. Mandibulate, or "chewing," insects, such as beetles, caterpillars and grasshoppers, may be killed by spreading stomach poisons on their food, for these insects bite off and swallow solid particles. Sucking insects, such as aphids, scale insects and leafhoppers, cannot be killed in this way but must be hit directly with a contact insecticide. It is theoretically just as easy to kill a chewing insect as a sucking one with a contact poison, but the most serious pests with chewing mouth parts usually have heavy body-wall protection. Furthermore it pays to use a stomach poison when possible because the digestive tract is perhaps the most vulnerable part of the body that can be exposed to the penetration of an insecticide. Another advantage of the stomach poison is that it can be applied to plant foliage whether the insects are present or not. A contact insecticide is usually of no value unless the insects are hit directly. Fumigants are gases toxic to insects. They are comparable to stomach poisons in efficiency for they penetrate the vulnerable tracheal system to reach the vital organs of the insect.

It must not be assumed that because one or two species are easily killed by a given insecticide that this poison is as effective in killing other

42

kinds of insects. Many insecticides, particularly organic compounds, are more or less specific in their action upon insects. In other words insecticide *A*, which is valuable against one pest, may be useless against another because of the innate resistance of the latter species. Insecticide *B*, which is effective against the latter insect, may, however, have little effect upon the first pest. This phenomenon in insecticides is spoken of as their *specificity of toxic action.*

In general there are two methods of applying stomach or contact insecticides: *spraying* and *dusting.* In either case the insecticides may be solid or liquid. Finely powdered solids are dusted over infested plants or suspended in water and then sprayed on the plants. When an insecticide is used as a dust it may be diluted with a carrier such as lime or talc so that not too much of the actual poison will fall in any one place. The water used in a spray is also a carrier and serves to distribute the poison evenly over a wide surface. Liquid insecticides ordinarily are diluted with water and sprayed, but sometimes they can be absorbed on the solid particles of a carrier and then used as a dust. Dusts are applied by means of mechanical *dusters*, machines arranged to blow out the dust either by a rotary fan or by bellows. *Sprayers* are usually pumps for producing air pressure to force a liquid spray through a fine nozzle at the end of a hose. When the operations are on a large scale and conditions are suitable for flying, airplanes are sometimes used, chiefly for dusting. Whatever the method of application, for good results the insecticide must be evenly distributed over the treated surface.

### STOMACH POISONS

Arsenicals were the earliest stomach poisons used on a large scale and still are the most important ones. During the last two decades, however, nonarsenical compounds have been found of practical value, at least for certain kinds of insects or under special conditions. It is important to remember that practically all stomach poisons are dangerous to man if taken internally, some even upon exposure to the poison externally. For convenience, the stomach poisons may be grouped under the two headings: arsenicals and nonarsenicals.

### ARSENICAL STOMACH POISONS

The first essentials of a good arsenical for insecticidal purposes are (1) effectiveness against insects and (2) insolubility in water. Arsenic is effective as a poison only when it is dissolved but soluble arsenic also injures foliage. The ideal arsenical, therefore, is one in which its solubility in water is low enough to be safe on foliage, yet in the digestive juices of the insect its solubility is sufficient for the compound to be effective as an insecticide. Low cost and other factors are generally secondary although highly important considerations.

Arsenic, as a chemical element, forms two oxides: (1) the trioxide, $As_2O_3$, arsenious oxide, also commonly known as white arsenic and (2) the pentoxide $As_2O_5$, arsenic oxide. These, combining with bases such as lead or calcium, produce two corresponding sets of salts. Those formed from the trioxide are called *arsenites;* those from the pentoxide, *arsenates.* The arsenites are not only inherently more toxic but they are more soluble in water and hence more rapidly absorbed by a given organism than the arsenates. They are therefore frequently too dangerous for application to plant foliage, although they would be effective insect poisons.

It is natural to suppose that the arsenical containing the highest proportion of arsenic by weight would be the most economical insecticide. Although this is worth consideration the other factors that make for an ideal insecticide are so important that they overshadow that of arsenic percentage. It is better to use more of an insecticide than to sacrifice the safety of a growing plant.

**White arsenic** is the common name applied to commercial arsenic trioxide. It is too soluble for use on foliage. Since it has a high content of elemental arsenic (75.7 per cent) it is valuable, however, where plant injury is not a factor, as in poison baits for grasshoppers and cutworms, or in ant sirups. White arsenic is also the fundamental material used in the manufacture of other arsenicals. To form the arsenites it is combined directly with a base such as sodium hydroxide. In the case of the arsenates it must be oxidized and then combined with the appropriate base.

**Paris green** was the first stomach poison used in large quantity against insects, being first employed in 1867 for the control of the Colorado potato beetle. Chemically it is a combination of copper, arsenic and acetic acid, and is therefore known as copper acetoarsenite. When pure it contains 58.6 per cent arsenic trioxide (equivalent to 44.4 per cent elemental arsenic), which is high as compared to most other arsenicals in common use.

Paris green as an insecticide has three serious disadvantages. It is liable to burn plants sprayed with it, even when lime is added as a corrective for soluble arsenic; it is heavy, settling quickly in the spray tank so as to result in uneven distribution on foliage; and it does not adhere well but is quickly washed off leaves by rain. Notwithstanding these faults it is still used in large quantities for the control of the Colorado potato beetle as well as for certain special purposes.

**Lead arsenate** is the most extensively used of all stomach poisons. Its value was discovered in 1892 in the course of work conducted by the state of Massachusetts on the control of the gypsy moth. Lead arsenate in paste form was developed commercially about 1895. Lead arsenate powder appeared on the market by 1909, gradually superseded the paste and has become the only form in common use.

The following formula for making a lead arsenate spray of average strength, referred to in the succeeding chapters as the "standard formula," is

|  | Per Barrel | Per Gallon |
|---|---|---|
| Lead arsenate powder | 1½ lb. | 9½ tsp. (level) |
| Water | 50 gal. | 1 gal. |

Mix a small amount of the water with the arsenate before diluting to spray strength. Wash the insecticide into the spray tank while the agitator is going.

Several lead arsenates are known chemically but only two are of importance as insecticides, the common acid lead arsenate, $PbHAsO_4$, and the basic lead arsenate, $Pb_5OH(AsO_4)_3$, the latter formerly thought to be neutral lead arsenate. The market for basic lead arsenate is limited to an area in California where foggy weather conditions compel the use of an arsenical less soluble on the foliage than acid lead arsenate. Acid lead arsenate contains about 21 per cent elemental arsenic ($= 33$ per cent $As_2O_5$), basic lead arsenate 15 per cent ($= 23$ per cent $As_2O_5$).

The advantages of lead arsenate are several. Although it is a heavy compound, commercial preparations are so fluffy, in other words the bulk of the dry product is so great, that the arsenical particles settle relatively slowly in the spray liquid. Lead arsenate adheres to foliage better than the other common arsenicals. Under most conditions it is less likely to injure plant life, although for the same reason it acts slowly on insects. Not only is its solubility low but it has a rather low arsenic content.

So much lead arsenate is applied to apples in commercial growing areas (estimated at 7,000,000 pounds annually in one valley in the Pacific northwest), that it has been necessary for the Federal government to regulate the residue of both arsenic and lead permissible upon fruit handled in interstate commerce. The tolerances in force have varied from time to time; those made legal on Aug. 10, 1940, were for arsenic, 0.025 grain per pound of fruit (in terms of arsenic oxide, $As_2O_5$, not metallic arsenic); for lead, 0.05 grain as the element. It is now customary for most commercial apple growers to wash their fruit with weak chemicals to remove excessive spray residues.

**Calcium arsenate** in the powder form came into use about 1914 as a substitute for lead arsenate. In 1919 it was first used for dusting the cotton crop, now its most important use. Like lead arsenate, this arsenical occurs in several chemical forms, but their commercial preparation is not so well understood and standardized as in the case of the lead salt. Commercial calcium arsenates are probably mixtures of two or three forms. The content of arsenic oxide in the average commercial product is about 45 per cent.

The chief advantages of calcium over lead arsenate are its high arsenic content, low cost and light weight. Because of the last factor this insecticide is adapted for dusting on a large scale. However, calcium arsenate injures certain types of foliage that are safely treated with lead arsenate. Sometimes this disadvantage can be overcome by the addition of hydrated lime (calcium hydroxide). Still calcium arsenate has disappointed entomologists in not being better adapted as a substitute for lead arsenate and the resulting elimination of lead as a residue problem.

**Spreaders and stickers.**—Wetting and spreading are closely related phenomena usually exhibited by the same substance. Spreaders are added to both stomach and contact poisons so that uniform rather than spotty deposits will be formed. Soaps and calcium caseinate are characteristic materials used for this purpose.

Stickers, or adhesives, are used to increase the resistance to weathering of deposits of arsenicals and other stomach poisons on foliage. Although spreaders are often more or less adhesive, some special stickers find application, as adding fish oil to lead arsenate in spraying forest areas for control of the gypsy moth. The use of a sticker, however, may add too much to the cost of a spray to make it worth while.

**Compatibility of insecticides.**—Whenever possible, sprays are combined to save the labor of separate applications of stomach poisons, contact insecticides and fungicides. However, such combinations cannot be made indiscriminately because some insecticides react upon others, either interfering with the killing efficiency of one or more ingredients or actually forming compounds injurious to plants. For instance, if soap is added to lead or calcium arsenate, the arsenical is broken down to form soluble arsenic dangerous to foliage and the lead or calcium forms an insoluble lead or calcium soap.

**A corrective** is a chemical added to a spray formula to neutralize some injurious effect, usually to overcome the excessive solubility of the insecticide which otherwise is likely to result in plant injury. The corrective most commonly used is hydrated lime added to arsenical sprays to combine with any arsenic that becomes soluble during spraying or after exposure to moisture on the foliage. Because of certain disadvantages of hydrated lime for this purpose, such compounds as ferric oxide, ferrous sulfate and zinc sulfate, either alone or with hydrated lime, have recently been used with some success as corrective agents.

**Poison baits** are often used to control insects, particularly grasshoppers, cutworms and ants, which cannot be reached by spraying or dusting. The bait is composed essentially of bits of poisoned food, as bran, sometimes sweetened or otherwise made attractive. The food habits of the insect must be taken into account in selecting a base for the bait. There should not be serious competition from foods already in the infested area. The best poison for most bait purposes is a relatively soluble or active one. It may be an arsenite, such as Paris green, white arsenic or sodium arsenite, or a fluorine compound such as sodium fluosilicate. Sugar sirup poisoned with sodium arsenite or sodium arsenate forms the average ant bait.

## NONARSENICAL STOMACH POISONS

Fluorine compounds form the most important group under this heading. They are of three chemical types: the fluorides, the fluosilicates and the fluoaluminates. *Sodium fluoride*, NaF, is the only fluoride important as an insecticide. It is used chiefly as a dust in cockroach control, in controlling ants and for dusting poultry and other animals to rid them of chewing lice. It acts upon cockroaches chiefly as a contact insecticide when applied directly on the insects although it also serves as a stomach poison when the insects take it into the alimentary tract. It is too soluble to be used upon foliage. *Sodium fluosilicate*, $Na_2SiF_6$, can be substituted for sodium fluoride, although it is less effective as a cockroach poison. It is useful in grasshopper and cutworm baits, apparently being less repellent than arsenicals. *Barium fluosilicate*, $BaSiF_6$, is the only fluosilicate used on plants on a commercial scale. *Sodium fluoaluminate*, $Na_3AlF_6$, known more commonly as *cryolite*, is much less soluble than the other fluorine compounds mentioned. It is used effectively in dusting truck crops for the control of insect pests where fluorine residues do not become a problem. The Federal tolerance for fluorine is 0.02 grain per pound of food. This substance, however, is not safe for use on tree fruits as it sometimes causes serious injury to the fruit. In the Pacific northwest, though, it has proved satisfactory.

The powdered roots of the East Indian plant derris, of cube from Peru and of timbo from Brazil are now coming into general use for dusting truck crops such as cabbage, cauliflower and green beans which may be rejected by the Federal authorities if they contain heavy arsenical residues. All three act as both stomach and contact insecticides. They do not seem to be of great value, however, as sprays on tree fruits. Hellebore, usually the powdered roots of the European *Veratrum album*, was formerly used more extensively than today to control currant worms and similar garden pests. It is a mild stomach poison which loses its strength upon exposure to the air for a few days, thus eliminating the problem of a poisonous residue on food crops.

# CHAPTER VIII

## CONTACT INSECTICIDES: SPRAY COMBINATIONS

Contact insecticides are used mainly for the control of three general types of sucking insects. The aphids and other soft-bodied insects form one of these groups. Many of these insects reproduce so rapidly that one or two survivors on each plant can lead to a general reinfestation even in a few days. Although otherwise rather easily killed they often cause irregular, curly leaves which protect them from an insecticide. The second type includes the scale insects and mealybugs whose waxy coverings are not easily penetrated by the ordinary sprays intended for aphid control. Such hardy hemipterous insects as the squash bug, which form the third group, can be controlled only in their early stages, when their presence on the lower surfaces of leaves is frequently overlooked.

### OILS

Oils from many sources are used as insecticides: petroleum or mineral oil, coal-tar distillates, pine oil and pine-tar distillates and vegetable and animal oils. In the United States petroleum products are the most important, but this is not true in most of Europe, Asia and Africa. Kerosene was formerly the petroleum product most used for this purpose but, although it is still useful where a cheap homemade insecticide is required, heavier oils of the light lubricating types are now more generally used, especially in the control of scale insects and red spider.

Oils are too injurious to plants to be used without dilution in the control of plant pests. Because they are not soluble in water they must be emulsified before or at the time of dilution. In order to make an oil emulsion a third substance, called an emulsifier, is added to the water before the oil is stirred in. When the emulsion is made properly the oil exists as tiny droplets suspended in the water. It is then an oil-in-water emulsion. A reversed, or water-in-oil, emulsion cannot be used as a spray. Soaps (particularly fish-oil soap), blood albumen and a wide variety of other materials may be used as emulsifiers.

The standard, or Riley and Hubbard, formula for homemade kerosene emulsion is as follows:

Laundry soap (or its equivalent)...................................... ½ lb.
Soft water................................................................. 1 gal.
Kerosene.................................................................. 2 gal.

48

Dissolve the soap in the water; then while the mixture is beaten vigorously add the kerosene gradually. The best method of mixing is to pump the ingredients through a spray pump with a fine nozzle and back into the container from which the liquid is being taken. In a few minutes the mixture should become creamy and thick. When it is too stiff for further pumping the preparation is completed. It is now a stock emulsion which may be diluted for application. As a spray for the control of aphids and other soft-bodied insects, one part is mixed with about nine parts of water; for tougher insects one part is diluted with four or five parts of water. The stock emulsion should keep several weeks before breaking down into separate layers of water and oil.

Although homemade lubricating oil emulsions are sometimes recommended now for use in special situations, emulsions prepared commercially are more dependable and easier to apply. Two types of preparations, miscible oils and stock emulsions (often called oil-emulsion stocks), are on the market.

**Miscible oils** are more or less clear solutions of an emulsifier in oil, together with other materials to ensure ready emulsification when water is added. Because miscible oils contain little if any water they are not affected by freezing temperatures. Since many of the emulsifier formulas used are liable to injure foliage, miscible oils are usually limited to dormant spraying.

**Oil-emulsion stocks** contain the minimum percentage of water (20 to 30 per cent) necessary to make an actual emulsion of oil in water ready for dilution. They have an appearance and consistency similar to mayonnaise. Most ready-prepared summer oils are now marketed in this form. In emulsion stocks the oil droplets are surrounded by water so these preparations are liable to injury by water evaporation and by freezing.

**Coal-tar distillates** are emulsified for application in Europe where lubricating oil emulsions cost far more than in America. However, neutral tar oil is favored in some localities in the United States for the control of aphid eggs on dormant orchard trees. Certain of the coal-tar creosotes are used as animal dips. *Pine oil* and some *pine-tar* fractions are added to fly sprays or otherwise employed for their repellent properties. Pine oil has some value also in sprays for the control of plant lice and similar pests.

Such *vegetable oils* as cottonseed oil, palm oil and peanut oil are emulsified and used as contact sprays in parts of the world where they are of less value than petroleum products, as in China and North Africa.

## SOAPS

Soaps may be utilized alone in the control of such soft-bodied insects as aphids, although nicotine or some other insecticide is usually added to increase their efficiency. By themselves soaps are so low in effectiveness that applications must be thorough and repeated. Soaps are of the most value (1) in improving the spreading ability of other insecticides, in other words, in increasing the contact of the poison with the surface of the insect, and (2) in the emulsification of oils.

**Fish-oil soap.**—Although any vegetable or animal oil might be employed in making soap for insecticidal purposes, fish oil is the most common one cheap enough to be so utilized. Potash fish-oil soap is semiliquid and can be diluted without much trouble whereas sodium fish-oil soap is a hard product that can be dissolved only after considerable time and heating.

## SULFUR AND SULFUR COMPOUNDS

Sulfur, in the form of either elemental sulfur or lime-sulfur, is more important as a fungicide than as an insecticide. Large quantities, however, are used in the control of scale insects and mites on growing plants as well as external parasites on domestic animals.

**Sulfur** for dusting purposes is ground very fine so that it will be adhesive as well as more effective. Wettable sulfur for use as a spray contains an added wetting agent such as flour or glue. Colloidal sulfurs are adapted for use wherever the minute division of the sulfur particles adds sufficiently to their effectiveness to justify their greater cost.

**Lime-sulfur.**—When sulfur and lime are boiled together in water a mixture of calcium polysulfides, chiefly calcium pentasulfide, $CaS_5$, is formed. Either quicklime, $CaO$, or hydrated lime, $Ca(OH)_2$, may be used. Air-slaked lime (calcium carbonate) is not suitable. The commercial manufacture of lime-sulfur solution has largely eliminated home preparation. A hydrometer, usually graduated in degrees Baumé, is used for determining the strength of lime-sulfur concentrates. The Baumé hydrometer must be for liquids heavier than water; lighter liquids such as oils require a separate instrument with a different Baumé scale. Fresh concentrates usually test 32 to 34 Bé. Tables of density, Baumé readings, and the dilutions for both dormant and foliage use can be obtained by applying to a state agricultural experiment station or to the U.S. Bureau of Entomology and Plant Quarantine. Strong lime-sulfur sprays are used for the control of scale insects during the dormancy of trees, weaker solutions chiefly for disease control while the trees are in foliage. Lime-sulfur concentrate should be kept in a tight container to prevent decomposition by the action of the air.

**Dry lime-sulfur** was developed commercially as a substitute for the liquid concentrate to prevent deterioration in storage and the nuisance of transporting and handling a liquid. It is not so efficient as the liquid concentrate.

## PLANT PRODUCTS

**Nicotine** is most often rated as a contact insecticide because of its method of application, although in many spray combinations and most dusts it is gaseous nicotine that is largely responsible for insect mortality. It is the principal alkaloid in tobacco. Formerly tobacco stems and waste were soaked in water and the resulting extract used for spraying plants. But commercial nicotine preparations of standard strength are now used almost exclusively.

**Nicotine sulfate.**—Here the nicotine base has been neutralized with sulfuric acid to lower its volatility because the base itself is usually too volatile for best use in a contact spray. The standard strength of concentrated nicotine sulfate is 40 per cent, which refers to nicotine base at a strength of 40 per cent with sufficient acid added for neutralization, not to nicotine sulfate at a concentration of 40 per cent. Nicotine sulfate is commonly used both outdoors and in greenhouses as a spray for delicate insects, the spray strength being 1 part of 40 per cent concentrate to 800 or 1,000 parts of water, equivalent to about 0.4 to 0.5 pint of nicotine sulfate in 50 gallons of spray. For more resistant insects the dilution may be only 1 to 500. Soap is often added at the rate of 2 or 3 pounds in 50 gallons to increase the spreading and adherence of the spray. The alkali which is present in a weak solution of soap, reacts with the non-volatile nicotine sulfate to release the volatile nicotine base. Even in solution, nicotine base is more rapid than the sulfate in its action upon insects.

The standard formula for nicotine sulfate spray at a dilution of 1 to 800 is as follows:

|  | Per Barrel | Per Gallon |
|---|---|---|
| Nicotine sulfate, 40 per cent | ½ pt. | 1¼ tsp. |
| Soap | 2 to 3 lb. | 1 oz. |
| Water | 50 gal. | 1 gal. |

Three-eighths of a pint in 50 gallons of water, or 1 teaspoonful in a gallon, gives a dilution of roughly 1 to 1,000.

Concentrated **nicotine base** is sold for the preparation of certain types of nicotine dusts and for greenhouse fumigation. It is dangerous to handle because it passes through the unbroken skin to cause severe poisoning and, like nicotine sulfate, is highly poisonous by mouth.

**Nicotine dusts** have been employed rather extensively in the control of some truck crop insects. Originally ground tobacco was used but synthetic dusts composed of a carrier, such as lime, gypsum or clay, into which is mixed a quantity of nicotine sulfate, are more satisfactory because they are of more uniform strength. By changing the carrier the rate of evolution of nicotine vapor can be varied, an alkaline carrier such as lime promoting nicotine evolution, a colloidal carrier as clay retarding it. Gypsum is a relatively inert carrier. The average nicotine dust contains about 2 per cent nicotine.

**Pyrethrum (insect powder)** is derived from the blossoms of *Chrysanthemum cinerariœfolium*. It is exported chiefly from Japan, appreciable quantities coming also from Dalmatia (in Yugoslavia), from Kenya (in East Africa) and from southern Brazil. Most of the crude pyrethrum flowers in world trade are shipped to the United States. After being made into sprays for household and garden use, large quantities are then reshipped to other countries. In recent years annual imports of pyrethrum flowers have varied from twelve to twenty million pounds.

Pyrethrum contains two insecticidal compounds known as pyrethrins I and II. These compounds are unstable and oxidize rapidly when pyrethrum powder is exposed to air and sunshine, or hydrolyze to ineffective decomposition products when pyrethrum extract is diluted with water, especially in the presence of soap. Pyrethrins are nontoxic to man when they are ingested with the food, in so far as can be determined. Although large quantities of pyrethrum are used against insects a larger proportion of them recover than is often realized. Pyrethrum is purely a contact insecticide and has no practical stomach poison or fumigant value.

Most pyrethrum is utilized in one of three forms: (1) pyrethrum dust, known as insect powder, (2) oil-base pyrethrum extracts for the control of household pests such as flies and cockroaches, (3) water-soluble extracts for use against soft-bodied, plant-infesting insects. Pyrethrum extracts keep rather well if packed properly but powdered pyrethrum as well as the whole flowers deteriorate, especially if not kept in airtight containers; hence care must be taken in their purchase and storage.

**Derris, cube, rotenone.**—The roots of a number of trailing, leguminous shrubs, such as derris in the East Indies and cube in South America, are the source of rotenone and some closely related insecticidal compounds. The powdered roots are used as dusts, usually at a strength of about 0.75 per cent rotenone when they are intended for application to truck crops. Extracts are applied as sprays, sometimes in combination with pyrethrum. Insects are not likely to recover once rotenone takes effect upon them although the action is deceptively slow. As used in insect control these insecticides are relatively free from danger to man. They do not seem to be of great value against fruit tree insects. As in pyrethrum the toxic constituents are unstable. They act as both stomach and contact insecticides but being nonvolatile they have no fumigant value.

Rotenone-containing dusts are ordinarily composed of the ground roots of derris or cube mixed with a chemically inactive carrier such as talc, clay or sulfur. The rotenone content varies from 0.5 to 1.5 per cent, but related toxic compounds in the roots raise the percentage of active ingredients somewhat above these figures.

## SYNTHETIC INSECTICIDES

Within recent years a number of effective insecticides have been synthesized in chemical laboratories and made available commercially. The most successful is a patented organic thiocyanate marketed for the past decade as a contact insecticide for garden and greenhouse use, and in an oil base as a substitute for pyrethrum in fly sprays. Other promising synthetics have not received the same test of time.

## CONTACT SPRAY COMBINATIONS

Lime-sulfur and other sulfur preparations are sometimes recommended in combination with oil emulsions, but frequently such mixtures cause serious injury to the foliage of deciduous trees. Such injury may occur also when an oil spray follows the application of sulfur by some weeks or months.

Pyrethrum and derris are unstable in the presence of weak alkali or even when allowed to stand long after dilution with water. Bordeaux mixture and lime-sulfur are alkaline in reaction and should not be combined with pyrethrum or derris. Soap combinations with these insecticides should be used immediately after dilution.

Calcium and barium compounds, as calcium arsenate, hydrated lime, lime-sulfur and barium fluosilicate, will react with nicotine sulfate to produce insoluble, noninsecticidal sulfates. Soap should not be added to nicotine if the latter is to be combined with an arsenical.

# CHAPTER IX

## INSECT FUMIGANTS

Theoretically, fumigation is the best method for the control of insects, because every crevice in which an insect can hide is more certain to be penetrated by a gas than by a spray. The difficulty of producing concentrations of gas in the open, great enough to kill insects, limits outdoor fumigations to trees that may be covered with canvas tents, and to soil plots treated with calcium cyanide or other suitable chemicals. The term fumigation is therefore usually reserved for the gas treatment of closed spaces, although some so-called contact sprays and dusts kill largely by their vapor toxicity.

Fumigants are used mostly for the treatment of dwelling houses, manufacturing plants, warehouses, railroad cars, greenhouses and citrus orchards. Many buildings that are the most in need of fumigation are so loosely constructed that they cannot be treated economically with a gas. The gases most used for general building fumigation are hydrocyanic acid, sulfur dioxide and chloropicrin; for the local fumigation of individual rooms, bins and boxes, chloropicrin, ethylene dichloride, paradichlorobenzene and naphthalene. Hydrocyanic acid, nicotine, methyl bromide and naphthalene are the ones usually used for fumigating greenhouses and nursery stock. Formaldehyde, although important for other purposes, is not an effective fumigant for the control of insects.

Because of the absorptive capacity of closely packed materials, unusually high concentrations of gas are required to fumigate grain, flour, tobacco, cotton, etc. Specially built, gastight, fumigation chambers are utilized in the industrial gas treatment of many stored products. Baled cotton, sacked flour and such materials not easily permeated by a fumigant are often treated in vacuum chambers. When most of the air has been removed the fumigant is introduced, the vacuum drawing it rapidly into the pores of the product. Vacuum chambers are now in use large enough to admit loaded railroad cars. In so-called atmospheric chamber fumigation, the vacuum feature is lacking. The gas is usually circulated by fans to obtain a uniform concentration and to avoid the settling of heavy fumigant vapors and inadequate exposure to the gas near the top of the chamber. Although it is frequently recommended that liquid fumigants be exposed in shallow pans it is better to spray the chemical into the space to be treated, or at least to splash the fumigant over a large

54

surface so as to build up an effective gas concentration as rapidly as possible.

The temperature of the fumigated material influences the results tremendously. Below 60 to 65°F. most insects become inactive and much less susceptible to the gas. Furthermore the gas is taken up by the fumigated products more when the latter are cold, less gas then being available to kill the insects.

The only fundamental difference in the mode of action of fumigants from that of other insecticides lies in the fact that fumigants enter the body of an insect through the respiratory system rather than by way of the alimentary tract or directly through the body wall. Fumigants, however, do not act necessarily as true respiratory poisons; nicotine affects the nervous system, and sulfur fumes corrode the tissues by their acid action. In fumigation it is more important than in any other method of chemical control to use sufficient insecticide and to expose the insects to its action long enough, for there may be no kill at all at gas concentrations or exposures that are only a little less than those required for complete kill.

Arrangements for ventilation at the end of a fumigation are important, especially in chamber and general building fumigation. Unless a gas mask is used so that windows can be opened from within the fumigated space, some arrangement must be made for airing out the gas by opening from the outside. Industrial fumigation chambers are equipped with exhaust fans which remove the gas to a safe distance from buildings. In no case should there be opportunity for any unauthorized person to enter a space fumigated with hydrocyanic acid or methyl bromide, either in ignorance or in willful disregard, before adequate ventilation has been accomplished. Moderate inhalation of small amounts of carbon disulfide or ethylene dichloride usually results only in a headache or drowsiness, a warning that it is time to seek fresh air.

**Hydrocyanic acid.**—This gas, often called hydrogen cyanide, HCN, is the most important and effective insect fumigant as well as the most dangerous one to handle. Persons having no experience in its use should not attempt cyanide fumigation. Detailed directions for the guidance of fumigators can be obtained from a state agricultural experiment station or the U. S. Department of Agriculture.

Three general methods of evolving hydrocyanic acid gas are employed: (1) the reaction of dilute sulfuric acid upon sodium cyanide, (2) the action of atmospheric moisture upon calcium cyanide and (3) the release of the gas from heavy cylinders of liquid hydrocyanic acid.

The first, known as the pot method, is frequently used in dwelling fumigation. The gas is evolved in suitable acid-resistant containers, distributed according to the cubic space in each room. From 12 to 16 ounces of sodium cyanide are used per 1,000 cubic feet. For each ounce of cyanide 1.5 fluid ounces of sulfuric acid are used. The acid is diluted with not less than an equal amount of water, not over 1.5 times as much water as acid. The time allowed for the average house fumigation is about 24 hours including several hours for thorough ventilation. Both the concentration and the exposure time can be varied to suit individual conditions. Sometimes a modification of the pot method is employed, sodium cyanide and acid being brought together in a machine from which the evolved gas is piped into the space to be fumigated.

**Calcium cyanide** comes as flakes or dust containing up to 40 or 50 per cent of calcium cyanide. It is used commonly in greenhouse fumigation, as well as for the treatment of ordinary dwellings and larger buildings and for the control of soil insects. In the latter case the slower evolution of gas from calcium cyanide is an advantage, but in building fumigation leakage may disperse much of the gas before the required concentration can be reached. By the pot method of cyanide evolution, the entire charge of gas is released within a few minutes, whereas several hours are required for its release from calcium cyanide. Hydrocyanic acid is evolved more rapidly from calcium cyanide if the atmospheric humidity is high. Moist cloths may be hung about rooms to be fumigated or water may be splashed on the floor in the case of a warehouse. The cyanide should be spread so that it will not come in actual contact with water.

Liquid hydrocyanic acid is employed only by professional fumigators, mostly in citrus fumigation in California and in the treatment of large buildings piped especially for its use. In the latter case the cyanide is pumped under pressure from outside the building through pipes to nozzles located in the machinery or the spaces to be treated. Liquid cyanide is inflammable but in the proportions used for fumigation it becomes noninflammable as soon as it is vaporized and thoroughly mixed with the air.

Licensed fumigators do practically all the citrus tree fumigation as well as most of the building fumigation in the larger cities. Ordinances prohibit the occupation of any part of a building while another part is being fumigated with cyanide. Hence, individual rooms or apartments cannot be treated with this gas without the evacuation of the entire building.

Hydrocyanic acid has a very rapid effect upon a person exposed to it. It is not safe to remain long in the gas even while wearing a gas mask because the gas penetrates rapidly through the skin. Once the gas takes effect a person is soon made unconscious.

Plants are killed if left in a house during cyanide fumigation. Greenhouse treatment with hydrocyanic acid must be done only after dark, at moderately low temperatures (about 65°F.) and a low level of atmospheric moisture (not recently watered). The concentration of cyanide for the fumigation of living plants is much less than that desirable for dwelling fumigation, and the exposure time is only three-fourths to one hour. Many kinds of plants are too susceptible to the gas to survive even this treatment. Dormant nursery stock is frequently fumigated with cyanide but at a higher dosage than for greenhouse treatment, in fact at about the same strength as for the fumigation of citrus trees which is done while the trees are most nearly dormant from October to January.

**Sulfur dioxide,** $SO_2$, is the gas given off in the fumes of burning sulfur. For fumigation it is produced by the burning of either ready-made sulfur "candles" or piles of powdered sulfur moistened with alcohol. Sulfur is used at the rate of about two pounds per thousand cubic feet. Sulfur dioxide is a potent insect fumigant but has fallen somewhat into disrepute because it tarnishes certain metals and in the presence of moisture may bleach colored paper and fabrics. Because sulfur fumes are absorbed by water to produce sulfurous acid which will rot curtains and clothing, sulfur fumigation should be done only in dry weather. Metal may be protected with a coating of Vaseline. Living plants and seeds, as well as food products like flour, are injured by the gas. Precautions against fire must be taken by placing the containers of burning sulfur on metal sheets or pans raised on bricks.

Because sulfur can be burned by a person of average intelligence without much danger and because the other fumigants are expensive in comparison, sulfur dioxide can be recommended for home use under suitable conditions, especially when the need for insect extermination is great enough to outweigh any possible injury to furnishings.

**Chloropicrin,** $CCl_3NO_2$, is the tear gas commonly known in chemical warfare during the European war of 1914–1918 as vomiting gas. It is so repellent that harmless traces will prevent a person from entering an atmosphere contaminated with it. It is a noninflammable liquid boiling at 112°C. The chief advantage of chloropicrin, aside from its warning properties, is its persistence in a fumigated space, leakage not affecting its concentration as rapidly as in the case of most other fumigants.

Chloropicrin is used at the rate of one to two pounds or more per thousand cubic feet. A full-face gas mask must be worn while handling it, except in the open when the liquid can be poured while the operator stands on the windward side. Farm granaries are sometimes treated with chloropicrin, although more experience is required than for the usual liquid grain fumigant composed chiefly of ethylene dichloride.

**Methyl bromide,** $CH_3Br$, was discovered only recently to have value for this purpose, but it is already a highly successful commercial fumigant, marketed in heavy metal cylinders.    It is a noninflammable liquid which boils at about 4°C. (40°F.).    Since it is more penetrating than most fumigants, it is particularly useful in the chamber fumigation of flour and other closely packed products.    The fact that it can be used more successfully than any other gas in the fumigation of living plants is another important reason for its rapid development.    It is not adapted for use where leakage is a serious factor.    Considerable danger lies in its lack of a marked warning odor.    One to two pounds per thousand cubic feet is the usual dosage.

**Carbon disulfide**, $CS_2$, produces a highly inflammable and explosive vapor.    It boils at 46°C. (115°F.), so its volatility is relatively high. Large quantities have been used in the past as a fumigant.    The vapor is easily exploded by an open flame, electric or other spark, or heated pipes.    Although somewhat less effective in killing insects, ethylene dichloride is much safer and is now usually recommended in place of carbon disulfide, especially for use in or near buildings of value.

**Ethylene dichloride**, $C_2Cl_2H_4$, is a colorless liquid boiling at 84°C. (183°F.).    It is only slightly inflammable but, to eliminate all danger of burning, it may be mixed with carbon tetrachloride at the rate of three parts by volume of ethylene dichloride to one of carbon tetrachloride. The mixture is used at the rate of fifteen to twenty pounds per 1,000 cubic feet if the space to be fumigated is fairly tight and its contents of average absorptivity.    Larger amounts must be used in stored grain fumigation, from three to five gallons (about thirty-five to fifty-five pounds) per thousand bushels of grain (a space equivalent to 1,245 cubic feet).

**Nicotine as a fumigant.**—As indicated in the previous chapter, free nicotine (nicotine base) is volatile.    If it is applied as a "contact insecticide" against aphids and similar plant pests its action is due partly to the nicotine fumes which enter the tracheae of the insect and partly to the nicotine passing directly from the spray solution through the body wall.    Nicotine is important as a fumigant in the usual or practical meaning of the word, chiefly in greenhouse fumigation.    Liquid nicotine base is evaporated over a heater, or nicotine absorbed in some inflammable carrier is burned, to produce nicotine fumes.

**Paradichlorobenzene** is a white, volatile, crystalline compound used in insect control principally against the peach tree borer and clothes moths. **Naphthalene** is similar in appearance but is less volatile.    It is used for bulb and greenhouse fumigation and for the protection of woolen and fur clothing and furnishings.    It may be obtained in flake form or as moth balls.    Both compounds are more effective as flakes than when compressed into balls or cakes.

**Soil fumigation** is sometimes practiced against wireworms, grubs and other soil-inhabiting organisms. It is practical only under intensive cultural conditions, as in experimental plots, golf greens, plant nurseries, truck gardens and greenhouses. The most promising fumigants for this purpose are carbon disulfide, chloropicrin, naphthalene, dichloroethyl ether and ethylene dichloride. Dichloroethyl ether has been developed recently and shows some promise along this line. Those fumigants which are liquids are frequently emulsified in water by means of soap before application.

# CHAPTER X

## THE RELATIONSHIPS OF INSECTS

Classification may be defined as the orderly arrangement of different objects into groups. Any articles can be classified in one way or another: chairs, for example, can be brought into groups according to the kinds of wood of which they are made, or whether they are upholstered or not, or according to their price; and any of these might be equally useful. With living things, however, the problem becomes one of a "natural" as opposed to an "artificial" classification.

It is now the general belief that the first animals were extremely simple in structure, and that in the course of generations (and centuries) variation in their descendants led to the production of different forms, and finally to all the multitudes of kinds now in existence. This development has often been pictured as a tree, the trunk representing the original animals, which, varying as individuals of the same kind always do, began after a time to show several distinct lines along which the variation took place. This would be represented in the tree by the lowest branching of the trunk. Each main limb under the influence of the same conditions would fork in its turn, perhaps into two, perhaps more, and this process repeated again and again would finally produce the terminal twigs—the present animals. Thus each twig would represent all the individuals of the same kind, *i.e.*, a single species; those nearest it the other species most closely related to it; and those on another part of the tree, though species and also related, would be only distantly so and, of course, quite different.

A natural classification of animals, therefore, is an attempt to express the actual relationships of the animals, placing nearest each other those most closely related. To do this, the total of their differences and resemblances must be taken into account. Classification based on a single character, then, is almost always unreliable. The division of insects into three main groups based on their metamorphosis is an example of this, for, although it is entirely correct as a statement of facts, a classification using this character would bring near together many insects which in reality are only distantly related.

The largest limb of the animal tree represents the original insects, not because they were so numerous at first, but because insects now form such a large part of animal life. This limb is usually called a class, whereas the still more comprehensive groups considered in Chap. I are called phyla. These are the main divisions of the tree. In this case the Hexapoda is the name given to the insect class (Fig. 36).

From all the evidence available, the original insects were at least comparatively small, wingless and with practically no metamorphosis. After a time many of their descendants began to develop wings, and a fork of the class was produced, one branch (or subclass), the Apterygota, apparently retaining much of its former character, and the other sub-

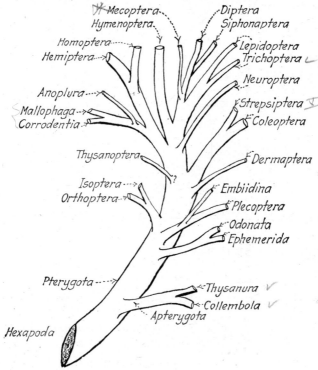

Fig. 36.—Diagram suggesting possible relations of the orders of insects to each other, expressed in a tree-like way; the hexapod limb.

class becoming the Pterygota or winged insects. These have increased greatly in abundance, and their variations have resulted in the production of many branches passing outward toward the twigs, named in sequence, orders, families, genera and species. Intermediate branchings between these often also need recognition and are called suborders, super-families, etc., as may be necessary. The twigs each represent a single species, but here we may recognize subspecies, varieties, races, etc., among which the individuals that together constitute the species are distributed.

In any consideration of the different groups of insects one must necessarily follow after another through the book, and when four groups, for example, are equally near relatives the first and fourth treated may thereby appear more distant than is really the case.

| Class | Subclass | Order | Suborder | Common Name or Examples |
|---|---|---|---|---|
| | | Protura | | (No common name) |
| | Apterygota | Thysanura | | Silverfish, etc. |
| | | Collembola | | Snow fleas, etc. |
| | | Ephemerida | | May flies |
| | | Odonata | | Dragonflies |
| | | Isoptera | | Termites or white ants |
| | | Orthoptera | | Cockroaches, grasshoppers, crickets, etc. |
| | | Dermaptera | | Earwigs |
| | | Plecoptera | | Stone flies |
| | | Embiidina | | (No common name) |
| | | Corrodentia | | Booklice; psocids |
| | | Zoraptera | | (No common name) |
| | | Mallophaga | | Biting or chewing bird lice |
| | | Thysanoptera | | Thrips |
| | | Anoplura | | Sucking lice |
| Hexapoda | | Hemiptera | | True bugs |
| | Pterygota | Homoptera | | Aphids, scales, leafhoppers, etc. |
| | | Coleoptera | Coleoptera vera | True beetles |
| | | | Rhynchophora | Snout beetles |
| | | Strepsiptera | | Stylopids |
| | | Neuroptera | | Corydalis, aphis lions, ant lions, etc. |
| | | Trichoptera | | Caddice flies |
| | | Lepidoptera | Heterocera | Moths |
| | | | Rhopalocera | Butterflies |
| | | Mecoptera | | Scorpion flies |
| | | Diptera | | Flies |
| | | Siphonaptera | | Fleas |
| | | Hymenoptera | Symphyta | Sawflies, horntails |
| | | | Apocrita | Ichneumon flies, ants, wasps, bees, etc. |

Between the fork of the insect limb which produced the Apterygota and the Pterygota, and the twigs representing the species, the actual divisions of the branches are more or less uncertain. The species in general group themselves quite easily into different genera and these into families; but although these last can in most cases be definitely placed in their orders, their correct relation to each other is often debatable. The relation of the orders to each other is far from settled; and although some are evidently more closely allied than others, within certain limits one order could follow another in almost any sequence without any serious loss to the expression of relationships. Where orders appear to be closely allied to each other, this will be indicated in connection with their consideration.

With the relations between the orders and also the families within the orders still uncertain in many cases, a tree showing these must of necessity express only the views of the individual who drew it. Such a tree carried to the species would be entirely too large for these pages (there are about eighty families of beetles, and many of the other orders have large numbers also), but one carried to the orders is given here (Fig. 36) simply to illustrate the general idea of a tree-like classification without any attempt to show the real relations of the groups to each other.

In the following chapters the names of the orders here used are followed in parentheses by other names which have been applied to these groups.

# CHAPTER XI

## SUBCLASS APTERYGOTA

### ORDERS PROTURA: THYSANURA: COLLEMBOLA

The Apterygota are all relatively small, wingless insects, some being as small as one-fiftieth of an inch; the largest are not more than two inches in length. They are all land animals though a few live near the ocean and are often found in tide pools. They are widely distributed, some living in arctic conditions and others occurring in the tropics, but most of them require a more or less humid atmosphere.

In this group the mouth parts seem to be typically of the chewing type. In many cases they are as much exposed as in most insects, but, in some, folds of the cheeks extend over them so that they are almost concealed. Under such conditions they are often so slender as to be no longer of value for chewing and are probably used for piercing and sucking.

Some Apterygota have traces of abdominal legs; spine-like appendages, attached to the hinder margins of some of the abdominal segments beneath and called styli, may also be present.

Bringing together these facts, the Apterygota may be characterized as *Wingless insects having the mouth parts either exposed and of the chewing type, or almost entirely concealed by folds of the cheeks. Then they are often slender and probably used for piercing and sucking. Metamorphosis is extremely slight.*

Not all wingless insects belong here. Some wingless forms had winged ancestors and have now lost their wings by degeneration under conditions where their presence would be of no use to the insect or even a distinct disadvantage. The Apterygota are believed to be survivors of the original insects that never had wings.

Very few of the Apterygota are of great importance from an economic standpoint, but they are of much interest, being the simplest insects known and throwing some light upon the subject of the ancestry of the insect group.

Three subdivisions, the orders Protura, Thysanura and Collembola, are now recognized in the Apterygota, of which over two thousand species are known.

### ORDER PROTURA

This order contains a small number of tiny insects, the largest being only about three-fiftieths of an inch long. They occur in many parts of the world in

64

damp places and so far as known are not injurious. Some species have no tracheae, obtaining air through the extremely thin cuticula of the surface of the body.

## ORDER THYSANURA

In this order the insects average much larger than in either of the other two groups of the subclass. The abdomen is composed of ten or eleven segments and at its end is a pair of cerci, thread-like except in a few species in which they resemble forceps. Styli, slender appendages, each having two segments, occur on the underside of the abdomen and sometimes on some of the thoracic segments also, the former attached to large plates believed to be the bases of former abdominal legs. In some Thysanura the body is covered by scales suggesting those on butterfly wings. The order may be described as

*Apterygota with styli on the underside of the abdomen; usually with slender, many-segmented cerci or forceps-like structures at the end of the abdomen which is composed of ten or eleven segments.*

Only a few Thysanura are of any great importance in the United States, the chief ones being the silverfish or "slicker" and the firebrat.

**The silverfish** (*Lepisma saccharina* L.).—This little household pest is found in both Europe and this country. It is silvery gray in color, usually less than half an inch long, very active and hard to catch (Fig. 37). Besides the two long cerci at the hinder end of the body it has a similar "caudal filament" giving the insect the appearance of having three "tails." It prefers dark places and feeds on anything containing starch, the sizing in paper, wallpaper or rayon and on damp wheat flour. It often loosens wallpaper by feeding on the starch used to paste it to the wall. It prefers temperatures of about 80°F. but is often found in much cooler places.

FIG. 37.—Silverfish (*Lepisma saccharina* L.); about twice natural size. (*After 14th Rept. Minn. State Entomologist.*)

**The firebrat** (*Thermobia domestica* Pack.).—This insect greatly resembles the silverfish, but its back is mottled with whitish and darker spots; its favorite temperature is at about 98°F. and so is most abundant in fire rooms, near ovens and similar hot places. Its food is like that of the silverfish and in many places it is called the asbestos bug for it feeds on the sizing used in the manufacture of the asbestos insulation for steam pipes.

*Control for the silverfish and firebrat.*—Dusting pyrethrum where the insects exist, using sodium fluoride in the same way, and poison baits, using a starchy base and a stomach poison, are often of value. Make a boiled paste of flour 1 pint; white arsenic or sodium fluoride ½ ounce; water enough to make a thin paste after boiling; spread on cards marked "Poison" and place where the insects are found. A powdered bait composed of finely ground oatmeal 200 parts by weight; either barium carbonate or sodium fluoride 16 parts; powdered sugar 10 parts; and common salt 5 parts, has been effective when scattered under crimped paper in uncovered shallow boxes placed where the insects have occurred.

### ORDER COLLEMBOLA

The Collembola are usually very small insects and, being dark colored in most cases, are not often noticed. Most of this group have a "spring" attached near

Fig. 38.          Fig. 39.

Fig. 38.—Springtail (*Papirius fuscus* Lucas), showing forked "spring" projecting forward toward the head beneath the body. Greatly enlarged. (*From Lubbock.*)

Fig. 39.—Snow flea (*Achorutes nivicola* Fitch); greatly enlarged. Real length ½₁₂ in. (*From Folsom.*)

the hinder end of the body beneath. This consists of a single piece to which a pair of others are joined and the whole is carried pointing forward when not in use (Fig. 38). When the spring is suddenly pressed against the ground, the entire body of the insect is thrown into the air and a peculiar hopping or leaping motion results. On the underside of the first abdominal segment is the collophore, an organ very differently developed in different species. It secretes a sticky fluid which aids the insect in holding on to smooth surfaces.

The Collembola may be described as

*Apterygota without styli on the underside of the abdomen; cerci absent or very small; abdomen of six segments, often so much condensed as hardly to show that number; with a variously developed collophore on the first abdominal segment beneath; with a ventral spring in most cases; insects usually much smaller than the Thysanura.*

Familiar members of this order are the snow fleas sometimes seen in enormous numbers on snow, where their dark color and hopping movements make them very noticeable (Fig. 39).

The greatest injury caused by these insects is to tender plants, especially seedlings, and to mushrooms. They make tiny holes in the leaves, stems and roots in different cases, destroy root hairs and small rootlets and make places where spores of fungi and bacteria can enter. With mushrooms they feed on the mycelium and also on the stems and caps, sometimes ruining them completely.

*Control.*—For mushrooms, dusting with a 2 to 3 per cent nicotine and lime dust has proved excellent. Naphthalene and paradichlorobenzene appear to have considerable value used in greenhouses, and tobacco dust and air-slaked lime have given good results in seed beds and with field crops.

Folsom states that about two thousand species of Collembola have been described.

# CHAPTER XII

## SUBCLASS PTERYGOTA: ORDER EPHEMERIDA

The subclass Pterygota includes practically all our common insects and is the main branch of the class Hexapoda, the Apterygota though of equal rank, being a mere twig in relative size.

As a whole the Pterygota are characterized by the presence of wings, though many of them for one reason or another have lost these structures.

Almost all the characters present in insects may be found in this section without referring to the Apterygota; practically all the pests and all the beneficial forms belong here, and their differences are so great that a large number of subdivisions—orders—have been established for them.

The early entomologists did not regard these differences as of great importance and called the groups families or gave them even lower rank. Linnaeus in 1758 placed all insects in seven orders only. More recent workers, however, have considered the differences as being of greater importance and have divided the Pterygota into twenty-three orders and the Apterygota as already indicated into three others. It is not unlikely that some of these may be divided as the insects now placed in them are studied more.

### ORDER EPHEMERIDA
### (Ephemeroptera: Plectoptera)

The Ephemerida, May flies or shad flies as they are often called (Fig. 40), are insects of medium or small size. The adults have delicate bodies and gauzy, fragile wings, the latter usually with many cross veins. The forewings are much larger than the hind ones, which in some cases are absent, and the former are in general rather strongly triangular in outline. When at rest they are held vertically above the body. At the end of the abdomen two or three long threads, each composed of many segments and often called caudal filaments, are usually present, the lateral ones being cerci corresponding to those in the Thysanura.

The mouth parts of the adult May fly are of the chewing type, but so poorly developed that it is doubtful if they are ever made use of. In some cases they are even rudimentary. The reproductive organs differ from those in all the other groups, the ducts being not united on the middle line below, but opening separately to the outside—apparently the retention of a very primitive condition. The early stages are passed in the water, the nymphs breathing—at least after the first few molts—by tracheal gills. These are delicate, usually wing-like in form, and are outgrowths of the body wall. Into them pass tracheal trunks which branch again and again so that only their own walls and those of the gill itself separate the air in the tracheae from that in the water outside, and so thin are these layers that the oxygen in the water can pass through them into the tracheae, and carbon dioxide gas pass out (Fig. 41).

These insects add to their list of peculiarities also the fact that, after becoming full grown and being able to fly, they molt once more, even a thin layer over the final wings being shed.

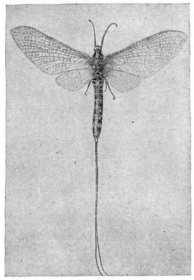

Fig. 40.—Adult May fly (*Hexagenia variabilis* Eaton) showing the long cerci; natural size. (*From Folsom.*)

From these statements the group may be characterized as

*Insects having as adults delicate bodies and usually four wings, the front pair much larger than the others (which are sometimes absent), and generally with many cross veins; end of the abdomen with two or three long caudal filaments composed of many segments; reproductive organs with two openings to the exterior; mouth parts of the chewing type but practically rudimentary; nymphs living in water and with an incomplete metamorphosis, the final molt coming after the wings have become fully developed.*

May flies are most abundant near streams and lakes, as their nymphs live in the water. The fully mature nymphs leave the water, usually in greatest numbers about sunset, and, suddenly molting, extend their wings and fly off but, as previously stated, usually molt again within a few hours. As their flight generally begins about dusk and as they are strongly attracted to lights, they are often seen in multitudes around street lights during the evenings.

The adults live only a few hours—not more than a few days at most—but during this time the eggs are laid in the water. The nymphs (naiads) which hatch from them feed mainly on vegetable matter at the bottom, though some are possibly partly carnivorous. They live for one, two or three years, according to the species concerned (some have two genera-

Fig. 41.—Nymph of a May fly showing tracheal gills on the abdomen above; enlarged (*After Needham; from Comstock, Introduction to Entomology, Comstock Publishing Company.*)

tions each year), feeding and molting with unusual frequency for insects (Lubbock observed twenty-one molts in one species), until they are full-grown. During this time the mouth parts are well developed and of the chewing type, but in the adult they become practically useless.

These insects are of no economic importance except perhaps to a very slight degree as scavengers in the water, feeding on matter that might otherwise decay and become objectionable, but their value for this is probably small at best. They are fed upon as larvae, and to some extent as adults, by fish and some carnivorous insects of other groups and for this reason also may be rated as slightly beneficial. At present about eight hundred kinds are known (Austin), but the group has not been very thoroughly studied. Many fossil ephemerids have been found, which suggests that the insects are possibly less abundant now than was once the case.

# CHAPTER XIII
## ORDER ODONATA
(Paraneuroptera)

The Odonata are such large and noticeable insects that they have received many common names, such as dragonflies, snake doctors, devil's-darning-needles and snake feeders. They are most plentiful near water, as in this they spend their early lives, though the larger and more powerful members of the group are frequently seen flying high in the air and at some distance from their more usual habitat.

The dragonflies have rather long, slender bodies, the abdomen being less shortened by the fusion and telescoping of its segments than in most insects. The head is large, generally rather spherical, though concave behind, and a great part of its surface is occupied by two very large compound eyes, each of which, in some species, contains more than thirty thousand facets. As these insects are carnivorous and capture their prey as it is flying, the advantage of large eyes which are also, because of the curvature of the surface of the head, capable of seeing in almost every direction is evident. There are also three ocelli. The antennae are short and not very noticeable.

The mouth parts, which are of the chewing type, are large and well developed. The food appears to be captured by the legs and held by them while it is being eaten. 

Four wings are present, all of about equal size, though the hinder pair are somewhat larger except in the section known as the damsel flies. The main veins are stout and are connected by many cross veins. Near the middle of the costa of each wing is a slight notch called the nodus, at which point there is a particularly stout cross vein. When at rest the wings are held either nearly vertical over the body (damsel flies) or extended laterally, much as in flight. The metamorphosis is by progressive changes at times of molting; and though the nymph can hardly be said ever greatly to resemble the adult, development may be considered as being by an incomplete metamorphosis.

The Odonata may then be characterized as

*Insects which as adults usually have long, slender bodies, large heads and large eyes; wings four, membranous, the hinder pair as large as or larger than the front pair, and each has near the middle of its front margin a notch, somewhat resembling a joint, called the nodus; mouth parts for chewing and well developed. Metamorphosis is incomplete.*

71

There are two groups of dragonflies. In one the insect is slender, the two pairs of wings are of about equal size and when not in use are held almost vertically above the body (Fig. 42). These insects are often

Fig. 42.—Damsel fly (*Lestes uncata* Kirby) showing position of wings when at rest. (*After Needham, N. Y. State Mus. Bull.* 68.)

Fig. 43.—Dragonfly (*Anax junius* Dru.); natural size.

called damsel flies. In the other group the body is stouter and proportionally shorter, and the wings when at rest extend out horizontally at the sides of the body (Fig. 43).

The bodies of dragonflies are often brilliantly colored and in some cases covered with a "bloom," giving them a whitish appearance (Fig.

44). The adults feed on almost any flying insects smaller than themselves which they may capture during their flight. Flies and mosquitoes form a favorite food, and the attempt has been made to "tame" dragonflies and keep them in houses on this account, but without success. They are very voracious, one specimen having been known to consume forty house flies in less than two hours.

Fig. 44.—Dragonfly (*Plathemis lydia* Dru.) showing "bloom" on abdomen; about natural size.

Many dragonflies fly very swiftly either in direct lines or with sudden changes of direction while hunting their prey and are perhaps unequaled in this regard by any other insects. They mate in the air. The eggs are laid either in the water, attached to water plants, or in the stems of plants under water. In the latter case they are laid singly but otherwise they are usually in clusters containing either a small or a large number of eggs.

Fig. 45.—Nymph of a dragonfly with mask (labium) extended forward; enlarged one-third.

The eggs may hatch after a few days or, if laid in the fall, may not produce nymphs until the following spring. The young nymphs stay at the bottom of the water and are carnivorous, feeding on larger and larger animals as they grow, individuals of the largest species attacking small fish in some cases, though the bulk of their food is undoubtedly the aquatic larvae of insects. They lie on the bottom waiting for their prey to come within reach, and when it is near enough they thrust out the underlip (labium) and seize it (Fig. 45). This labium has been remarkably developed from its usual form, being drawn out into two long pieces with a pair of jaws or claws at the end. When not extended the piece connected at one end with the head is bent backward under the body; the second piece, hinged to the other end of the first, extends forward so that its front end with the jaws lies near the front of the head, which it somewhat conceals. This has led to calling the structure a mask. When this is extended forward it enables the nymph (naiad) to capture animals that are not very close to it.

In the nymphs of the damsel flies breathing appears to be, in part at least, by means of long and rather large tracheal gills at the end of the abdomen, which are also used for swimming. In the other section of the order, the gills are found in the rectum, into which water is drawn, bathing the gills there, after which it is expelled; if this is done quickly the recoil carries the nymph forward, thus providing one means of locomotion.

Molts are frequent, and when full-grown the nymph crawls out of the water and molts for the last time, whereupon the wings grow to full size and the adult insect is produced. Some dragonflies have two generations a year or possibly even more; in other cases more than a year is necessary to a generation, but one each season is the usual condition.

Despite tradition and their bad reputation, dragonflies are in no way injurious to man, not stinging—they have nothing to sting with—nor biting to such an extent as to cause the slightest pain, their jaws being too weak even to break the skin. They are beneficial insects as both young and adults, because so much of their food consists of injurious insects such as flies and mosquitoes, whereas the injury they cause by feeding on fish is usually so slight as to be negligible.

Dragonflies are sun-loving animals, concealing themselves during dark, cloudy weather. Over five thousand kinds are known, the greatest number of which occur in the warmer regions. Fossil dragonflies or insects resembling them are numerous, and some of them were very large, one measuring more than two feet from wing tip to wing tip.

## CHAPTER XIV

### ORDER ISOPTERA

These insects arc commonly called white ants or termites, the former name being used because, though not nearly related to ants, they live in colonies and in many of their ways resemble these insects.

The white ants, as their name suggests, are whitish in color (the winged adults may be brown or blackish). The group is essentially a tropical one but some of them are found as far north as Canada. The

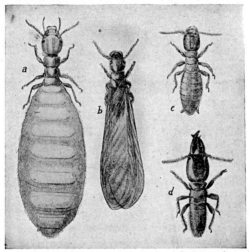

Fig. 46.—Castes of a termite colony: *a*, queen; *b*, male; *c*, worker; *d*, soldier; all much enlarged. Observe space between the nota of the abdominal segments in *a*. (*After Jordan and Kellogg, Evolution and Animal Life, D. Appleton-Century Company.*)

tropical species differ so markedly in many of their ways from the northern ones that separate descriptions almost sccm necessary. In all, however, there is a colonial life and a division of the insects into several groups or "castes."

A colony normally consists of one or more males or "kings" (Fig. 46*b*), one or sometimes several females or "queens" (Fig. 46*a*) and a variable but generally large number of other individuals, nearly always at least, of two castes, known as workers and soldiers (Fig. 46*c* and *d*). These may be individuals of either sex which have not developed to reproductive maturity. During a short period of their lives the kings and queens have fully developed wings, four in number, long, narrow and quite similar in

75

appearance, which when at rest are laid flat upon the back. Near the base of each wing is a line marking where it will easily break off. The part between this point and the body is horny; the remainder is at most only somewhat leathery. At the end of the abdomen is a pair of short cerci. Development of the young is by an incomplete metamorphosis.

The group may accordingly be characterized as

*Insects living in colonies and of several castes, of which only the kings and queens ever have wings. These are four in number, long, more or less leathery, narrow, similar, laid flat on the back when not in use and easily broken off near their bases. The bodies of the insects are soft and usually*

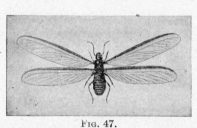 

FIG. 47.                                     FIG. 48.

FIG. 47.—Adult male of a tropical termite (*Termes spinosus* Latr.); about half natural size. (*After Desneux.*)

FIG. 48.—Laying queen of a tropical termite (*Termes gilvus* Hag.); reduced nearly one-half. (*From Desneux.*)

*whitish in color. The abdomen has a pair of cerci at its hinder end. Mouth parts are for chewing. Metamorphosis is incomplete.*

The food of termites is mainly dead wood, though living trees and other plants sometimes suffer from their attacks. Their nests in the tropics are made of earth, wood that has been chewed up and their excrement. They are often prominent objects, sometimes twenty feet or more in height, and seem to vary in form to some extent according to the species.

Termites "swarm" at some seasons, enormous numbers of winged kings (Fig. 47) and queens leaving their nest at about the same time and flying off. After alighting, the wings are broken off and each pair of individuals turns its attention to the establishment of a new colony. In the tropical species which form large nests and have thousands of individuals in a colony, the abdomen of the queen gradually becomes distended by the developing eggs until this part of the body may become several inches long and an inch or more in diameter, so that the insect is entirely helpless and unable to move (Fig. 48). The workers, which are generally blind, provide for the queen, carry away the eggs, feed and care for the young, construct the nest and indeed do all the work of the colony. The soldiers are generally regarded as a caste produced for the protection of the colony, but numerous observations which show the workers to be better fighters throw doubt upon the real duties of this caste.

Other castes besides those already mentioned have been discovered in different species of termites, at least fifteen having been recognized, though not for any one species. In addition to the royal pair, workers and soldiers, however, a caste consisting of individuals generally called complementary kings and queens or neoteinic members of the colony is generally present, at least in the older colonies. This caste is capable of reproduction, though less abundantly than the true queen, and appears to be produced to continue the colony after her death.

The most generally common species of termite in the United States (*Reticulitermes flavipes* Kol.), except perhaps in the far south and on the Pacific coast, does not appear to form large colonies (see Fig. 46). Its nests occur under logs and in them, in fence posts, timbers of buildings or other structures or in tunnels in the ground, though here usually in near proximity to wood. Centering here, they go out through tunnels, always protected from the light, mining in woodwork, honeycombing it and leaving only a thin film on the surface to conceal them and shut out the light. If necessary to reach the wood they desire, they may construct small covered passages over the surface of stone, brick or similar materials, through which they pass. They will also attack books and papers, pasteboard, leather, etc., if stored in dark and moist places. In some cases they attack trees, infesting roots and the heartwood near the base. Citrus trees in the south are often seriously injured by them. Field crops are also affected, the roots being fed upon; plants in gardens and greenhouses are often attacked, the termites sometimes coming up to the benches through covered tubes, in the latter location, and working first in the wooden bench sides and then passing to the plants themselves. True queens have seldom been found in the nests of this species.

*Control.*—Protection of wooden structures can best be obtained by taking care that no wood comes in contact with the ground and that light and dryness are ensured as much as possible. Timbers thoroughly treated with coal-tar creosote are repellent to the insects. With houses a thin sheet of metal, placed between the foundation and the lowest timbers, extending all the way around and projecting out on all sides about an inch, will prevent covered passages being built up over the foundation to the wood. Poles to be set in the ground may be treated with coal-tar creosote under considerable pressure after removal of any water in them; this will give good protection. Spraying them with cement has also been successful.

When termites are already in the wood, all infested parts will generally need to be removed and the nest should be located, if possible, and destroyed by using kerosene or by fumigation.  Treat all wood exposed to attack, but not yet infested, with creosote or other tested wood preservative.  Treatment of the soil near a building with a mixture of trichlorbenzene one part, fuel oil or creosote two parts, aids for a few years in keeping termites away.

The termites are not a large group, numbering between fifteen hundred and two thousand species, but the size of their nests in the tropics attracts attention, and their habits and colonial life are of much interest.  They appear to be most closely related to the Orthoptera. Fossil species are quite numerous.

# CHAPTER XV

## ORDER ORTHOPTERA

The Orthoptera is a large group of insects containing about twenty thousand species. Many of them are very large and striking in appearance and common names have been given to different families in the group, but none to it as a whole.

The insects belonging here are so diverse in structure, appearance and habits that it is difficult to give distinctive characters, but they all have well-developed chewing mouth parts. The majority of them have four wings, the front pair being slightly thicker than the others, somewhat leathery in texture and overlapping more or less when folded. The hind wings are almost always larger and fold in plaits. In many of the group, however, the wings are lacking or very small in the adults; in this case it is sometimes difficult to tell from these structures whether the insect is a short-winged adult or a nymph in which the wings have not as yet completed their development. The Dermaptera were at one time placed in this order.

In some of the families the hind legs are much developed and the insects have the power of jumping; in others this is not the case and walking and running are their methods of locomotion on the ground. On this basis the order has often been divided into two sections, Cursoria or running Orthoptera, and Saltatoria or leaping Orthoptera.

The Orthoptera may be defined, despite the difficulties above indicated, as

*Insects which when adult have mouth parts for chewing; usually four wings, the front pair thicker than the others; the hind pair larger and folded in plaits when at rest. A pair of cerci is always present. Metamorphosis is incomplete.*

Many students of the group are of the opinion that the insects included in this order should really be placed in two or three, but at present such a separation seems hardly advisable. Most of the families are quite distinct. The group is frequently divided into eight or ten families, but for the purposes of this book six will be considered. These are

Cursoria { Blattidæ, cockroaches.
Mantidæ, mantids.
Phasmidæ, walkingsticks.

Saltatoria { Acrididæ, locusts and short-horned grasshoppers.
Tettigoniidæ, long-horned grasshoppers and katydids.
Gryllidæ, crickets.

79

*Family* **BLATTIDÆ** (the cockroaches; roaches).—These insects are known by a variety of common names such as cockroaches, roaches, water bugs and black beetles. The group is primarily one living in warm countries with many kinds living in houses, and many more, some of them several inches in length, occurring wild. In more northern climates only a few are wild. Several are household pests, these last when adult ranging from less than an inch to nearly two inches in length. In the north the wild species are found under logs and stones and seldom enter houses. They are of various shades of brown and the winged adults are an inch or slightly more in length.

FIG. 49.—Egg case of American cockroach; *a*, side; *b*, end view; both considerably enlarged. (*Modified from U.S. Dept. Agr. Farmers' Bull. 658.*)

Cockroaches are generally brown or dark colored, though some are green. They are broad and flattened, with the head bent under the body so that the mouth opens backward and the eyes look downward. The antennae are long, slender and of many segments. Wings are usually developed in the adults and the hinder pair fold once. The mouth parts are strong, the legs long and in most species bear many spines. Cockroaches are active at night, hiding in dark places such as cracks and crevices during daylight and running very rapidly when disturbed.

The household pests of this group consume foods and food materials freely; gnaw woolen goods, leather and anything that has paste on it, and thus often injure book bindings; in fact they are practically omnivorous. Besides eating, they leave a disagreeable "roachy" odor which spoils food where they have been. When abundant they become very troublesome and vigorous measures must be taken for their control. They lay their eggs in packets, the number per packet varying with the species, and the outside case (oötheca) is horny in nature (Fig. 49). In some species this case may be carried around partly projecting from the body of the parent for several days or even weeks. The young are active, feed freely and molt several times.

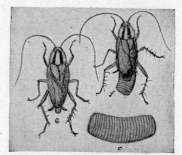

FIG. 50.—German cockroach or Croton bug (*Blattella germanica* L.): *c*, egg case much enlarged; *e*, adult, natural size; *f*, adult carrying egg case. (*From U.S. Dept. Agr. Farmers' Bull. 658.*)

**The German cockroach** (*Blattella germanica* L.).—This insect, in some places called the Croton bug, came from Europe and is generally the most common domestic cockroach in the northern United States, but less so in the southernmost states (Fig. 50). The adult is from one-half to three-fourths of an inch long, pale brown with two darker brown stripes. It is very active and increases in numbers rapidly, frequenting kitchens more than the other common species. Unlike the others, the female carries its egg case until the eggs are nearly or quite ready to hatch. In heated buildings there are from two to three generations a year.

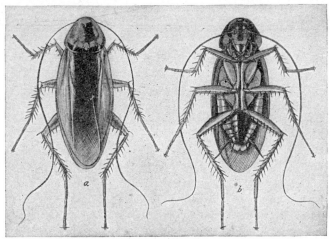

Fig. 51.—American cockroach (*Periplaneta americana* L.) adults: *a*, from above; *b*, from beneath, about natural size. (*Modified from U.S. Dept. Agr. Farmers' Bull.* 658.)

**The American cockroach** (*Periplaneta americana* L.).—This is the largest of the house cockroaches, being from one and a fourth to one and a half inches long when adult. It is dark reddish brown, with a more or less definite yellow band around the margin of the pronotum (Fig. 51). It is a native of the warmer parts of this country and southward but has spread northward and is now abundant in

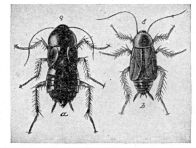

Fig. 52.                    Fig. 53.

Fig. 52.—Australian cockroach (*Periplaneta australasiæ* Fab.). Adult, about two-thirds natural size. (*Reduced from U.S. Dept. Agr. Farmers' Bull.* 658.)

Fig. 53.—Oriental cockroach (*Blatta orientalis* L.) adults about three-fourths natural size: *a*, female; *b*, male. (*Reduced from U.S. Dept. Agr. Farmers' Bull.*.658.)

warm basements of city buildings as far as Canada. A generation requires ten to twenty months to develop.

**The Australian cockroach** (*Periplaneta australasiæ* Fab.).—This is somewhat smaller and apparently broader than the preceding, with the yellow band around the pronotum brighter and a yellow streak on the costa of the forewing extending part way to the tip (Fig. 52). It is particularly common in the southern states.

**The oriental cockroach** (*Blatta orientalis* L.).—This insect is the "black beetle" of Europe. It is almost black and the wings of the adult male are considerably shorter than its body, while in the female they are hardly more than stubs. It is a stout-bodied insect, generally distributed in the central states from east to west and is the most common species in Europe (Fig. 53). It occurs in locations similar to those frequented by the American cockroach. The time required for its young to develop is about the same as for the American species.

Within the last few years the **brown-banded cockroach** (*Supella supellectilium* Serv.), very abundant in Cuba, has become a pest of homes and apartments throughout the southern states and in many cities farther north. The **smoky brown cockroach** (*Periplaneta fuliginosa* Serv.) is a rather common cockroach invading houses in the southern states.

*Control for cockroaches.*—Dusting sodium fluoride in dark or concealed places where these insects are found is the most generally effective control method. Those which are dusted directly are killed by contact with the powder. Those which crawl through the dust or in other ways get the poison on their antennae or legs, clean these parts by drawing them between their mouth parts so that the fluoride then acts largely as a stomach poison. Where sodium fluoride is dangerous to use, frequent applications of pyrethrum powder or spray should be substituted.

Other kinds of cockroaches are occasionally found in the northern states, brought there in bunches of bananas or with other southern fruits, but they do not appear to be able to live long in the colder climates.

*Family* **MANTIDÆ** (the mantids).—The mantids are usually quite large insects, with bodies much longer than wide and a broad head which moves very freely upon the thorax. The prothorax, with few exceptions, is very long and, for grasping the prey, bears legs which are well provided with spines, the insects walking on the other four. In nearly all members of the group the wings are well developed, the hinder pair larger and folding in plaits when at rest with the other pair on the back of the abdomen. They are often called rearhorses, devil-horses, soothsayers, praying mantids or mule killers.

The mantids are carnivorous, feeding on flies and other insects, and are therefore beneficial. Fifteen to twenty kinds occur in the United States, particularly in the south, but the group is mainly found in tropical countries where it reaches its greatest development and includes some remarkable forms.

Mantid eggs are laid in cases composed of a thick material which quickly dries. They are usually laid in the fall and hatch the following spring. Some of the cases are very noticeable, being an inch or more long. They are usually attached to plant stems (see Fig. 55).

The common Carolina mantis (*Stagmomantis carolina* L., Fig. 54) is found as far north as southern New Jersey, Pennsylvania and Ohio. It is about two and one-half inches long when adult, green or brown, or a mixture of the two colors, and is found not only on plants but also often on houses, sheds or other places where it may obtain its prey. It locates in some spot, then raising its prothorax and head somewhat, with its

FIG. 54.                    FIG. 55.

FIG. 54.—Carolina mantis (*Stagomantis carolina* L.); slightly reduced.

FIG. 55.—Egg case of Carolina mantis; natural size.

forelegs partly extended, quietly waits until an unwary insect comes within its reach. When this happens, a quick motion of its forelegs and the prey is seized, the spines aiding in holding the insect, which is then fed upon.

FIG. 56.                    FIG. 57.

FIG. 56.—European mantis (*Mantis religiosa* L.); natural size, with wings spread.

FIG. 57.—Egg case of European mantis; natural size.

In 1897 a mantid from China (*Tenodera sinensis* Sauss.) was discovered near Philadelphia where it successfully established itself and it is now found in many parts of this country. It is much larger than the common native mantis, being about four inches long. In 1899 the common European mantis (*Mantis religiosa* L.) was found near Rochester, N. Y., where it appears to be quite common. It much resembles our native form but is slightly larger (Figs. 56, 57).

As these insects are beneficial, attempts have been made to establish them in other places, but thus far they do not seem able to withstand severe winters, and in the case of the last-named species it has until now apparently been unable to live north of Ontario, and colonies placed in New England have died out.

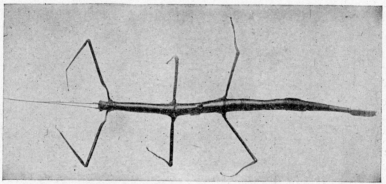

FIG. 58.—Common walkingstick (*Diapheromera femorata* Say); natural size.

*Family* **PHASMIDÆ** (the walkingsticks).—The phasmids are generally called walkingsticks. Their bodies are usually long and stick-like, owing largely to their very long and slender meso- and metathoracic segments. Their legs and antennae are also generally long, and the fifteen to twenty kinds found in the United States are wingless, or with only wing stubs, which adds to their stick-like appearance. They are brown or green in color and thus much resemble the twigs on which they rest. Only one species (*Diapheromera femorata* Say) is abundant except in the more southern states, but this is quite generally present (Fig. 58).

Walkingsticks feed on foliage and, when abundant, may entirely strip many acres of forest trees of their leaves, though this does not often happen. Their eggs are laid in the fall, being usually dropped singly wherever the insects happen to be, and falling to the ground remain there until the following spring, or in some cases until the second spring, before hatching.

Where forest areas are attacked, no entirely satisfactory method of control is known. In the case of a few trees or plants easily accessible, spraying with a stomach poison is sufficient to prevent further injury.

FIG. 59.—A tropical leaf insect (*Phyllium bioculatum* Gray); about half natural size.

This group is mainly a tropical one, over six hundred kinds being known, very variable in size and appearance. One species has a body nine inches or more in length and, with its front legs extended forward and its hinder ones backward—a position it often assumes—may measure sixteen inches or even more, while its body has a diameter of less than one-quarter of an inch. In the tropical forms wings are often present, and in some cases colored and marked to resemble leaves. This resemblance is increased in *Phyllium bioculatum* Gray (Fig. 59), found in the East Indies, by leaf-like expansions of the femora and tibiae and of the body itself.

The insects belonging to the three families of this order, treated thus far, are all walkers or runners (Cursoria). Those now to be considered are leaping forms (Saltatoria), the hind legs being longer than the others and provided with powerful muscles. Their heads are generally strongly hypognathous, the mouth being directed downward and in some cases even a little backward. Sounds sometimes called musical are produced by most members of these families.

*Family* **ACRIDIDÆ** (the grasshoppers).—The insects belonging in this group are commonly called grasshoppers. A few kinds when adult

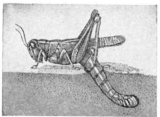 

|  |  |
|---|---|
| Fig. 60. | Fig. 61. |

Fig. 60.—Two-striped grasshopper (*Melanoplus bivittalus* Say) laying eggs.
Fig. 61.—Sac, or "eggpod," of grasshopper eggs in the ground; about natural size. (*Both figures reduced from U.S. Dept. Agr. Farmers' Bull. 747.*)

migrate, often in such enormous numbers as to look like clouds in the sky. These migrating species are sometimes spoken of as locusts.

Grasshoppers are feeders on grass and vegetation in general and are injurious, the amount of injury they cause varying with their abundance. Their antennae, shorter than the body, and their tarsi, consisting of three segments (only two in the fore- and middle legs of the grouse locusts) quickly distinguish them from the related family Tettigoniidæ. The pronotum is extended backward somewhat, and down on the sides of the prothorax almost to the base of the forelegs. In the female there is a short, stout ovipositor composed of six parts, and the rather narrow forewings, usually somewhat leathery in texture, cover the large, delicate hinder pair when these, folded in plaits, are at rest above and along the sides of the body. Some adults have only short wings (Fig. 64) and some none at all.

Most grasshoppers lay their eggs in the ground, usually in the fall, and these hatch the following spring. The female works its ovipositor into the soil a short distance, then pushes apart its four outer pieces and deposits its eggs in a cluster containing from twenty-five to perhaps eighty eggs, covered by a fluid which hardens and forms a protecting case or "pod" (Figs. 60, 61). More than one pod may be formed by the same insect. The young, on hatching, work their way out of the ground and feed, molting several times and becoming adult after two or three months.

Only a few kinds of the grasshoppers found in the United States are sufficiently migratory in their nature to deserve the name locust. Notably during the periods from 1862 to 1887 and from 1930 to the present time (1942) but also to some extent every year, inhabitants of the states west of the Mississippi River have suffered great crop losses by the ravages of swarms of the "Rocky Mountain locust," a form of the lesser migratory grasshopper (*Melanoplus mexicanus* Sauss.). However, in all parts of the country grasshoppers may lay large numbers of eggs in uncultivated ground such as pastures, resulting in spring damage caused at first by the feeding of the nymphs and later by the adults.

*Control.*—Plowing and harrowing the ground in the fall or spring will destroy large numbers of grasshopper eggs but the most successful control is by using poison bait.

The formula most often used in cooperative control campaigns is

| | |
|---|---|
| Wheat bran | 25 lb. |
| Sawdust | 3½ bu. |
| Sodium arsenite solution (32 per cent arsenious oxide[1]) | 2 qt. |
| Water | 10 gal. |

Mix the bran and sawdust dry. After diluting the sodium arsenite with the water, sprinkle it over the bran and sawdust, then mix again. If the sawdust is wet, the proportion of water is so reduced that the resulting mash is dry enough to be broadcast without being lumpy. Sodium fluosilicate (three-fourths pound) is often substituted for the sodium arsenite.

Another common formula for grasshopper bait is

| | |
|---|---|
| Wheat bran | 25 lb. |
| White arsenic or Paris green | 1¼ lb. |
| Blackstrap molasses | 2 qt. |
| Water | 2½ gal. |

In this case the arsenical, molasses and water are mixed thoroughly, then stirred continually to prevent settling until the entire quantity has been sprinkled over and mixed with the bran.

Lubricating oil, 20 to 30 S.A.E. rating, one-half gallon is sometimes used in place of the water, and the molasses is omitted. This is to keep the bait moist as water baits dry quickly and then are not eaten by the grasshoppers.

There are many kinds of grasshoppers in the United States. The more injurious ones in their general order of importance are as follows. The lesser

[1] This strength of sodium arsenite is known as four-pound material because it contains four pounds of arsenious oxide equivalent in a gallon of solution.

migratory grasshopper (*Melanoplus mexicanus* Sauss.), although only about an inch long (Fig. 62) is a strong flier; it is found nearly everywhere in the United States but becomes seriously abundant west of the Mississippi River. The differential grasshopper (*Melanoplus differentialis* Thos.) is somewhat larger, present nearly everywhere, but rare in the east. The two-striped grasshopper

Fig. 62.                          Fig. 63.

Fig. 62.—Lesser migratory grasshopper (*Melanoplus mexicanus* Sauss.); about natural size. (*Reduced from U.S. Dept. Agr. Farmers' Bull.* 747.)

Fig. 63.—Red-legged grasshopper (*Melanoplus femur-rubrum* De G.); about natural size. (*Reduced from U.S. Dept. Agr. Farmers' Bull.* 747.)

(*Melanoplus bivittatus* Say), about the size of the last and with two yellow stripes along its back, is generally distributed except in the south Atlantic states. The red-legged grasshopper (*Melanoplus femur-rubrum* De G.), smaller, its hind legs red, is the most widely distributed of the injurious species (Fig. 63). The clear-winged grasshopper (*Camnula pellucida* Scudd.) is also small but often

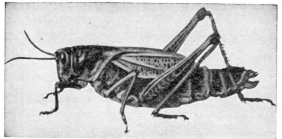

Fig. 64.—Eastern lubber grasshopper (*Romalea microptera* Beauv.); about natural size. (*From U.S. Dept. Agr. Farmers' Bull.* 747.)

very injurious; it is distributed throughout the northern United States. All of these species attack various cereal and forage crops.

In the southern and western states are large, short-winged grasshoppers which are very stout and from their appearance and clumsy movements are called lubber grasshoppers (Fig. 64). They attack grass, alfalfa and other crops.

The Carolina grasshopper (*Dissosteira carolina* L., Fig. 65), one and a half inches or more in length, is gray or brown, varying somewhat with the color

Fig. 65.—Carolina grasshopper (*Dissosteira carolina* L.); natural size.

of the ground where it lives. It is most noticeable along roads. When it is startled into flight its black hind wings with yellow margins and the crackling sound often produced at such times are sufficient to attract attention. It is found throughout the entire United States.

In one section including the smallest grasshoppers, generally called "grouse locusts," some of which are less than half an inch in length, the pronotum

FIG. 66.—Two types of "grouse locusts" somewhat enlarged.

extends back to, or even beyond, the end of the abdomen and the forewings are reduced to mere stubs. Two common species are shown in Fig. 66.

The hind wings of grasshoppers are often brightly colored, yellow, red or black. Such species are rarely injurious. The legs also often show bright colors.

The sounds produced by grasshoppers are made in one or the other of two ways. In some species the hind legs are drawn up and down across the forewings, ridges on the inner face of the femur scratching against a heavy vein on the wing and giving a rasping sound. In others the sound is produced while flying. Here the front edge of the hind wing is struck against the under surface of the forewing, making a short, sharp sound, which, quickly repeated, gives a kind of "crackling." Apparently the organs of hearing are located on each side of the body just above the base of the hind leg (Fig. 10). Each is a rather large, smooth disk, suggestive of an ear-drum membrane, connected by nerve fibers with a small ganglion which in turn connects with the main nervous system.

FIG. 67.—Broad-winged katydid (*Amblycorypha rotundifolia* Scudd.); natural size.

*Family* **TETTIGONIIDÆ** (the green grasshoppers and katydids).— Some of the insects of this family are called green grasshoppers, long-horned grasshoppers or meadow grasshoppers; others are the katydids. Their tarsi consist of four segments. Most of them are green in color, and all have antennae longer than their bodies. Some of the katydids have broad forewings and these live among trees and shrubs, feeding on the leaves and even on the more tender twigs (Fig. 67). Others have narrow forewings and appear to prefer bushes or tall weeds and grass as their abiding places (Fig. 68). The meadow grasshoppers resemble the narrow-winged katydids but average smaller and are most abundant in fields and pastures, particularly where the grass is thick and tall. In most members of the group the ovipositor is long or at least large enough to be quite noticeable.

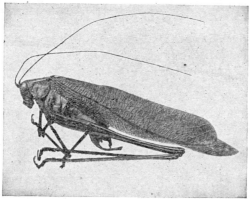

FIG. 68.—Narrow-winged katydid (*Scudderia curvicauda* De G.); slightly enlarged.

Some of the tettigoniids are wingless and come out only at night, hiding under logs or stones or in dark places during the day. They are of various shades of brown or gray, and the species found in different parts of the country vary much in appearance (Fig. 69). They are called wingless grasshoppers, camel crickets, shield-backed grasshoppers, Jerusalem crickets, etc., according to their kind and the local usage.

Sound in this family is produced by the males. The base of the forewing is modified, not necessarily in the same way in all the species, but in such a manner that rubbing these wings together will produce a sound. The organ of hearing is a small, oval membrane located near the base of the tibia on each side of the front leg. Inside

FIG. 69.—"Wingless grasshopper"; natural size.

the membrane are a hollow space or resonance chamber and a nerve supply. The sounds made by these insects are produced chiefly toward evening and at night, though in dense woods they may sometimes be heard earlier in the day.

The members of this group are rarely serious pests, though katydids have been known to injure orange groves and presumably some forest trees suffer more than is generally realized, when these insects are abundant. One exception to the general unimportance of the family is the so-called Mormon cricket (*Anabrus simplex* Hald.) (Fig. 70). This insect is native in the higher hills of the Rocky Mountains in certain sections from northwestern Montana southward to northern Nevada, Utah and Colorado.  When it becomes abundant it migrates into near-by cultivated valleys where it may cause much damage to crops.  It is of less economic importance in the Pacific northwest, southward to New Mexico and Texas, and eastward in the Great Plains region to Manitoba and Kansas.  Its

Fig. 70.—"Mormon cricket" (*Anabrus simplex* Hald.); slightly enlarged.  (*After Gillette.*)

eggs hatch in the spring and the insects become adult in June and July.  The eggs are deposited in the ground singly, oviposition continuing all summer.  The adult is stout, about an inch long, dark brown to black, and the ovipositor in the female is long and stout.  The wings are rudimentary in both sexes, so migration is on the ground, but even so they may travel over a mile in a day.  Control is chiefly by dusting with a mixture of sodium arsenite powder 1 part with hydrated lime or diatomaceous earth 4 parts.  Recently poison baits have given good results and have been widely used.  The usual formula is wheat bran 100 pounds, sodium fluosilicate 3 pounds, water 10 to 15 gallons.  Crude arsenic may be used for the fluosilicate at the rate of 4 pounds to 100 pounds of bran.

Fig. 71.—Common field cricket (*Gryllus assimilis* Fab., var.); natural size.

*Family* GRYLLIDÆ (the crickets).— Crickets are familiar insects, often seen walking or leaping over the ground.  Their wings, though usually present, are sometimes reduced in size.  In some cases they are lacking.  When present, the front pair are so bent that one part lies flat over the back while the other lies against the side of the body when not in use.  The antennae are, in most cases, longer than the body.  A convenient grouping of these insects is into the field crickets, the mole crickets and the tree crickets.

The sounds are produced by the wings of the males, which are rubbed over each other.  On one wing is a strong vein which bears cross ridges, and on the other is a thickened area.  These two parts (termed file and scraper by Comstock) when rubbed together cause the sound. Ears in crickets are located, as in the preceding family, on the forelegs, but the two on the same leg differ somewhat in appearance.

FIG. 72.—Northern mole cricket (*Gryllotalpa hexadactyla* Perty); slightly enlarged.

The common field crickets (Fig. 71) are black or brown, and a long ovipositor is present in the females. They are rather indiscriminate feeders, consuming either vegetable or animal materials, and may even be cannibals. In houses they will eat foods and injure linens and clothing, but are rarely abundant enough to become serious pests.

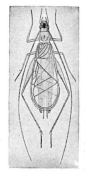

FIG. 73.                              FIG. 74.
FIG. 73.—Adult male tree cricket (*Œcanthus niveus* De G.); somewhat enlarged. (*Reduced from N. Y. Agr. Expt. Sta. Tech. Bull. 42.*)
FIG. 74.—Female tree cricket ovipositing in a twig; enlarged about one-half. (*Reduced from N. Y. Agr. Expt. Sta. Tech. Bull. 42.*)

The mole crickets are larger and stouter than the common field crickets and because of their habit of burrowing in the ground are less often seen (Fig. 72). They are brown in color and their forelegs are broad and flat, forming most effective digging organs (Fig. 18*E*). The eyes are much reduced and the hind legs, not being used for leaping, are not so greatly developed as in the other crickets. They prefer rather moist land in which to make their burrows and feed on plant roots, earthworms and insect larvae and sometimes become quite injurious.

The changa (*Scapteriscus vicinus* Scudd.) of Puerto Rico attacks the roots of various crops in that island, causing much injury, and is now present in some of the southern states where it injures cotton and other crops and at times is a serious pest.

The tree crickets differ greatly in appearance from the field and mole crickets, being slender, greenish white and only about half to three-quarters of an inch in length (Fig. 73). They occur on trees and bushes and attract attention from July till frost by their shrill, steadily repeated note or song, beginning as it grows dark and continuing through the night, the rapidity of the note being so closely related to the temperature that by timing the number of repetitions per minute a close approximation to the thermometer reading can be obtained.

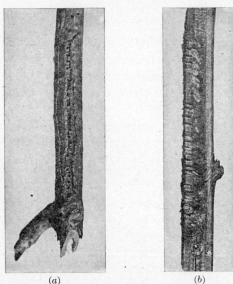

(a)         (b)

FIG. 75.—Raspberry canes showing; a, row of egg punctures along the cane, inducing cracking open; b, cane split open to show the depth of the punctures; natural size.

The tree crickets are rather serious pests as during the fall the females make long rows of punctures in the twigs of trees and in berry canes (Fig. 74), laying their eggs in these punctures which usually are nearly as deep as the diameter of the twig or cane (Fig. 75). The general result is the drying and splitting open of the portion of the plant attacked, causing its death, besides providing an opportunity for the spores of fungous diseases to enter and attack the plant. These insects are controlled quite well by spraying or dusting with lead arsenate in the early summer while the crickets are young. Injured parts of the plant, with the eggs contained in them, should be cut off and destroyed in the spring before the eggs hatch.

A few species of crickets live a semiparasitic life in ants' nests and in consequence are so much modified as to show little resemblance to the common forms.

# CHAPTER XVI

## ORDER DERMAPTERA

### (Dermaptoria: Euplexoptera)

The insects belonging in this group are commonly called earwigs, because of a mistaken belief that they crawl into the ears of sleeping persons. They are most abundant in warm climates, very few being found in the more northern states. Both winged and wingless species are known, the wings always shorter than the body and the front pair tough, leathery and shorter than the hinder pair. The latter are very broad, nearly half-moon shaped, with veins radiating from a point behind the costa and about one-third the distance from the base to the apex. These wings first fold in plaits like a fan, then twice across to reduce their length and thus are brought under the forewings, the forceps aiding in this. At the end of the abdomen is a pair of prominent, horny cerci, shaped like forceps, differing in form in the two sexes. The mouth parts are well developed and of the chewing type. The order may be characterized as

*Insects which when adult are usually rather long and narrow in form; with chewing mouth parts and a pair of forceps-like cerci at the end of the abdomen. Wings may be absent or present; in the latter case the front wings are leathery and shorter than the others which are broad and fold in plaits from a center and in addition fold crosswise. Metamorphosis is incomplete.*

Earwigs are not generally of great importance as pests in North America, though in the south and on the Pacific coast, as they generally feed on fruits, blossoms and other vegetable matter, they may occasionally cause some injury. This appears to be more frequently the case in Europe than in this country.

They hide in crevices, among leaves and in the ground in the daytime, coming out at night to feed. In the northern states the most common species is the little earwig (*Labia minor* L.), brownish in color and only about a quarter of an inch long. It is sometimes attracted to lights at night. A much larger, dark-brown, wingless species (*Anisolabis maritima* Géné), a native of Europe, has now reached this country and is found on the sea beaches of the eastern United States, under seaweed near high-water mark, probably feeding chiefly on decomposing vegetable matter (Fig. 76).

In 1911 the common European earwig (*Forficula auricularia* L.), which is about three-quarters of an inch in length when adult, was found to have established itself at Newport, R. I., and another colony of this

species was discovered at Seattle, Wash., in 1915 (Fig. 77). They are now found in British Columbia, Idaho, Oregon, California, Utah, Colorado, New York, Massachusetts and probably in other parts of the country, also.

The adults lay their eggs in the ground in the fall and the adult females winter there also. The nymphs feed on green plant shoots, injuring garden plants and flowers during the spring, and later in the season turn their attention to blossoms, eating the stamens and bases of the petals. The adults, too, feed on these and also on fruits and vegetables, dead flies, larvae and even dead or dying

*a*        *b*
FIG. 76.—Adults of a wingless earwig (*Anisolabis maritima* Géné): *a*, male; *b*, female; natural size.

individuals of their own kind. Their actual injuries, however, are far less serious than the annoyance caused by their presence in residences, where they crawl over everything at night and hide under chair cushions, dishes, in folds of clothing and in all crevices in and about the houses during the day.

*a*                                    *b*
FIG. 77.—Males *a*, and females *b*, of the European earwig (*Forficula auricularia* L.); about twice natural size. (*From U.S. Dept. Agr. Bull.* 566.)

*Control.*—The U. S. Bureau of Entomology recommends the use of a poison bait prepared as follows:

| | |
|---|---|
| Bran............................................................ | 12 lb. |
| Sodium fluosilicate........................................ | 1 lb. |
| Fish oil...................................................... | 1 qt. |

Mix the bran and fluosilicate dry, very thoroughly; add the fish oil and mix thoroughly again. Add no water.

Scatter this thinly over lawns, gardens and wherever the earwigs are found, paying particular attention to places such as about trees and along fences and woodpiles. Do not sprinkle after spreading the bait till this has been out at least two nights.

In Europe this earwig is not a serious pest, perhaps being kept in check by natural enemies not present in this country.

The Dermaptera as a whole cannot be considered as a group of great economic importance. They have sometimes been regarded as a family of the Orthoptera and sometimes as a separate order akin to the latter, but recent studies seem to indicate a closer relationship to the Coleoptera or beetles. About nine hundred fifty species of this group are now known.

# CHAPTER XVII

## ORDER PLECOPTERA

### (Perlaria)

The most usual common name for the Plecoptera is stone flies. They range from small to good-sized insects whose bodies are quite long, flattened and with rather parallel sides. The wings are nearly always well developed and with many cross veins, though in a few cases they are very small and in some species the cross veins are few. In considering only the more usual condition, the forewings extend well behind the end of the body when closed and have a considerably smaller area than the hind wings which are so broad that when they are at rest upon the

Fig. 78.—Adult plecopteran (*Pteronarcys regalis* Newm.); slightly reduced. (*From Folsom.*)

upper side of the body they must be folded lengthwise into plaits to reduce them to the necessary width (Fig. 78).

The antennae are long and composed of many segments. In most members of the group a pair of cerci is present at the end of the abdomen. The mouth parts are of the chewing type but are generally so weakly developed as to be practically useless. The nymphs (naiads) live in water and differ considerably in appearance from the adults.

The group may be described as follows:

*Insects which as adults have four membranous wings, usually longer than the body and generally with many cross veins. Hind wings larger than the front ones and when at rest folded lengthwise and lying, covered by the front pair, on the abdomen. Antennae long; a pair of caudal cerci*

96

*usually present; mouth parts for chewing but generally poorly developed. Metamorphosis is incomplete.*

Adult stone flies are most numerous near streams, particularly those with a rapid current. The eggs, which are often several thousand in number, are laid in the water and the nymphs locate on the underside of stones. Some breathe through the surface of the body. Tracheal gills, when present, are not leaf-like as in the May flies but are tufts of numerous short, thread-like structures containing tracheae, a tuft or bundle just behind each leg, on the underside, and also on the first two abdominal segments. When fully grown the nymphs leave the water and molt for the last time on land. They feed on small insects, probably largely May fly nymphs, and possibly on vegetable matter (diatoms) and are themselves a favorite food for fish.

Some species of stone flies appear in enormous numbers just as the ice is breaking up in the streams, in the northern United States; others are found on the snow even earlier in the season on warm days. In general the group is without economic importance, but a few kinds of adults have recently been observed in the northwest injuring the buds and foliage of fruit trees as these first develop, and in these species the mouth parts are much more strongly developed than in the others. Only one thousand to fifteen hundred species are known.

# CHAPTER XVIII

## ORDER EMBIIDINA

### (Embioptera)

This is a small group of insects, only about sixty species having been described. They live in warm climates either under stones or on plants in crevices of the bark or elsewhere, spinning silken tunnels in which to live. The largest species known is less than an inch long (Fig. 79).

Wings are present in the males of some species only. The females are always wingless. Wing veins are few in number and each lies in the

FIG. 79.—*Embia major* Imms, about 1½ times natural size. (*Reduced from Imms. Trans. Linn. Soc. Lond.*, 1913.)

middle of a brown band so that the wing as a whole shows alternating light and dark bands.

The tunnels appear to be formed at least partly for protection, but perhaps also as an aid in preserving moisture, for when dry weather comes on they are carried deeper into the soil in the ground-inhabiting forms. The silk seems to be produced, in part at least, by glands in the tarsi of the front legs. The metamorphosis differs somewhat in different members of the order, approaching a complete metamorphosis in those which have winged males when adult. The mouth parts are of the chewing type.

The food of these insects is probably vegetable matter, but the injury they do to plants, as thus far reported, is slight. Even where they are most abundant, they are seldom seen except by those looking for them. A few fossil specimens belonging to this group have been found preserved in amber. The embiids appear to be more closely related to the Plecoptera than to any of the other orders of insects.

# CHAPTER XIX

# ORDERS CORRODENTIA AND ZORAPTERA

## ORDER CORRODENTIA

### (Copeognatha; Psocoptera)

Most of the Corrodentia are very small, even tiny insects, though a few giants of the group found in South America have a wingspread of about an inch. Some of the group are wingless and are most often noticed as small, whitish, gray or brown specks running over the leaves of old books. These are generally called booklice. The winged forms (frequently called psocids, though this name really applies to the entire group) when adult are somewhat larger and are found on tree trunks, weathered fences and other places where lichens grow and furnish them with their food. In general the members of the group eat animal or vegetable refuse, mold, fungi and similar materials. Nearly seven hundred kinds are known.

The body in the Corrodentia, though quite soft, is well developed, but the prothorax is small and concealed in some cases between the head and the mesothorax. In others it is distinct, but, as the meso- and metathorax are grown together in those cases, only two of the three thoracic segments are evident. The antennae are rather long and slender, and the mouth parts are for chewing but considerably different in some details from the typical structure. The wings when present are four in number, with very noticeable veins, few of which are cross veins. When at rest the hinder margins of the wings of the opposite sides are brought together over the back of the insect with their upper surfaces sloping down at the sides, thus assuming the position of a steep house roof. They are often more or less dusky or mottled. The tarsi consist of only two or three segments. Ocelli may be present in the adults but not in the nymphs. These are quite similar to the adults otherwise and develop through a series of molts into the adult condition.

The group may be characterized as follows:

*Small, soft-bodied insects, with or without wings when adult. In those having wings there are two pairs, with prominent veins; when at rest they are held at a sharp angle over the body, hinder margins uppermost. Antennae are long and slender. Mouth parts are for chewing. Tarsi consist of two or three segments. Ocelli are sometimes present in the adult condition. Metamorphosis is incomplete.*

This little order contains few species of much economic importance. The wingless forms—booklice (Fig. 80)—found in buildings, eat the paste and paper of old books and are also found in birds' nests where

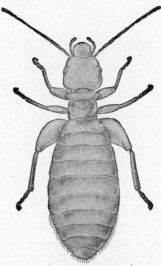

Fig. 80.—Adult booklouse; about fifty times natural size.    (*From U.S. Dept. Agr. Farmers' Bull.* 1104.)

they find their food in feathers and other organic debris. The winged forms, often called psocids, are found in various places, but perhaps most frequently on the trunks of trees, generally in clusters and often in

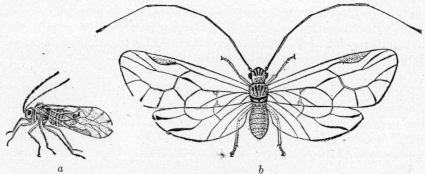

a                                                    b

Fig. 81.—Adult psocids: *a*, side view showing position of wings at rest; *b*, psocid (*Psocus lineatus*) with wings spread; both greatly enlarged.    (*From Sanderson and Jackson, Elementary Entomology; a, after Kellogg: b, after J. B. Smith.*)

various stages of their development.    They have the power of producing silk and sometimes the clusters appear to be covered, at least partly, by a web of this.

Some of the booklice are able to make a ticking sound something like that of a watch, which is often called the death watch. Since such a sound is also produced by a small beetle, the possibility of the booklice also being able to make it has been questioned, but it is now certain that they can produce it. It is heard chiefly in old houses at night or when everything is quiet, as a faint, rapidly repeated tick-tick-tick, and is in all probability the call of an insect to its mate.

A few winged Corrodentia (psocids, Fig. 81) are known to be of a little economic importance. Where the wingless forms (booklice) become extremely abundant in buildings, relief may be obtained by a thorough cleaning of the infested places. Light and air, particularly dry air, are unfavorable to them, and heating a room to quite a high temperature for a few hours and the exposure of all the furniture to sunlight for a time on a bright day will generally free the place from these insects. All stages except the egg appear to die at the beginning of winter.

## ORDER ZORAPTERA

About 1913 a group of insects was discovered, living in Ceylon, Africa, Java and Costa Rica, which seemed to differ so greatly from those previously known as to justify placing them in a new order. Those first found were tiny and wingless, with only vestiges of eyes at most and a thorax as long as the abdomen. Cerci are present. The insects average about a twelfth of an inch in length. The legs are similar. in form and used for running. The tarsus consists of only two segments and the mandibles are well developed, the mouth parts being of the chewing type. More recent discoveries of these insects in the southern United States from Maryland to Texas and elsewhere show that the adult females may have well-developed eyes, wings in some cases at least, which they shed like the termites, and, while the head resembles that of the Plecoptera, the hinder end of the body resembles that of the termites. They are found under the bark of fallen trees and stumps, often near termite nests which have similar locations. The metamorphosis is incomplete.

These insects have some features similar to the termites and some to certain Orthoptera, but on the whole they most closely resemble the Corrodentia. Until more is known about them it seems best to place them as an order by themselves.

# CHAPTER XX

## ORDER MALLOPHAGA

The Mallophaga are generally called bird lice but, as they feed by biting off particles of feathers, hairs and scales of the skin from the animals on which they live, the names biting or chewing lice would be better, as it would distinguish them more accurately from a large number of very similar insects found in many cases on the same animals, which feed by sucking the blood of their hosts and which are called sucking lice.

The bird lice or biting lice (Fig. 82) are very small insects, ranging from about one twenty-fifth to one-tenth of an inch in length, rather

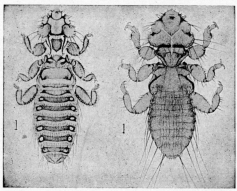

*a*                              *b*

Fig. 82.—Samples of Mallophaga or biting lice: *a, Trinoton luridum; b, Trinoton lituratum;* greatly enlarged; hair lines show actual length. (*After Kellogg.*)

whitish in color, much flattened and with an exoskeleton that is unusually hard for such small insects. They are wingless and are rarely found off the bodies of the birds and mammals on which they live. Development from the egg is gradual, through a series of molts which finally produces the adult. This type of metamorphosis appears to be the result of the parasitic habits of these insects.

The group may be described as

*Small, wingless insects, usually with a large head; mouth parts for chewing; body quite hard, flattened.* They are parasitic on the bodies of birds and some mammals and ametabolous as the result of parasitism.

About fifteen hundred kinds of Mallophaga are known, most of them living on birds, where they feed on feathers and skin scales. On mammals, hairs replace the feathers as their food. When Mallophaga are

102

abundant, bare areas on the bodies of birds appear where the feathers have been eaten or have dropped out as a result of the feeding of these insects. Birds normally dust themselves, working the dust in among their feathers, where it has been claimed it gets into the spiracles of the lice and suffocates them, but this explanation is now considered at least doubtful. Apparently the greatest injury to the fowls does not come from the feeding on the feathers and scales, but from the irritation produced by the scratching of the skin caused by the tarsal claws of the parasites as they move about, and this must be quite severe, for birds

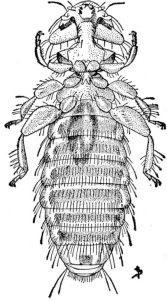

Fɪɢ. 83.—Female chicken body louse (*Eomenacanthus stramineus* Nitz.); greatly enlarged.
(*From U.S. Dept. Agr. Farmers' Bull.* 801.)

considerably infested become dull and act sick and are certainly less able to resist disease than usual.

The eggs of the lice are attached separately to the feathers or hairs of the host and hatch into nymphs, which on the whole considerably resemble their adults. They feed, molt, grow and become adult in a few weeks.

Though these insects are widely distributed on many kinds of birds and on a number of mammals, they are of importance from an economic standpoint mainly on the domesticated birds such as chickens, turkeys, geese, ducks and pigeons, though occasionally dogs, cattle and horses become infested.

Seven different kinds of biting lice are fairly common on domestic fowls. Of these, some prefer the head for their location, others the body

(Fig. 83), etc., though not found exclusively in those locations. Four kinds are often present on turkeys and quite a number occur on geese and ducks. Pigeons and guinea fowls have several species.

*Control of Lice on Poultry.*—Various methods of control for poultry lice are in use, but, in most cases at least, the best one is the use of sodium fluoride, dry or dissolved in water. Either the commercial or the chemically pure grade can be used but the commercial is somewhat easier to work with, particularly for dusting the fowls.

The first step in treatment is to shut up all the fowls. Then each bird is taken and, while it is held either by the wings or legs with one hand, pinches of the powder are placed in among the feathers, "one on the head, one on the neck, two on the back, one on the breast, one below the vent, one on the tail, one on each thigh, and one scattered on the underside of each wing when spread." For young birds dusting rather than dipping is advisable.

If dipping is preferred for the older birds, use warm water in a tub, measuring the water put into the tub and adding from three-fourths to one ounce of the commercial fluoride (or two-thirds ounce of the chemically pure fluoride) to each gallon of water. Dip the birds in this, holding the wings over the back with one hand and ruffling the feathers with the other, below the surface of the water. Then duck the head of the bird once or twice, take it out of the water, let it drain for a moment and then let it go. After a little experience, three-fourths minute per bird will be an ample amount of time for this treatment.

The water in the tub will be reduced in quantity, of course, by use, and more, having the proper amount of fluoride dissolved in it, should be at hand to add from time to time.

Derris dusts and dips are effective if used properly. A common practice is to apply in warm weather undiluted nicotine sulfate, one ounce for each fifteen to twenty feet, along the top of the roosts just before roosting time. This should be repeated in one to two weeks to kill the lice which were in the egg stage at the time of the first application.

Boxes of road dust, available in poultry houses during the winter months for the birds to dust themselves in, are desirable. Formerly supposed to aid the birds in freeing themselves from the lice, they may indicate that lice are present and that treatment is needed.

The houses in which poultry are kept should be thoroughly cleaned each year.

For biting lice on mammals it seems best to use raw linseed oil as advised for sucking lice in Chap. XXII.

# CHAPTER XXI

## ORDER THYSANOPTERA

(Physapoda or Physopoda)

The Thysanoptera are very small insects, peculiar in many ways. The common name for the members of the group is thrips, spelled the same whether one or many are referred to.

As a whole these insects appear to have some affinities with the hemipteroid groups (Anoplura, Hemiptera and Homoptera), yet to be considered, but are generally looked upon as forming an order by themselves, though in some regards they seem to have certain relations to the Corro-

FIG. 84.—Side view of the head and prothorax of a thrips to show the mouth parts.   (*From U.S. Dept. Agr. Bur. Ent. Bull.* 68, *Part* II.)

dentia and Mallophaga. It is not improbable that they form a group originating not far from the common trunk of all the above-named orders.

Thrips vary from one-fiftieth to one-third of an inch or more in length. Their mouth parts (Fig. 84) form in part a short, stout cone attached far back on the underside of the head, composed of the labrum, a portion of the maxillae and the labium. Within this cone are three bristles consisting of the lobes of the maxillae and one mandible, the other not being developed. The animals are sucking insects. Four wings are usually present, rather long and narrow, with few veins, and fringed behind and generally in front also, with slender hairs, longer than the breadth of the wing itself (see Fig. 85). When at rest the wings lie flat on the top of the abdomen. In some cases they are greatly reduced in size or may even be wanting entirely. The tarsi are composed either of one or two segments, usually the latter; at the tip is a bladder-like portion which can be drawn into the segment or pushed out. The abdomen consists of ten segments, the last either conical or tubular in form.

105

Summarizing these facts, the adult Thysanoptera may be described as *Small insects with greatly modified mouth parts forming a cone attached to the back part of the head beneath and used for sucking. Wings four, generally present, long, narrow, with few veins, and fringed behind (usually in front also) with long hairs. Tarsi of one or two segments, the tip with a bladder-like swelling capable of being drawn into the tarsus. Abdomen of ten segments, the last either conical or tubular. Metamorphosis is incomplete but approaching completeness.*

Thrips feed on plant juices, puncturing the tissues and extracting the sap, leaving white marks or streaks where the cells without their

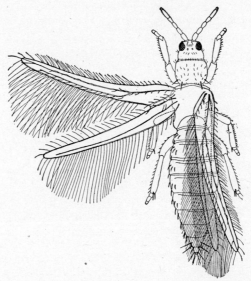

Fig. 85.—Onion thrips (*Thrips tabaci* Linde.): adult enlarged about fifty times. Left wings spread to show the fringes of bristles. (*From Metcalf and Flint, Destructive and Useful Insects.*)

juices have dried. They attack stems, leaves and blossoms, in the last case often blighting them and preventing the setting of fruit. On leaves of plants the under surface appears in most cases to be the preferred place of attack and the insects do not move about much. With grasses and cereals the stems as well as the leaves suffer, thus checking the growth of the top, and in some cases the kernels of growing grain are also fed upon. Some species live under loose bark and a few have been reported as feeding upon other insects. In many cases the injury caused by these insects is very serious. Over sixteen hundred species of thrips are now known.

In one section (suborder Terebrantia) the female has an ovipositor with which she saws slits in the epidermis of plants, placing an egg in each slit. In the other section (suborder Tubulifera) there is no ovipositor and the eggs are laid upon the surface of the food material. The nymphs considerably resemble the adult. After from two to four molts they leave their food to find some more protected place and there molt again, at which time wing stubs appear and other changes can be seen. After another molt the insect becomes quiet unless disturbed, not feeding, and marked changes become evident, bringing it more nearly like the adult. The completion of these changes is followed by a molt that produces the adult itself. This is more than a typical incomplete metamorphosis, yet not entirely comparable with a complete one. It may be regarded therefore as intermediate between the two.

In some cases parthenogenesis, *i.e.*, the production of the next generation by unfertilized females, occurs. This is perhaps to some extent determined by weather conditions in this group. Parthenogenesis is frequently present here and there among insects and will be considered more fully elsewhere. Driving rains are very destructive to all kinds of thrips. Ladybeetles and other insects of several species feed freely upon them.

**The onion thrips** (*Thrips tabaci* Linde.).—This pest is present practically everywhere in Europe and the United States, having first been noticed here about 1872 (Fig. 85). The adult is about a twenty-fifth of an inch long, rather light yellow, but turning brown as it becomes older. It feeds on a great variety of plants but, being the species that is particularly injurious to growing onions, is generally known as the onion thrips. The onion leaves are whitened by the removal of their juices, and soon begin to bend sharply downward, and later they may curl or twist and even die, an area much affected in a field being noticeably pale colored and the plants stunted, while the bulbs make little growth.

Winter in the north is spent as the adult in protected situations such as in dead grass close to the ground or in rubbish left on the field. In spring the young onion plants are attacked soon after they come up, first in the bud, later on the leaves, in which the eggs are laid. The life cycle from egg to adult is influenced by the temperature, varying from a little less than three weeks to over a month, and in the most southerly states the generations overlap so that practically all stages may be found at the same time. Sometimes in the north this insect becomes a greenhouse pest on roses, carnations, cucumbers and tomatoes, though the greenhouse thrips (*Heliothrips hæmorrhoidalis* Bouché) is most often responsible for this injury.

*Control.*—Any methods of farming that will reduce the opportunities for this insect to pass the winter successfully are of value. The destruction of all refuse on the field after the crop has been gathered; fall plowing of such fields, and burning over grasslands adjacent to them, at the proper time in the spring, are all beneficial. Cultivation and fertilization to push the crop ahead early to "keep it ahead of the thrips" are also helpful.

Spraying very thoroughly with nicotine sulfate 1 pint, soap (fish oil preferred), about 3 pounds in 50 gallons of water, is quite effective; nicotine dust, 4 per cent, gives fair results; crude naphthalene, ground fine, 4 pounds, mixed with talc powder, $3\frac{1}{2}$ pounds, and kept in an airtight container 24 hours, then mixed with $2\frac{1}{2}$ pounds of an alcoholic extract of pyrethrum is approved of in many places; and naphthalene ground to dust, 4 pounds, mixed with hydrated lime, 6 pounds, has given satisfaction. All of these are applied by machines—sprayers or dusters. Crude chipped naphthalene applied by hand along the rows also works well. The nicotine dust is rather expensive and the addition of the pyrethrum to the third treatment above may prove not to improve the mixture. All these controls may need to be repeated several times at 8- to 10-day intervals as long as the thrips are abundant.

**The flower thrips** (*Frankliniella tritici* Fitch).—This insect—also known as the wheat and the strawberry thrips—is widely distributed in this country. It feeds on wheat, apple and many other plants and where the blossom is attacked, as in the case of the strawberry, it is blighted, preventing the formation of fruit and producing the stunted structures known as buttons, instead. Leaves attacked often curl and become malformed, soon turning brown and dying. In California it is a particular pest of alfalfa.

The adult is about a twentieth of an inch long, yellowish in color. In the warmer parts of the south it is more or less active at all seasons of the year, but in the north it winters in protected places, many probably, like other species, in grass fields close to the ground.

The life history in the south requires about twelve days but is probably longer in the cooler temperatures of the northern states, and several generations are produced in a season.

*Control.*—In general, spraying with nicotine sulfate, 40 per cent standard formula or dusting with a fine derris dust is good treatment. Success with these materials, however, depends largely upon the thoroughness of the application and the number which are killed. A favorite formula in California consists of $1\frac{1}{4}$ gallons of commercial lime-sulfur, and $3\frac{1}{2}$ fluid ounces of nicotine sulfate 40 per cent in 50 gallons of water, applied as a spray. Where the adults are wintering in grass fields and it is practicable, burning these over will destroy many.

**The pear thrips** (*Tæniothrips inconsequens* Uzel).—This insect was first discovered in the United States in the central part of California and is now found as far north as British Columbia, attacking deciduous fruit trees, particularly pears, prunes and cherries, blighting the blossoms by the abstraction of their sap. Later it was found in the Hudson River Valley in New York, and still later in Pennsylvania, Maryland and England. Recently it has been learned that the insect was first discovered in Bohemia, feeding in blossoms.

The destruction caused by this pest in California has been very great during some years. The crop of prunes in the Santa Clara Valley alone has been estimated as having been reduced in the seven years, 1905–1911, by 141 million pounds. The injury is caused by the feeding of the young and adults on leaves, buds, flowers and fruit, and by laying eggs in the leaves and fruit stems and also in the small fruit.

The dark-brown—almost black—adults (Fig. 86) appear early in spring, coming out of the ground about the time the fruit buds are swelling and opening; as soon as these have opened slightly the insects work their way into them and feed on the most delicate parts. The eggs are laid mainly in the young leaf and fruit stems and young fruit and hatch on an average after about eight days.

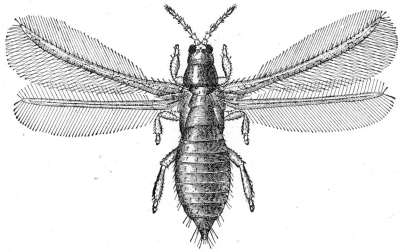

Fig. 86.—Adult pear thrips (*Tæniothrips inconsequens* Uzel); greatly enlarged. (*From U.S. Dept. Agr. Bull.* 173.)

The nymphs (Fig. 87) feed on the leaves and young fruit, forming a sort of "scab" on the surface of the latter, and remain on the tree for two or three weeks, though the time from the first young's appearance to the last young's disappearance may be more than two months. When through feeding they fall to the ground, which they enter for a varying distance, and there, after two to five or six months, they transform to the last stage before the adult, having previously molted once underground. Late in the fall or winter the final molt produces the adults which remain in the ground till early spring.

This remarkable life history, quite unlike anything known for any other Thysanoptera, permits but one generation a year, with active injury during only a rather short period in the spring.

*Control.*—These insects may be controlled by spraying with a miscible oil or an oil-emulsion stock diluted to give 2 per cent oil, to which is added one pint of nicotine sulfate for each hundred gallons of the diluted oil. It must be applied very thoroughly to be a success. Dusting, though not quite so effective, is satisfactory and is growing in favor. The dust used contains 2 per cent pure nicotine or is a nicodust containing 5 per cent of 40 per cent nicotine sulfate. The first treatment should at once follow the discovery of the thrips upon the swelling buds and should be repeated at least every two or three days until the buds are open or the thrips have become very few. No spraying should be done from the time the blossoms open until the petals fall. Then, if thrips are abundant on the remains of the blossoms, another treatment should be given.

**The citrus thrips** (*Scirtothrips citri* Moult.) is a rather serious pest in California and Arizona. It feeds upon the tender stems, leaves and fruit of citrus trees and occasionally also attacks the grape, apricot and other plants. With seedling plants the leaves and buds are injured and growth is checked. The

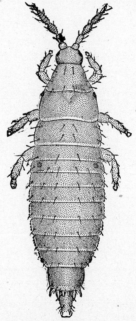

Fig. 87.—Nymph of pear thrips, greatly enlarged.   (*From U.S. Dept. Agr. Bur. Ent. Bull.* 68, *Part* I.)

fruit is injured by scars and scabs caused by the feeding and is greatly reduced in value, and some drop to the ground.

The adult is one of the smallest of the Thysanoptera, varying from one-fiftieth to one-twentieth of an inch in length, and is orange-yellow in color. The young appear in April and May and gather on the leaves and fruit where they remain until the midsummer hardening of these parts leads most of them to leave for various other food plants until August and September when they return to the citrus trees again and lay their eggs in the leaves and stems of the plant. These winter over and hatch the following spring. Following the production of adults from the hatching and development of these eggs, there may be six to eight generations during the season and all stages may be present at once on a tree as late as December, though these die with colder weather, leaving only the eggs to hatch in the spring. The last stage before the adult, during which the insect is quiet, is passed in crevices of the trunks or in rubbish under the trees, but not in the ground.

*Control.*—Lime-sulfur solution at 1½ to 2 per cent is now the chief control for this insect. About two sprays are usually needed. Dusting with fine sulfur is also effective, about one pound for an average tree at the time of the first warm spring weather, followed by lighter applications according to schedules that may be obtained from the state experiment stations.

**The gladiolus thrips** (*Tœniothrips simplex* Morison).— This pest of the gladiolus and some related plants was first found in Ohio in 1929 and is now present in most places where gladioli are grown. It is small and black, but whitish at the bases of its wings when adult and lemon yellow in its early stages. It sucks the sap from the bulbs (corms) while they are in storage causing them to become roughened and darker. On the plants the leaves turn silvery, then brown, and die, the flowers become deformed and the spikes may not produce blossoms.

*Control.*—After the corms have been brought into storage and are in bags or trays, sprinkle naphthalene flakes over them, using about 1 pound of flakes to each 2,000 corms; if in trays, cover them with wrapping paper and leave them for about 4 weeks. Then shake out all excess flakes and air. This may be done at any time during the winter, but best between early November and March. In the field the best treatment now known is to spray with force with tartar emetic 4 pounds, brown sugar 8 pounds, water 100 gallons and repeat six times at 5- or 6-day intervals, beginning soon after the plants come up.

In addition to the species of thrips given separate consideration here, numerous other species are frequently of some importance. Among these the grass thrips which sucks the sap from the stems of the lighter grasses, turning them white and killing them, thus causing silver top as it is called; the greenhouse thrips which attacks tomatoes, cucumbers and many other plants in greenhouses in the north and out of doors in the south; and the camphor thrips which is a serious pest of the camphor tree in Florida are perhaps the most important.

# CHAPTER XXII

## ORDER ANOPLURA

(Siphunculata: Parasita)

These insects are the sucking lice that attack mammals, and mammals only. They are small, wingless insects from about one twenty-fifth to one-fourth of an inch in length, and with mouth parts for sucking. The head is usually rather pointed in front and is often joined to the thorax by a distinct neck which permits its free movement. The distinction between thorax and abdomen is less evident, the constriction there being practically nonexistent. The legs, which join the thorax well out

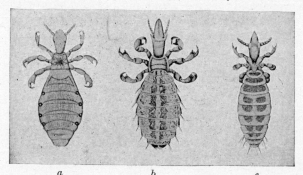

*a*　　　　　*b*　　　　　*c*

Fig. 88.—Samples of Anoplura or sucking lice: *a, Pedicinus eurygaster; b, Hæmatopinus suis; c, Linognathus piliferus;* greatly enlarged. (*After Dalla Torre.*)

on its sides, are constructed for climbing and grasping, and each ends in a single claw, so placed with reference to the rest of the leg that it can tightly grasp a hair, the claw on one side and the tibia on the other. The eyes are rudimentary or absent in some cases.

The group may be defined as

*Small, wingless insects with sucking mouth parts, feeding on the blood of mammals; eyes present or absent; tarsi each with one claw. Metamorphosis is practically absent, probably as the result of the parasitic habits of the insects.*

Anoplura (Fig. 88) occur on man, monkeys, domestic animals, rats, mice, rabbits, squirrels, the elephant, etc., and one genus is found on the seal. The mouth consists of a flexible proboscis which may be drawn in or pushed out, turning inside out as it goes and exposing some chitinous hooks which attach themselves to the skin of the host. Lodged in the head are two long, slender, sharp-pointed structures called stabbers, so

112

placed as to form a canal between them through which saliva may be injected into the wound they make.  These stabbers are forced through the skin within the area encircled by the proboscis, saliva is forced into the wound and after a few moments feeding begins, the blood of the host being pumped into the body of the louse.

Eggs or "nits" are laid singly, attached to the hairs of the host or, in some species, to the fibers of the clothing.  They hatch in from one to two weeks, according to the species and the temperature; but when the latter remains low, as where the eggs do not feel the effects of the warmth of the host, they will not hatch (at least with the lice infesting man).  The nymph stage probably requires eight to ten days, though practically nothing is known of the development except with the lice attacking man.  Several hundred eggs are usually laid by each female during a period of nearly a month, so that a heavy infestation becomes possible in quite a brief time.

The Anoplura were formerly considered degenerate Hemiptera, but with the division of the old order Hemiptera into separate orders—the Hemiptera in a more restricted sense and the Homoptera—it has seemed more logical to regard the Anoplura as also an order, most closely related to these, but still sufficiently different to entitle it to ordinal rank.

Fig. 89.—Body louse (*Pediculus humanus corporis* De G.); about eight times natural size. (*From Berlese.*)

Over two thousand species are now known.

The body louse (*Pediculus humanus corporis* De G.).—This pest (Fig. 89), which during the European war also received the common name of cootie, is now generally regarded as being of two races, the head louse (*Pediculus humanus humanus* L.), which is found chiefly on the head, and the body louse (formerly *Pediculus vestimenti*), found mainly on the clothing, rather than different species, but the races differ somewhat because of different conditions under which they live.  This insect under ordinary conditions of cleanliness can be easily controlled; in camp life it finds an opportunity to increase, often almost without the possibility of being checked.

Under ordinary conditions a simple treatment for the race living on the head is to wash thoroughly with tincture of larkspur, which can be obtained of a druggist, repeating this two or three times at intervals of about a week.  For the race living on the body, treatment is somewhat different, as the pests are largely on the clothing, reaching across from this to the skin to feed.  Here, boiling all clothing that can be so treated, dry heating the rest to 130°F. for half an hour and taking a hot bath will usually be sufficient.

**The crab louse** (*Phthirus pubis* L.).—This louse is quite different in appearance from the preceding, being smaller, shorter, broader, and with its legs projecting outward near together (Fig. 90). The forelegs are

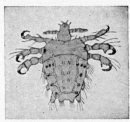

FIG. 90.—Crab louse (*Phthirus pubis* L.); about twelve times natural size. (*From Berlese.*)

slender but the others are stout and each has a powerful serrated claw which shuts against a projection of the preceding segment of the leg in such a way as to give a very firm grip on a hair. This insect is found primarily on the hairy parts of the body except the head, but in exceptional cases it may be found there also. It holds on to the hairs while feeding and in moving about always holds tightly to hairs on one side until it has obtained a grasp on others on the other side. This gives it a sideways movement which is responsible for its common name. Its life history is much the same as in the other species.

Washing thoroughly with tincture of larkspur as for the head louse is usually an effective treatment. An ointment made of four parts of crude naphthalene mixed with one part of soft soap rubbed on the underclothing in the infested region has also been found to be a very successful treatment.

**Lice on domestic animals.**—These are sometimes serious in their attacks, weakening the animal greatly if they are abundant. In the treatment of these pests it should be borne in mind that poisonous materials cannot be used because of the danger coming from the animals' licking themselves. Various materials have been used for livestock, but at present the favorite treatment seems to be the application of raw (not boiled or refined) linseed oil, using a hand brush. Only enough oil should be used for it to reach the skin; a pint is enough for four or five cows. After the application the animals should be kept out of the sun for a day or two and should not be allowed to become overheated and the application should not be made in cold weather. A second treatment ten to fifteen days later to kill the lice which were in the egg stage at the time of the first application is needed, with later treatments if examination shows that any lice are still present.

Where many animals are concerned, dipping them in vats is more economical of time. Directions for building the vats and for the entire process can be obtained by applying to the U.S. Department of Agriculture.

Another treatment for sucking lice on domestic animals is to boil 4 ounces of stavesacre (*Delphinium*) seeds and 1 ounce of white hellebore in a gallon of water until only two quarts remain. Apply this with a brush to the animals. It may need to be repeated if more lice appear, showing that eggs or some of the lice escaped the first treatment.

It has been discovered that the lice of man are concerned in the transmission of relapsing fever, trench fever and typhus fever. It does not at present seem that the causal agents of the first two of these are actually transferred to man by the feeding of the infested lice, but rather that these agents are present in their bodies and feces, and that, by scratching the parts irritated, fluids from crushed lice or the feces get rubbed into the irritated areas, are able to enter the body, reach the blood and begin the disease. This also appears to be true in the case of typhus fever, but here inoculation by the feeding of the lice also seems probable. In some cases where scratching does not occur but where relapsing or trench fever nevertheless develops, it is probable that the feces get into the feeding wounds and in that way cause the disease.

Our knowledge of the relation of insects to disease has grown remarkably during the last three decades. One such relation has just been mentioned and other cases are given later in this book. More than twenty diseases, some of them very dangerous, are now known to be carried by certain species of insects and, if we include ticks, which are not very far distant from insects, the number is greatly increased. Fortunately for the United States most of these diseases are tropical ones and seldom or never reach this country.

But insects and diseases have other relations to each other, which as a whole may be classified as follows: (1) Insects as carriers (vectors) of disease organisms to man or other animals: (a) as simple vectors, carrying the disease in what may be called a purely mechanical way, e.g., houseflies and typhoid-fever germs (page 322), or (b) as essential hosts in which the parasite must undergo a part of its life cycle before the insect can pass it on to another animal in which it produces the disease (page 307). (2) Insects as carriers of plant diseases from one plant to another. Of the many such diseases, bacterial wilt and fire blight of the pear are two examples referred to in these pages. (3) The diseases of insects themselves (see page 125). Our knowledge of all these relations has greatly increased in recent years.

# CHAPTER XXIII

## ORDER HEMIPTERA

### (Heteroptera.  With the Homoptera also—Rhynchota)

The Hemiptera is a large group containing many insects that are always injuriously active, and many more that occasionally become so. They vary greatly in size, some being minute whereas others may attain a length of four or five inches.  They are most numerous in species in the warmer portions of the globe, but an abundance of individuals in colder regions results in making them extremely common everywhere.

Most Hemiptera have the dorsal surface of the body rather flattened, though there are many exceptions to this statement; the wings when not in use rest upon this surface.  The wings are nearly always present, four in number, and the basal half, or sometimes more, of the front pair is thickened and horny, resembling the elytra of beetles.  The outer end, however, is membranous and veins traverse this portion, so that the forewings are appropriately called hemielytra.  The membranous part of one wing largely overlaps that of the other when they are at rest.  In a few families the difference in the texture of the two portions is not very perceptible but in most cases it is plainly evident.  The hinder wings are entirely membranous and when not in use are concealed beneath the others.

The body of the hemipteron, with few exceptions, shows no constriction at the junction of thorax and abdomen and is usually widest at the hinder end of the prothorax.  The attachments of the wings behind this do not occupy anywhere near all of the width of the body, and directly behind the pronotum, between the wings, the space is taken up by a rather large, usually quite triangular plate called the scutellum. In some families this becomes greatly enlarged, covering more or less of the dorsal surface of the body from the pronotum back, and in such cases the wings in closing slip under this so that little besides their costas show.

Hemiptera are sucking insects (Fig. 91), obtaining their food by piercing the surfaces of plants or animals and drawing into their own bodies the sap or blood.  The mouth parts in the group have been identified with those of chewing insects, but they have been greatly modified to form a beak or rostrum which is attached to the front of the underside of the head.  The details of structure of the rostrum differ in different

116

Hemiptera but agree in general plan (Fig. 92). The outside of the rostrum is a sheath which appears in the main to be derived from the labium or hinder lip of the chewing insect, being much elongated, and its sides rolled forward to meet or almost meet in front, forming a tube. The front part of this tube, however, near the head, seems not to be formed by the labium, leaving open a somewhat triangular place, and the labrum or front lip appears to have grown downward to close up this portion of the sheath more or less completely. Within the tube thus formed lie the mandibles and maxillae, which have become transformed into long and slender bristles with pointed tips. The surfaces of the

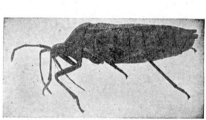

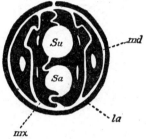

Fig. 91. Fig. 92.

Fig. 91.—Side view of a squash bug (*Anasa tristis* De G.) showing the rostrum and its attachment to the front of the head. Some of the mouth parts usually within the sheath have been pulled out and show in front of it. Rather more than twice natural size.

Fig. 92.—Diagram of a cross section of rostrum of a squash bug: *la*, labium; *md*, mandible; *mx*, maxilla; *Sa*, tube carrying saliva to the wound; *Su*, tube through which the food is drawn into the body. (*Modified from Tower, Ann. Ent. Soc. Am. VI, 1913.*)

maxillae which face each other have so changed their outline as to form two gutters or troughs and when the maxillae are pressed together, as is the case in the living insect, each gutter of one side coincides with the corresponding one of the other to form two tubes, half of each being contributed by each maxilla. The more anterior of the tubes is for sucking the nourishment into the bug; the other is for injecting saliva into the wound. The mandibles lie beside the maxillae and seem to function chiefly as piercing organs.

In feeding, the tip of the rostrum is brought into contact with the surface of the object to be fed upon and the tips of the mandibles and maxillae are then driven into it until sap. or blood, as the case may be, is reached. Then saliva is forced into the wound and this seems to be irritating or even poisonous in its nature and its presence in the wound causes (in animals at least) an increased flow of the body fluids to that point. Assured thus of a sufficient supply of food, the insect then begins sucking it into its body.

The eggs of Hemiptera are laid under greatly differing conditions. Some are inserted in twigs or stems; others are laid either singly or in clusters on leaves or twigs or in other places. The eggs themselves vary much in appearance, some being provided with circlets of spines, some with long filaments and some being smooth but of unusual form or color. They hatch into nymphs (Fig. 93) more or less closely resembling the adult, which stage they reach by a series of molts, changing with each molt.

The order Hemiptera may be characterized as

*Insects which when adult nearly always have four wings, the front pair in most cases partly horny, partly membranous; with a plate located between the bases of the wings, usually triangular in outline, in some cases covering more or less of the abdomen above; mouth parts for sucking, and attached to the front end of the underside of the head. Metamorphosis is incomplete.*

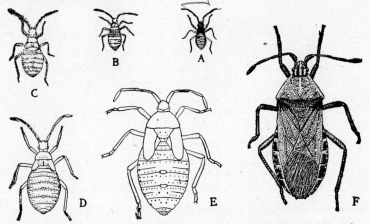

Fig. 93.—Metamorphosis of the squash bug (*Anasa tristis* De G.). Adult and nymphs of different ages; all twice natural size. (*From Folsom.*)

Hemiptera occur under almost every conceivable condition of life. Some live in water, coming to the surface only to obtain air; some are found on the surface of the water; some are found on the ocean hundreds of miles from land. Most of the group are terrestrial, however, and in many cases are widely distributed. Probably fifteen thousand species are already known but the group has been little studied as compared with some of the more attractively colored and marked orders. Those living in water are, at least for the most part, feeders on insects and other animals small enough for them to capture; those which live on the surface are also predaceous; of the land forms some consume other insects but probably the larger number are plant feeders. The Hemiptera are the true bugs, the general use of the term bug as applied to all insects being incorrect.

*Family* **PENTATOMIDÆ**.—This group consists of land forms, many of them producing a disagreeable odor which has resulted in applying to these insects the common name stinkbugs (Fig. 94). Most of them suck the sap from various plants, leaving behind the odor so often notice- able on berries. Others are carnivorous, attacking caterpillars and sucking their juices. Many of them are minor pests and potentially important ones, and their fair size—often half an inch or more in length— together with considerable width, giving them a broad surface, makes them fairly familiar objects.

**The harlequin bug** (*Murgantia histrionica* Hahn).—This pest, native to Mexico and Central America, has gradually spread northward, feeding on cabbage, kale, mustard, turnip, radish and other cruciferous plants, and its present northern limits are now in New Jersey and Long Island,

  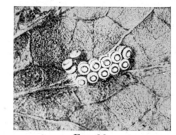

Fig. 94.            Fig. 95.                    Fig. 96.
Fig. 94.—Pentatomid bug (*Euschistus*); natural size.
Fig. 95.—Adult harlequin bug (*Murgantia histrionica* Hahn); slightly enlarged.
Fig. 96.—Eggs of harlequin bug; slightly enlarged. (*Modified from Essig. Inj. and Benef. Ins. Cal.*)

Ohio, Indiana, Wisconsin, Iowa, Nebraska, Colorado, Arizona, Nevada and Washington, though the insect rarely does much injury so far north.

The adults (Fig. 95) are about half an inch long, black or dark blue with bright red or orange marks, the brilliancy of the colors making the insects very noticeable and resulting in the common names calicoback, terrapin bug and perhaps fire bug as well. They winter in the adult stage under rubbish or wherever they can find protection, though in the far south they are more or less active nearly all the time and there the nymphs are also present.

Farther north the bugs become active during the early spring and attack various wild cruciferous plants and lay their eggs (Fig. 96). These are usually placed in clusters of about twelve, in two rows, and are somewhat barrel-shaped, white, with two black rings around each, and a third ring on the upper end, being both very noticeable and distinctive. They hatch in from three to eleven days according to the temperature and the nymphs suck the sap from the plants for one to two months, again according to the temperature, before becoming adult. When cabbage, cauliflower, kale, turnip, radish, etc., become available, the bugs go to these and thereafter devote their attention to these plants until late in the fall when various other kinds, such as egg plant, asparagus, tomato, beans and beets, may be attacked.

*Control.*—Insecticides which do not injure the plants the bugs are on are not usually effective against this pest and preventive methods have thus far given the best results. Planting a very early crop of kale, mustard or rape, to which the bugs when they first become active in spring may be attracted, is a good practice, for the insects seem to prefer these to the other plants. Here the bugs may be killed by spraying with kerosene, collected in nets and destroyed, or burned with a torch. The few that may escape this treatment can be picked by hand wherever found; but if the trapping method above is followed, few usually escape.

Clean culture is also helpful. As soon as the crops are gathered, all the stalks and leaves of the plants on which the harlequin bug feeds should be gathered and destroyed, both to leave them no food and to remove possible places where they might winter. Rubbish which might provide wintering quarters should also be carefully removed. If an insecticide must be used, derris sprays and dusts or similar synthetic contact insecticides should be applied directly on the insects.

*Family* **COREIDÆ.**—Many of the members of this large family are of considerable size for bugs, some being over an inch long, but their bodies are much more narrow in proportion to their length than in the Pentatomidæ. Some of the southern species have broad, flat expansions of the tibiæ, giving them a curious appearance. The insects of this group suck plant juices and a number are frequently more or less injurious to various plants.

**The squash bug** (*Anasa tristis* De G.).—The squash bug is common almost everywhere in the United States, feeding on squash and pumpkin and sometimes on cucumber and melon plants (see Fig. 93). The adult is a dark-brown bug, very finely mottled with gray or lighter brown in many cases, about three-quarters of an inch long. It winters as the adult under rubbish or in other protected places, and appears in spring, ready for its food plants when these come up. When the leaves of the plants develop, the bugs lay their eggs on their under surface in clusters which vary greatly in the number of eggs composing them. The eggs themselves are oval in outline, very convex, and being resin brown in color are very conspicuous against the green background of the leaf. In a cluster the eggs are not usually so laid that they touch but are somewhat spaced apart in most cases. At intervals before and during the egg-laying period the adults feed on the plants and when they are very abundant may seriously injure or in some cases even kill them.

The eggs hatch on an average in about ten days and the tiny nymphs, green and reddish in color, begin to suck the sap from the underside of the leaves, at first together, but scattering later. The reddish color of the nymph quickly changes to black and the green gradually becomes more of a gray. Feeding and molting five times result in the production of the adult after a period of from four to five weeks from the time the eggs hatch, and in the north the adults feed on the plants until fall; then they go into winter quarters. In the south the longer seasons which permit an earlier start in the spring and the higher temperature which causes the eggs to hatch more quickly permit the production, in some cases at least, of two generations each season.

The injury to the plants caused by the spring feeding of the adult is continued by the sucking of the young. Where these are plenty, growth is checked and the crop reduced. If the plants are killed by frost before the nymphs are mature, they often attack the fruits in order to obtain the nourishment they need to become adult.

*Control.*—Contact insecticides are not effective for the adult squash bug, which has an unusually thick shell. The usual methods for control are the removal as far as possible of all rubbish and places where the insects can obtain protection during the winter; stimulation of growth of the plants by fertilizers and cultivation; protection of the young plants by fine netting until they are so well started that they can thrive despite the bugs; traps of bark or shingles placed close to the plants, under which the bugs rest at night and from which they can be gathered and destroyed early in the morning (this can be begun even before the plants are up); egg masses being easily seen can be quickly found and crushed; and while the nymphs are small, spraying with a pyrethrum and soap mixture or dusting with pyrethrum powder will destroy them. The difficulty in reaching the nymphs on the underside of the leaves with the spray can in part be obviated by attaching the nozzle of the spray pump to a piece of tubing connecting at its other end with the hose, and bent in a loop so as to give an upward spray.

In the south one or two very closely allied species also attack the squashes and cucurbits and may be controlled in the same ways.

*Family* **PYRRHOCORIDÆ.**—The insects of this family superficially resemble the coreids and are of medium size. Only one is of any economic importance in the United States, and that in only a few of the southern states though it is also injurious in some of the West Indies Islands.

**The cotton stainer** (*Dysdercus suturellus* H. S., Fig. 97) feeds on cotton, and occasionally the eggplant and orange among cultivated crops. On oranges it attacks the fruit about the time it is ripening, puncturing the skin and thus hastening decay. On cotton the insect punctures the partly developed bolls and if the attack is severe these may be destroyed. If not, the fiber is more or less stained, apparently from the punctures in the seeds, reducing the value of the cotton anywhere from 5 to 50 per cent. As the bugs develop in colonies and remain close together for some time and in their early stages are red, they are easily located and knocked off into dishes containing kerosene. In fall and spring they are attracted to baits, of either cottonseed or sugar cane, where they can be killed with kerosene. The bugs also feed and breed freely on *Hibiscus* and the Spanish cocklebur, and the destruction of these plants near cotton fields will prevent their breeding there and spreading in larger numbers to the cotton.

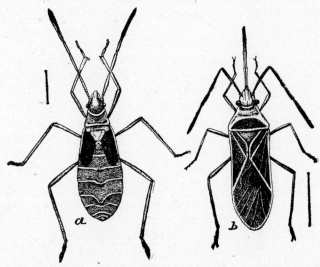

FIG. 97.—The cotton stainer (*Dysdercus suturellus* H. S.): *a*, nymph; *b*, adult; enlarged about three times. (*From U.S. Dept Agr. Farmers' Bull.* 890.)

*Family* **LYGÆIDÆ.**—There are many kinds of insects in this family but nearly all are small, being in most cases less than a third of an inch long. A number occasionally injure various plants, and one—the chinch bug—is one of the worst half dozen pests in the United States.

**The chinch bug** (*Blissus leucopterus* Say).—This little bug, less than a quarter of an inch long, feeds on all the grasses and cereal crops. It is apparently a native of tropical America which has migrated northward, up the Atlantic coast, the Mississippi Valley and the Pacific coast, and is now found everywhere south of the St. Lawrence River and the Great Lakes and also in southern Ontario, Minnesota, Manitoba, the Dakotas and along the eastern slope of the Rocky Mountains to Texas. It has also been found in Arizona, California and Washington. It is not a serious pest, usually, in the northeastern states and many of the others, but in the Mississippi Valley it often destroys crops valued at millions of dollars in one season.

The adult bug (Fig. 98c) is a tiny insect seemingly incapable of causing so much injury, but its enormous numbers make up for its small size. Its body is black or dark gray, with white and therefore conspicuous wings, each having a single black spot. There are two forms of adult, however: one with long full-sized wings, the other with short wings only partly covering the top of the abdomen. The former occurs in the Mississippi Valley; the latter is met with, together with the long-winged form, in the Atlantic states and to some extent inland from there along the more southern of the Great Lakes to Illinois.

The long-winged form passes the winter as the adult in grass tufts, under fallen leaves or in other places that give it protection. Corn shocks left out over winter often harbor enormous numbers. In spring the bugs leave their winter quarters and fly to the grain fields. Here they lay their eggs, several hundred in number, on the ground at the base of the plants or on the roots just below the surface, this process lasting about a

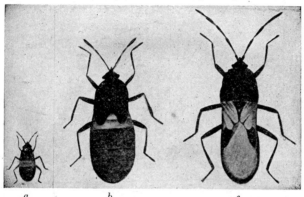

a        b        c

Fig. 98.—Different stages of the chinch bug (*Blissus leucopterus* Say): *a*, nymph in first instar; *b*, fourth instar nymph; *c*, adult; all enlarged about nine times. (*Modified from Ill. Agr. Expt. Sta. Bull.* 95.)

month. The average length of the egg stage is about two weeks and the young that hatch suck the sap from the plants for about forty days before becoming adult. The nymphs are yellow with an orange tinge about in the middle of the abdomen. This soon spreads over the greater part of the body. In later stages the red becomes vermilion, with a pale band across the front of the abdomen, the head and prothorax dusky, and before becoming adult the red becomes quite dark.

Development, at least for the individuals coming from the later eggs, is not complete before harvesting time, and to finish their growth they are obliged to migrate and find more food. They accordingly march in armies, often traveling some little distance on foot, and many that have already become adults, able to fly, march with them. In new feeding grounds development is completed and the eggs for a second generation are laid. This generation appears to feed more particularly on corn, kafir corn, millet and other similar crops, and its members become adult before winter and go into hiding until the following spring.

With the short-winged form, hibernation at a distance from its food plant is impossible because of its inability to fly. This form therefore winters in grassland and begins its work there in the spring. It is a question whether there is more than one generation a year for this form. Migrations, when they occur, are, of course, on foot, and corn is no more liable to be attacked than timothy or any other grass crop.

The chinch bug is particularly affected by weather conditions, dry weather being favorable and wet seasons unfavorable. Dry weather appears to induce migration, and a succession of several dry years favors a large increase in their numbers and consequently of the injury they cause. Rains during the hatching periods of the eggs are very destructive to the insect, and the suppression of a chinch-bug attack, anticipated because of the great abundance of the wintering bugs, by heavy rains at the right time in the spring is one reason why these pests are not even more serious than is the case.

A fungus (*Sporotrichum globuliferum* Speg.), generally called the chinch-bug fungus, frequently attacks this insect, particularly during periods of wet, cool, cloudy weather, and then kills enormous numbers of them. In dry seasons it seems to have little effect, and attempts to control the chinch bug by placing individuals inoculated with the fungus in infested fields, although successful from the experimental standpoint, have on the whole hardly produced the results hoped for. It is most valuable in seasons which are dry during the egg-hatching period but wet thereafter.

In seasons, then, when rains occur during the egg-hatching periods of the bugs, these and the fungus present will usually prevent serious outbreaks. In dry seasons, particularly where there are several in succession, artificial methods of control must be resorted to.

*Control.*—Numerous methods of control have been tested, with varying degrees of success. Only two of these, though, appear to be of great value and, unfortunately, neither will protect a crop actually being fed upon, though planting some vigorous growing legume in the hills with the corn is helpful, as the bugs prefer feeding where there is sunlight and the legumes shade the bases of the corn plants.

Burning over the fields while the bugs are wintering there will destroy great numbers of them, particularly where they winter largely in bunch grass. In the east this method is less effective, as the bugs are more scattered in hiding places.

The other method is available when, the grass or grain having been cut, the bugs still require food and must go elsewhere to find it and march in swarms together toward corn or some other grass. At this time a barrier around the field they are leaving, made by plowing a furrow around the field or across their line of march and putting a band of creosote 2 or 3 inches wide near the top of this furrow, on the side toward which the bugs are coming, will repel them. Renewal of this band daily for 10 days to 2 weeks is necessary to maintain the repellent odor which keeps the bugs back. If post holes 1½ to 2 feet deep are dug at intervals on the side of the creosote band to which the bugs are coming, and the tops of these holes dusted so the bugs can get no hold there, many will fall into these holes and be unable to escape. Thousands are often caught in this way. Kerosene poured into these holes will kill the bugs. Creosoted paper barriers are often substituted for the creosote barrier band, largely because they require much less creosote.

In the south this insect is often a serious pest in lawns planted with St. Augustine grass.

That insects like other animals suffer from the attacks of various diseases is, perhaps, not generally realized. This topic is also discussed on (pages 178 and 209). The list of these diseases is not a small one, but our knowledge of them is very limited.

Some of them are caused by bacteria and are diseases comparable to many of those from which man suffers. Others are caused by parasitic fungi which in one way or another enter the body of the insect and grow, consuming the nourishment they find there, finally killing the animal, usually making its body hard and firm, or "mummifying" it. A third type of disease is that known as the wilt disease, in which neither bacteria nor fungi have been discovered, where the insect "wilts" after a time, becomes soft and gradually decays. The causative agents in this class of diseases are still unknown, but they are infectious, spreading from one individual to another, and where the insects are abundant and weather conditions are favorable they cause a high mortality.

Attempts have been made to utilize diseases for the control of insect pests. The chinch bug has been the subject of one of the most thorough of these experiments, the fungus already referred to having been cultivated for the purpose. It was found that, by the use of appropriate methods, cultures of the fungus obtained in the fall could be grown during the winter, and bugs inoculated with it in the spring could be sent out to fields where the insects were abundant and liberated there to spread the disease. To some extent this was a success, but it was soon found that if the inoculated bugs were set free during dry weather the disease failed to spread rapidly enough to prevent great injury; if the weather was wet the fungus was in most cases already present and the addition of more diseased bugs at best only hastened its spread somewhat. As a business proposition, then, the artificial cultivation and distribution of the fungus have been given up.

In the case of a bacterial disease of grasshoppers which has at times been observed greatly to reduce the numbers of this insect, somewhat similar results have been obtained. In a few instances some degree of success has been secured by spreading the germs, but here the factor of cannibalism seems to enter into the problem. With species of grasshoppers that feed considerably on dead or dying individuals, there is some probability of successful treatment in this way, but such species are not numerous, and there also appears to be more or less immunity to the germ in some species.

The whole problem of control by disease appears to hinge on satisfactory answers to three questions: Can the disease be cultivated so that a supply can be obtained and continued? Can it be introduced successfully into regions where it is needed but not present? Will the disease establish itself there and become effective?

The answers to the first two of these questions are liable to be affirmative ones, though this is not always the case. The third is the most difficult to determine. It may be that the disease is not already present where it is desired to introduce it because conditions there are such that it will not thrive. Fungous diseases at least are influenced to a very large degree by the weather, most of them thriving best in warm, moist weather and if these conditions are not present they will amount to little.

Fig. 99.—Example of a tingid bug (*Gargaphia solanii* Heid.); enlarged about five times. (*From U.S. Dept. Agr. Farmers' Bull.* 856.)

At the present time it would appear that the success of artificially introducing diseases to control insect attacks is so dependent upon weather conditions that man can do little more than supply the disease and trust that the needed kind of weather may follow. Unfortunately the very conditions under which injurious abundance of the insect takes place appear in too many instances to be those distinctly unfavorable to the spread of the disease.

*Family* **TINGIDÆ.**—The insects (Fig. 99) of this family are delicate little bugs, usually having the pronotum broadly expanded and, with the hemielytra, covered with reticulated marks, giving them something the appearance of a bit of lace; this has been responsible for their common name—lacebugs. They are rarely more than an eighth of an inch long, usually whitish in color, and suck the sap from various plants, being generally found on the underside of the leaves. Their eggs are placed on the leaves, generally at the tops of small, brown, rather conical projections produced by the bugs, which somewhat resemble places where fungi project from the leaf surface. Several species are occasionally rather injurious.

*Family* **MIRIDÆ.**—This family until recently was called the Capsidæ. It contains a very large number of species, perhaps more than any other family of bugs, all small, and most feeding on plant juices. Some feed on grass; others on succulent stems; some make a specialty, at least at certain seasons, of sucking the sap from leaf and flower buds, distorting them or even preventing their development. Sometimes they are present in great numbers and do much injury. Fruit is attacked by some species while it is small and rapidly growing; such attacks produce "dimples" or small depressed areas, or they may even deform and thus greatly reduce the value of the fruit. Many secondary and potential pests belong in this family. On the other hand, some are predaceous, feeding on injurious insects. One species is an important enemy of certain kinds of aphids.

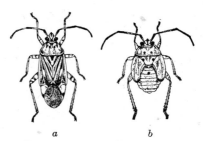

Some of the adults are bright red; others red and black, yellow and black or other colors. In those feeding on grass, grayish yellow or greenish yellow is a frequent color. In many cases it seems that this is in some way connected with the color of their food, as, for example, some species found on the stems of the red dogwood are themselves largely red, though in other

Fig. 100.—Tarnished plant bug (*Lygus pratensis* L.); *a*, adult; *b*, nearly full-grown nymph; nearly four times natural size. (*From U.S. Dept. Agr. Farmers' Bull.* 856.)

cases it is difficult to discover any such correspondence of color between the insect and its food plant.

**The tarnished plant bug** (*Lygus pratensis* L.).—The tarnished plant bug is widely distributed, in both Europe and this country. It is about a quarter of an inch long (Fig. 100) and varies greatly in its coloration. The general color is brown, variegated with shades of yellowish and brownish and with black spots in some places.

This pest feeds on over fifty different kinds of plants which are of value to man. The adults attack apple, pear, peach and in fact all fruit-tree buds, destroying or at least seriously injuring them; small fruits are often stunted or "buttoned" by them; flower buds of such plants as the chrysanthemum, dahlia, peony and aster are punctured and destroyed or malformed. Corn, wheat, oats and other grain and grass crops are also injured by this omnivorous feeder. With young peach trees in nurseries it causes the trouble called stopback by killing the terminal buds, and it is a carrier of the fire blight of the pear, conveying the bacteria causing this disease from infected to healthy trees. It is therefore a serious pest.

The insect passes the winter as the adult, and possibly as the nearly full-grown nymph also, in protected places and appears with the first warm spring days and attacks the buds of fruit trees and other plants. Its eggs are inserted in leaf veins and stems, flowers and similar places, and they hatch in about ten days. The nymphs feed on the juices of the plants and become adult in from three weeks to a month. There is, therefore, time for several generations in a season, though the actual number of these does not appear to have been worked out and probably varies somewhat according to the length of the season in different parts of the country.

*Control.*—No effective method of control has as yet been discovered for this pest, though many have been tried. Spraying the infested plants with kerosene emulsion, nicotine sulfate or soaps early in the morning has been found to kill some of them. Shields covered with tanglefoot, placed beside and over the plants, which are then jarred, will capture some; the destruction of near-by weeds and rubbish before the bugs come out of hibernation helps. Dusting with fine sulfur dusts has given fair control on some crops.

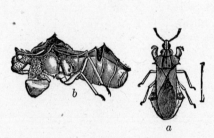

FIG. 101. FIG. 102.

FIG. 101.—Ambush bug (*Phymata erosa wolffi* Stal.): *a*, from above; *b*, from the side, showing the grasping front leg. Enlarged; true length shown by hair line. (*Modified from Sanderson and Jackson, Elementary Entomology, after Riley, U.S. Dept. Agr.*)

FIG. 102.—Reduviid bug; about twice natural size.

*Family* **PHYMATIDÆ.**—The ambush bugs (Fig. 101), as members of this family are called, are carnivorous bugs which usually hide in blossoms to capture insects visiting there. They are rather short and stout, generally less than half an inch long, and have colors so combined on their bodies as to render them very inconspicuous in the flowers. Their prey is generally any insect they can grasp with their stout forelegs, whether it is injurious or otherwise.

*Family* **REDUVIIDÆ.**—This large family consists of carnivorous insects some of which are small; others are considerably more than an inch long (Fig. 102). Though generally feeding on the blood of other insects, they may occasionally attack man and in such cases produce rather painful wounds. One species, most common in the southern states, often enters houses and feeds upon the bedbug, and from this habit has been called the masked hunter, the mask referring to dust which adheres to its rather sticky body before it becomes adult. Another species in the west and south is occasionally found in beds where it imitates the habits of the true bedbug. A similar but different species occurs in California.

The group as a whole, preying as its members do upon other insects almost entirely, must be regarded as a beneficial one. The family is most abundant in the warmer climates.

*Family* **CIMICIDÆ.**—The Cimicidæ is a very small group but well known through one of its members, the bedbug. All the insects belonging here are small, rather oval in outline, very flat and rather reddish in color. Birds, poultry and bats are attacked by species similar to but smaller than the bedbug and some of these, under unusual conditions, may enter houses and attack man.

**The bedbug** (*Cimex lectularius* L.).—This universally distributed and well-known pest (Fig. 103) appears to have originated in Asia and has now spread wherever man is found. It is a small, flat insect, reddish brown in color, about a fifth of an inch long when adult, and wingless, only tiny stubs of wings remaining to show that it has been derived from winged ancestors. It produces a very noticeable odor.

It is a nocturnal animal, hiding during the day in any cracks and crevices it may find, in the bedstead, behind loose wallpaper or elsewhere. In these places it lays its eggs, probably about two hundred in number, these hatching in from a week to a much longer period depending upon the temperature. The nymphs are yellowish white at first, turning brown gradually with increasing age. Nymphal life varies greatly in its length, being

Fig. 103.—Adult female bedbug (*Cimex lectularius* L.) gorged with blood; greatly enlarged. (*From U.S. Dept. Agr. Farmers' Bull.* 754.)

affected by the temperature and food supply; but when these are favorable, about seven weeks is required to produce the adult bug. Under less favorable circumstances the nymphs may remain unchanged, but alive, for a long period. The number of generations in a year may therefore differ greatly under different conditions but in warmed houses there are probably at least four.

Where human blood is not obtainable for food, that of mice, rats, or other animals where available may be taken instead, and living bedbugs in empty houses may perhaps be accounted for in this way. Without food, however, death within a year is a practical certainty.

The "bite" of the bedbug is quite poisonous to some persons but not to others and in some cases a sort of immunity is obtained by individuals continuously exposed to attacks.

Bedbugs have been accused of carrying certain contagious diseases of man, such as European relapsing fever, kala azar, bubonic plague, leprosy and others, but proof is thus far inadequate, or even negative as in the case of kala azar. The bedbug does not appear to transmit diseases except as the causative organisms contaminate its mouth parts and thus are more or less accidentally carried from one victim to another.

*Control.*—Where sulfur can be burned in a room, using four pounds for each thousand cubic feet of space, for twenty-four hours, the fumes will destroy all stages of this insect if the room is reasonably tight. A thorough treatment with kerosene or an oil-base contact spray of all places where the insects can hide and lay their eggs is also successful if the material penetrates all the cracks. Heating a room or house to from 120 to 130°F. in summer and keeping it that hot for an hour has proved effective. Bedbug

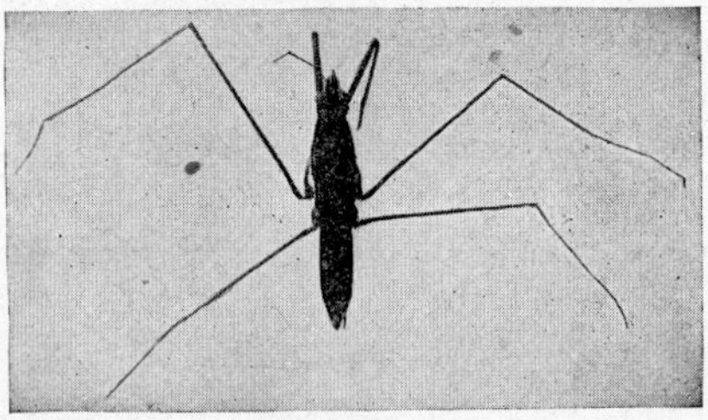

Fig. 104.

Fig. 105.

Fig. 104.—Water skater (*Gerris conformis* Uhl.); about natural size.
Fig. 105.—Notonectids and corixid: *A*, Notonectid at the surface of the water showing under surface; *A'*, swimming showing upper surface; *B*, Corixid swimming; somewhat enlarged. (*From Linville and Kelly, Text-book in General Zoology.*)

control on a commercial scale is largely by means of hydrocyanic acid gas. Persons obliged to stop at infested places can usually obtain protection by dusting pyrethrum between the sheets of the bed.

*Family* **GERRIDÆ.**—These insects, the water skaters or water striders (Fig. 104) as they are commonly called, are often noticed during the summer, skating over the surface of quiet pools of water. Their bodies are slender in most cases, less than half an inch long, usually black or brown, and their long, slender legs project some distance from the body. A few are shorter and broader. They feed on any small insects they are able to capture and winter either under sticks or stones under water, or in mud near the edge, under leaves and rubbish. A few live on the surface of the ocean in warm climates. They are interesting insects to watch but are of little if any economic importance.

*Family* **NOTONECTIDÆ.**—The back swimmers (Fig. 105*A*), as they are termed, live in fresh water. They are small, rarely more than half an inch in length and generally black and cream-colored. The back has sloping sides something like the bottom of a boat and they swim on their backs, propelling themselves by their long legs which are fringed with hairs. They occasionally come to the surface for air, a supply of which they carry down with them under their wings and between the fine hairs covering the underside of the body. They are carnivorous, feeding on other small insects, but are of little importance.

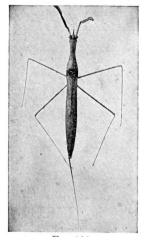

FIG. 106.                          FIG. 107.
FIG. 106.—Water scorpion (*Ranatra americana* Montd.); about natural size.
FIG. 107.—Giant water bug (*Lethocerus americanus* Leidy); natural size.

*Family* **CORIXIDÆ.**—Living in the same places and with similar habits to the back swimmers are small, greenish and blackish mottled insects, rather oval in outline with heads somewhat flattened in front, and known as water boatmen (Fig. 105*B*). They have long, fringed, oar-like legs but do not swim on their backs and in some way are able to remain under water without coming up for air for a much longer time than the back swimmers. Like the latter group they often leave the water and fly at night and are frequently attracted to lights.

*Family* **NEPIDÆ.**—The water scorpions, as these insects are called, live in fresh-water ponds and pools. Two types of form are included, one having a long, slender body and long legs (Fig. 106), the front pair of which, unusually long, are constructed for grasping their prey which consists of small insects. In the other type the body is short, rather broad and flat. In both a long tube, consisting of two pieces which can be pressed together to form the tube, joins the hinder end of the body and, while the insect is an inch under water in some

FIG. 108.—Male belostomid (*Belostoma flumineum* Say) carrying eggs on its back, natural size.

cases, this tube is pointed upward until its tip is out of water and through it the insect obtains air. The slender forms lying quiet on the bottom of pools resemble dead twigs and thus obtain the concealment needed to enable them to get within reach of their food.

*Family* **BELOSTOMIDÆ.**—These insects are generally termed the giant water bugs. Some of them are the largest members of the Hemiptera, being two, three or more inches long, broad, flat and brown in color (Fig. 107). They live in fresh water and feed on insects and even small fish and are thus sometimes injurious in the production of food fishes. They fly by night and are frequently attracted to electric lights, which has led to the larger species being sometimes called electric-light bugs. In some of the smaller species (Fig. 108) the eggs are laid on the back of the male who is thus obliged to carry them around until they hatch.

# CHAPTER XXIV

## ORDER HOMOPTERA

The Homoptera is a large group containing insects of many forms, often showing little resemblance to one another. They suck sap from plants through a beak, apparently very similar in structure to that already described for the Hemiptera, but it is attached not to the front but to the hinder part of the under surface of the head which is very closely joined to the prothorax so that the beak frequently appears to arise between the front legs. In some instances where the adults do not feed, this structure is lacking. The wings are often absent but when present are usually held, while at rest, sloping over the body like a house roof. They are of the same thickness and usually, though not always, transparent. In this group (except the male scale insects) the metamorphosis is incomplete. These facts may be summarized as follows:

*The Homoptera are sucking insects with the beak (when present) arising from the back part of the underside of the head which is very closely joined to the prothorax. The wings (frequently absent) are of uniform thickness throughout and when not in use are held sloping over the body. The metamorphosis (except in male scale insects) is incomplete.*

Few groups of insects show as great differences in their members as are found here. The cicadas, often two or three inches in length and with a wing spread of four inches or more, are among the giants of the order; some of the whiteflies and scale insects are hardly more than just visible to the eye. Most of the group move about freely, though some locate in one place soon after they hatch and remain there the rest of their lives. In one section the insect produces a protective scale which covers it, and, beneath this, degeneration of some parts of the body occurs.

Many Homoptera secrete a sweet, sticky fluid called honeydew, often in such quantities, when the insects are in abundance, that in falling it makes a noise like fine rain. Striking on leaves, fruit or bark, it adheres and dries, and a blackish fungus grows in it, giving to such places a sooty appearance. This secretion appears to be produced most abundantly by the soft scales, whiteflies, plant lice, jumping plant lice and some of the treehoppers. Ants and honeybees feed on the honeydew and frequently visit the insects producing it, for this food.

Nine families of Homoptera are generally recognized, but four of these may, for convenience, be combined here. The six to be considered therefore are:

Order Homoptera
{
Cicadas (Cicadidæ)
Leafhoppers and treehoppers (four families)
Jumping plant lice (Chermidæ)
Plant lice or aphids (Aphididæ)
Whiteflies (Aleyrodidæ)
Scale insects (Coccidæ)
}

*Family* **CICADIDÆ** (the cicadas).—Most of the members of this family are rather large insects, with bodies often two or three inches or even more in length and quite stout as well. Their wings are correspondingly large, and in some species have a spread of more than six inches. Though usually transparent and with prominent veins, they sometimes have pigmented areas of various colors.

The adults place their eggs in slits they make with their ovipositors in twigs. On hatching, the nymphs drop to the ground and make their way to the roots where they feed on the sap. Metamorphosis is more nearly a complete one than in the other families of Homoptera (except the scales), the nymph having but little resemblance to the adult, and the last two nymphal stages are rather transitional in appearance between the two.

The adult males have vocal organs located on the underside of the basal segments of the abdomen and covered by extensions backward of the metathorax. The sound produced is often so loud, especially when the insects are abundant, as to be very noticeable and even unpleasant. No auditory organ has as yet been discovered with certainty in either sex.

Fig. 109.—Adult periodical cicada; natural size.

Cicadas are particularly inhabitants of warm countries, though some species are abundant quite far from these regions. In North America they occur in Canada and probably in all the states farther south and are found as far north as England in the Old World. They are often wrongly called locusts.

**The periodical cicada or 17-year locust** (*Magicicada* (*Tibicina*) *septendecim* L.).—This remarkable insect is a native of North America. It is found from Vermont and Massachusetts to northern Florida and west to Wisconsin, Iowa, Kansas, (Colorado?) Oklahoma and Texas but is not of great importance near its northern limits.

The adult (Fig. 109) is about an inch long, with a stout black body, orange eyes, legs and wing veins. The wings when at rest extend considerably behind the body. In the far south it appears early in May but near its northern limits it may be as late as early June. The insects are usually in evidence for five or six weeks and are particularly noticeable in and near wooded areas. They suck the sap from various trees but do little injury in this way. The females lay their eggs in the smaller twigs of trees, shrubs and even in herbaceous plants, the oak and hickory, and in the case of fruit trees the apple seeming to be preferred for this purpose, though more than seventy-five kinds of trees are attacked. The eggs are placed in slits made in rows by the ovipositor and a twig thus punctured is liable to break off either entirely or in part. The eggs hatch in six or seven weeks and the nymphs drop to the ground and burrow to the roots where they feed until the seventeenth spring from the one when they entered the ground, most of them being between six and eighteen inches below the surface.

During the seventeenth spring the nymphs burrow upward nearly to the surface of the ground but do not usually come out until ready for the final molt producing the adult. In some cases, however, upon reaching the surface they construct earthen cones or chimneys sometimes six or eight inches high, within which the burrow is continued. It is supposed that these are constructed where the cicadas are in moist places and these structures will bring the insects out above the moisture, or that a shallow soil enables them to reach the surface before the normal time, or unusually warm conditions hasten their start, and on their arrival they are not ready for their final molt. Recent work indicates that length of day is a factor. Probably the last word on this subject has not yet been said.

Arrived at the surface of the ground and ready to molt for the last time, the nymphs crawl out of their burrows, the greater number of them in the afternoon and evening, and make their way to any objects such as a tree, stick or anything at hand and on these molt for the last time and become the adults that are ready for flight the next morning.

In the course of nearly seventeen years of underground feeding it is only natural that some finding an abundant food supply should be able to gain a little time and appear during the sixteenth year as "forerunners" of the main brood, and that others with scanty food should be delayed until the eighteenth season. These are few in number, however. In the south is a race with a thirteen-year life, the origin of which as related to the other race is not as yet explained.

Though a cicada's life is (except for the race just mentioned) seventeen years, they occur in one place or another every year, showing that in some way in the past these insects have diverged so that there are now seventeen broods. Some places are so unfortunate as to have several of these broods but, though the cicada may appear there every four or five years, the descendants of any one of these will not be found until seventeen years have elapsed.

Some of the broods are more abundant and widely distributed than others. Brood II, due in 1945; brood VI, due in 1949; brood X, due in

1953; and brood XIV, due in 1957, are the most important in the 17-year race; brood XIX, due in 1946 and brood XXIII, due in 1950, are the most important in the 13-year race.

Numerous enemies of the periodical cicada are known, many of them being parasites. Some birds feed on them and a fungus causes disease of the adults. Various mammals feed on them as they are coming out of the ground.

*Control.*—In forests nothing can be done to control these insects; but when they appear in sufficient numbers in parks and orchards to make treatment desirable, certain methods for preventing injury or for

the destruction of the insects are feasible. In some cases, collection of the adults by hand has paid. In others, spraying the tree trunks and other objects on which they rest while molting after leaving the ground, aiming to hit as many of the insects as possible and using a strong kerosene emulsion for the spray material, has proved quite effective, for where the cicadas are not killed they are

FIG. 110.—Adult dog-day cicada (*Tibicen linnei* Sm. and Grsb.); natural size.

crippled by the action of the particles of the spray which strike them. This treatment, however, to be successful must be repeated every evening about sunset or very early in the morning, before the insects begin to fly, as long as they continue to come out of the ground.

In the case of fruit trees anywhere, pruning is not advisable, if spring cicadas are due in that locality, until after the eggs are laid. Then, pruning and burning the punctured twigs before the eggs hatch are desirable. In some cases young trees suffer so severely that it is not advisable to set out nursery stock the year before cicadas are due. Apple "whips," however, can usually be safely planted the same spring that the cicadas come, being generally too small to suffer much by the attacks of these insects. Hogs allowed to run under trees known to have cicadas at their roots will kill many of these pests as they come to the surface to become adult in May and June of their seventeenth year.

Various species of cicadas are common in nearly all parts of the United States. In the east the dog-day cicadas (*Tibicen linnei* Sm. and Grsb., and others) are often noticeable (Fig. 110), singing in the trees during late July and August. Most of these species are somewhat larger than the periodical cicada and generally black and olive green, with a white powder or "bloom" on the underside of the body. They are supposed to have about a two-year life history and, as individuals occur every year, two distinct broods. A few of these species greatly resemble the periodical cicada in color but are smaller, and, as they appear more than a month after the latter have disappeared, no confusion should lead to the belief that the periodical cicada has appeared at that season.

**Leafhoppers and treehoppers.**—The four or more families included under this heading contain a large number of kinds of insects, many of which are extremely numerous. Among them are the lantern flies of South America and the candle flies of China and India which are quite

FIG. 111.—Treehoppers showing remarkable forms of the pronotum; enlarged about twice.

large insects, a number of which at least are luminous. Some of the insects here included are highly colored and some secrete quantities of wax which is often used for candles and other purposes.

In one of the families—the treehoppers—the pronotum is largely and often remarkably developed, sometimes giving these insects a very grotesque appearance. In this country, however, such forms are not usual, the development of this section of the body being mainly in the line of horns or humps and the enlargement of this plate in width or height and in its extension backward until it covers most or all of the body (Fig. 111). The treehoppers of the United States are all small insects, less than half an inch long, and as they sit on twigs their peculiar forms seem to give them resemblances to buds, swellings or other characters, which suggests that their odd outlines may be for resemblance to these structures and thus secure the protection from their enemies which this would give.

FIG. 112.—Adult buffalo treehopper; view from above; enlarged about twice.

In general the treehoppers puncture the twigs of plants and are injurious, though only a few kinds are ever so abundant and attack plants of such importance as to need consideration.

Among these the most common is the buffalo treehopper (*Ceresa bubalus* Fab., Fig. 112), found practically everywhere in the United States except perhaps in the most southerly portions, which injures the twigs of fruit trees by its egg punctures made in the fall. Two rows of punctures are made, nearly parallel to each other, the two rather resembling parenthesis marks, and in each a number of eggs is laid. These hatch the following spring. Injury caused by the feeding of the nymphs and adults is slight, and in fact most of the young feed mainly on weeds, but the egg punctures (Fig. 113) cause distorted growth and weaken the twig. A dormant oil spray, 4 to 6 per cent, will kill a large proportion of the eggs that overwinter. Weeds should be kept down and legume cover crops avoided for a year or two.

The leafhoppers (Fig. 114) are extremely abundant insects some of which must do much injury to the grass crop, as it has been estimated that there are frequently as many as one to two millions of them per acre. Most of them are very small.

Some leafhoppers have one generation a year, others more, and different species appear to hibernate in different stages. In addition to various grasses,

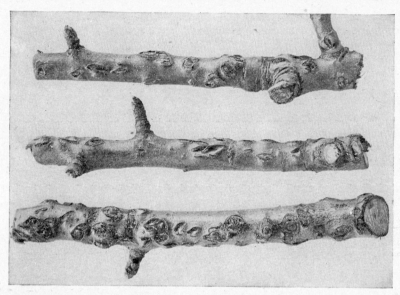

Fig. 113.—Twigs showing injuries caused by the buffalo treehopper in laying its eggs; about natural size. (*From Britton, Fifteenth Rept. Conn. Agr. Expt. Sta., 1915.*)

grain, alfalfa, clover, sugar beets, grape and rose, the apple, elm, willow and other trees have their juices extracted by the feeding of these insects.

**Apple leafhoppers.**—Several species of leafhoppers attack the foliage of the apple, though two of them are primarily feeders on other plants. The potato

Fig. 114.—Three kinds of leaf-hoppers; enlarged about twice. The two left-hand figures are of "spittle insects."

leafhopper (*Empoasca fabæ* Harr.) seriously injures the potato in many parts of this country. It is a pale-green insect about one-eighth inch long. These insects winter as adults under leaves, etc., and become active in the spring, feeding on various plants; when the potatoes come up they pass to them and lay their eggs which hatch in one to two weeks. The nymphs suck the sap from the leaves and become adults in one to four weeks according to the temperature. Some now pass to the later potatoes where a second generation is produced and, if time permits, a partial third generation. During all this time many may pass to and attack the apple, particularly nursery stock, causing a curling of the leaves and checking of growth, but the injury here is not usually important on older trees. On the potato this insect produces "hopper burn," a browning, usually first at the leaf tip, then on its sides and spreading inward. The spots are closely related to the tips of the veins.

*Control.*—On the potato, spraying with 4–6–50 homemade Bordeaux mixture is quite effective. Apply this when the potatoes are about 6 inches high and repeat every week to 10 days for four or five sprayings. As Bordeaux mixture is a useful fungicide for the potato, this treatment serves a double purpose. On the apple, spray with nicotine sulfate, 40 per cent, 1 part in 900 to 1,200 parts of water with the addition of soap. Pyrethrum dust has also proved effective.

The apple leafhopper (*Empoasca maligna* Walsh) spends its entire life on the apple, wintering as the egg under loose bark or other protected places. During the summer the nymphs suck the sap from the leaves, causing these to show a whitening of their upper surface. This species, which has only one generation a year, occurs nearly everywhere east of the Rocky Mountains. Its work is most serious in the older orchards and its control is the same as that for the potato leafhopper on the apple.

The rose leafhopper (*Typhlocyba rosœ* L.).—This European insect is now present practically everywhere in the United States and in parts of Canada. It is a general feeder and will probably attack most plants of the family Rosaceæ but appears to be particularly injurious to the rose and apple. The adult is almost as large as the apple leafhopper and is creamy white to light yellow. It lays its eggs during the fall in the bark of rosebushes, apple trees, berry canes and other plants and there they remain until spring, when they hatch. The nymphs suck the sap from the underside of the leaves of the plants, producing a mottled appearance, and as the injury increases the leaves may turn yellow and dry up, but they do not curl. There are two generations of this insect a year, the eggs for the second generation being laid in July. Most of the wintering eggs are deposited in rose stems.

This insect is a serious apple pest in the northwest and is occasionally important in New England. Rosebushes often suffer by their loss of sap and the failure of their injured leaves to perform their proper functions. Spraying or dusting infested plants with nicotine sulfate as soon as the nymphs are observed is usually sufficient to prevent further injury.

The beet leafhopper (*Eutettix tenellus* Bak.) is a western species, also reported from Mexico and Argentina. It is about three-sixteenths of an inch long, varying from pale green to dark brown in color. It winters as the adult and in spring may feed on many kinds of wild plants but later passes to the sugar beet, often flying in swarms for many miles. As it feeds on the beets, a curling of the leaves called curly top is produced if the insect has previously obtained the curly-top virus from some diseased plant. Its effect on the beet is to reduce its sugar content and stunt or kill the plant attacked, often causing a loss of millions of dollars a year to the crop. Breeding in the beet fields, there may be from one to four generations a year. No satisfactory control for this pest has thus far been found, as it flies too quickly for contact insecticides to be very effective and sugar-beet raising has been given up in many places on this account.

Many other leafhoppers are at times serious pests. The grape leafhopper is sometimes so abundant that grape leaves in vineyards are turned brown and much injured. The six-spotted leafhopper attacks some grains and grasses, and other species, generally of slight importance, at times assume prominence. In general, nicotine sulfate, prepared as previously indicated, is an effective control material for these insects wherever conditions permit its use.

A group of tiny leafhoppers known as froghoppers or spittle insects (Fig. 114) is also included here. They are common on grasses and other herbaceous plants and also on some trees such as the pine. The nymphs produce a fluid and liberate air in this in such a way as to form a sort of froth or "spittle" in which they live. They are very abundant in the northern states practically across the entire continent, and one species, the lined spittle bug (*Philœnus lineatus* L.), is often so common as to wet the shoes of a person who walks through the grass in June. The nymphs suck the sap from the grass stems, withering and turning white the upper parts of the stems and the blossoms, much as do the grass thrips. Burning over old grass fields where these insects

 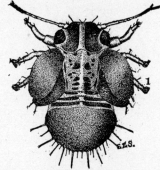

Fig. 115.    Fig. 116.

Fig. 115.—Adult pear psylla (*Psylla pyricola* Foerst.); about ten times natural size. (*From Britton, Third Rpt. Ent. Conn. Agr. Expt. Sta.*, 1903; *after Slingerland.*)

Fig. 116.—Nymph of pear psylla; greatly enlarged. (*From Britton, Third Rpt. Ent. Conn. Agr. Expt. Sta.*, 1903; *after Slingerland.*)

are most abundant, in early spring, will destroy many of these insects in their winter quarters close to the ground.

*Family* **CHERMIDÆ.**—The jumping plant lice, as the members of this family are usually called, are very small insects which feed on various plants but are rarely abundant enough to become of economic importance. One exception to this occurs and a consideration of that species will also give something of a general idea of the insects of the group as a whole.

**The pear psylla** (*Psylla pyricola* Foerst.).—The pear psylla is a European pear pest which seems to have reached this country about 1832 and is now present nearly everywhere in the eastern United States where pears are grown and is a serious pest in the pear orchards of the Pacific northwest. When it is abundant it is very injurious, seriously checking the growth of the tree, so that many of the leaves turn yellow and drop off, as does much of the young fruit, and the entire vitality of the tree is reduced and it makes little or no growth.

The adult (Fig. 115) is about a tenth of an inch long, the body black with reddish markings, and long antennae are present. Except for this last feature it greatly resembles a tiny cicada. The adults pass the winter hiding in crevices of the bark or similarly protected places and in spring lay their eggs on the twigs. The eggs hatch in two to three weeks according to the temperature. The nymphs (Fig. 116) suck the sap from the axils of the leaves and fruit stems and, if abundant, gather around the bases of these and spread to the under surface of the leaves themselves. They move about but little and secrete large amounts of honeydew (see page 133), sometimes so much, when they are very numerous, as to cover the leaves and branches. They are broadly oval, flat creatures, yellowish at first but blackish with reddish marks later and with bright-red eyes. They become adult in about a month and lay their eggs, this time on the underside of the leaves or on the leaf petioles. These eggs hatch in a week to ten days and

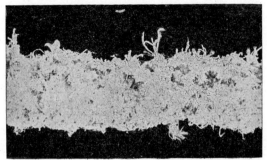

Fig. 117.—Alder twig covered by woolly aphids, the "wool" entirely concealing their bodies; somewhat enlarged.

adults are produced in about a month. There are three or four generations a year in New England and more in the South.

*Control.*—Methods for checking the injuries caused by these insects center around their control in winter and early spring. Most of the adults winter under the loose bark of the trees or in tufts of grass and rubbish near the trees. Scraping off all loose bark and removal of all rubbish late in fall is desirable. Spray thoroughly, as soon as the leaves have fallen, with a miscible oil. In spring, just as the clusters of blossom buds begin to separate from each other, but before the blossoms open, lime-sulfur, diluted at the rate of one part to eight or nine of water, will kill the eggs and any newly hatched nymphs. Give particular attention to the fruit spurs and the undersides of the twigs with this spray. Strong nicotine dusts are also useful.

*Family* **APHIDIDÆ** (aphids or plant lice).—This is one of the most important groups of insects from an economic standpoint, as all its members are injurious, often very abundant, and a species usually doing little harm may at any time become a serious pest.

Aphids are tiny, soft-bodied insects, the largest being less than a third of an inch long, generally with long legs and antennae, and are of various colors, green, black, various shades of red and brown, white and gray being the most usual ones. Some are more or less completely concealed (Fig. 117) beneath long, white waxy threads, giving them a "woolly" appearance; others have a sort of dust or "bloom," like that on a plum, coating their bodies; but the majority (Fig. 118) are without any covering. Many species of aphids have a pair of tubes, called cornicles, projecting upward from the top of the abdomen. These were formerly believed to be the exit ducts through which honeydew, abundantly produced by the insects, escapes, but it is now known that this substance is expelled through the anus, often in such quantities that when the insects are abundant it forms a sort of fine rain which can be heard falling on the leaves and ground. This fluid, which is sweet and sticky, is eagerly fed upon by ants. Falling on twigs and leaves it dries there and a fungus grows in it turning it black; plants where aphids have been abundant often show this by their black appearance. Some aphids produce galls

within which they live for at least a part of their lives, but most of them are not thus enclosed, living on leaves, twigs, succulent plant stems or roots. Though there are great variations in the life histories of different aphids, certain general facts hold for most of the group. In most cases eggs are laid in the fall, on a food plant of the species concerned, and these hatch the following spring. The nymphs soon become full-grown and are known as stem mothers and without fertilization (there are no males in the spring generations) produce eggs,

FIG. 118.—Portion of leaf showing aphids; somewhat enlarged.

or in most cases living young which like the stem mother are all females and on reaching maturity produce young in a similar way. The production of young without fertilization of the parent is not uncommon in insects and is called parthenogenesis or agamic reproduction. In this case the production of these young alive rather than from deposited eggs introduces the additional fact that these insects are also ovoviviparous except in (generally) one generation. The number of young produced by each parent varies but will perhaps average about ten, a few being born every few days, and the number of generations is variable but is also likely to be about ten, though the first-born young in each generation, being a week or two older than the last-born young, will gain enough time during the season to produce more generations than the others. In fact, in some species a range from eight to twenty-one generations for late- and early-born individuals has been observed, and an average number of twenty-eight young produced per parent, so that the figures given above may be regarded as conservative. But even with this moderate estimate, allowing only ten young to a generation and ten generations a season, the total product from a single egg hatching in the spring, and itself counted as the first generation, would be over a billion insects; this would be far below the actual number in most cases, were it not for the enormous destruction of these insects by their enemies and by unfavorable weather conditions.

In many species instead of ten young being produced per female as an average, the number is likely to be nearer a hundred, and in those species which also have more than ten generations the total number of individuals which would theoretically be produced in a season "would be sufficient to completely cover the entire world with a continuous layer of plant lice."

With such a marvelous reproductive power as this it becomes evident that, despite natural checks to their increase, plants infested are liable after a few weeks to be entirely unable to provide food for the hordes of aphids upon them. Accordingly we find that in most of the generations winged individuals may be produced so that they can migrate to other plants. Winged and wingless forms may therefore be found at almost any time during the summer, and a wide distribution of the insect is obtained in this way.

When cold weather approaches in the fall, a generation appears consisting of both sexes, and the females of this generation lay fertilized eggs which winter over and hatch the following spring. In some cases this does not happen until the second fall and, in a few species at least, sexual individuals have not been discovered and may occur only at long intervals, if at all. This is particularly true of species found in greenhouses, where exposure to winter conditions does not exist.

Many aphids do not feed entirely on one kind of plant but spend a part of the year on one species, and the rest on another. One of the species that is injurious to the apple remains on this tree from fall until May or June when it migrates to grain and spends the summer months there. Another species, living on the elm during the fall, winter and spring, passes to the apple for its summer residence. A long list of aphids having alternating food plants is now known.

Aphids suck the sap from plants and often produce curling or malformation and even wilting of the leaves, frequently accompanied by discoloration. Root-attacking forms produce knots and deformities affecting the health of the plant, and young fruit becomes hard at the attacked spots and remains small. The punctures made by aphids often enable the spores of fungi and bacteria that cause plant diseases to enter the plants, and aphids may even transfer these from one plant to another. Among the diseases transferred are an oat blight, fire blight of the pear and cucurbit wilt. Indirectly by the honeydew in which spores can live for several days, it is probable that the diseases can also be widely distributed through the agency of other insects which visit and feed on honeydew. In general a year when aphids are abundant over a large part of the country is certain to result in great injury to plants of all kinds affected by these insects.

Ants not only gather the honeydew produced by the aphids, but in some cases the relation is closer, particularly with root-feeding species (see page 149).

Aphids have many enemies which destroy great numbers of them. They are also affected by the weather, cloudy, wet periods being favorable, though driving rains destroy many.

Some aphids attack evergreens and produce rather soft, fleshy galls, generally at the bases of the outer shoots. These appear during the spring months and are of full size by midsummer. They then dry and crack open, showing little cavities occupied by the plant lice, which now leave the galls for other parts, either of the same or of some other kind of tree, according to the species concerned. The gall formation interferes with the growth of the tree by preventing wholly or in part the circulation of the sap in the shoot at the base of which the gall is located, and this results, by the death or checking of the growth, in trees which look thin rather than dense, and in some cases they may become worthless as lawn ornaments. In the east the spruce is often seriously injured in this way.

Many kinds of aphids often become seriously abundant for periods of two or three years, then disappear for a time. The potato aphid, the beet root aphid, the cabbage aphid, cherry aphids and others are often destructive for a year or two at a time and outbreaks of these or others may be expected any year.

*Control.*—In general, the best control of aphids is by using nicotine sulfate, 40 per cent, 1 part; water, 800 to 1,000 parts; soap flakes enough to form suds on adding. Nicotine sulfate dusts also give good results. Rotenone compounds may also be used. In enclosed places such as greenhouses, calcium cyanide is a good fumigant if care be taken not to apply it too strong for the plants. In fact any contact spray is effective if the insects can be reached by it, but they are so small and often so protected that this is difficult to do.

**The apple aphids.**—Though a number of aphids occur on the apple only three are of great importance and one of these differs much from the others, attacking the roots as well as the leaves.

**The apple aphid** (*Aphis pomi* De G.) and **the rosy apple aphid** (*Anuraphis roseus* Baker) in the fall lay their eggs on apple twigs. These hatch in early spring and the young nymphs suck the sap from the buds and opening leaves, often doing much injury. These nymphs all develop into stem mothers (Figs. 119, 120), so called, no males being produced, the apple aphis having a uniformly green body and the rosy apple aphis becoming greenish blended with purplish brown.   These stem mothers by parthenogenesis produce numerous young which give birth to others in their turn.

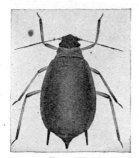 

FIG. 119.                                    FIG. 120.

FIG. 119.—Apple aphid (*Aphis pomi* De G.) stem mother; greatly enlarged.   (*From a drawing by Dr. Robert Matheson, Cornell University, New York.*)

FIG. 120.—Rosy apple aphid (*Anuraphis roseus* Baker) stem mother; greatly enarged.   (*From a drawing by Dr. Robert Matheson, Cornell University, New York.*)

After a generation or two, winged forms (Fig. 121) begin to appear, which in the case of the apple aphid may migrate to other apple trees where they pass the summer, multiplying there.   With the rosy apple aphid the migration is to the narrow-leaved plantain.

FIG. 121.—Winged migrant of apple aphid; greatly enlarged.   (*Modified from Cornell Agr. Expt. Sta. Mem. 24.*)

In the fall a migration back to the apple occurs and here a generation of both males and females is produced.   Eggs are then laid which hatch the following spring.

A third species, the **apple grain aphid** (*Rhopalosiphum prunifoliæ* Fitch) is often abundant on the apple in spring, but on the whole is seldom common enough to be of great importance.   The same is true of the **clover aphid** (*Anuraphis bakeri* Cowen) which, though feeding on the apple in early spring, soon leaves it for alfalfa, clover and other plants and often causes serious injury to the clover seed crop in the west.

Injury to the apple by these aphids is by checking the growth of buds and young leaves, by the curling of the latter and often by checking the growth of the fruit as well.

*Control of the apple aphid and rosy apple aphid.*—Spray when the buds begin to show green, with a commercial tar-oil emulsion according to the manufacturer's directions, or with nicotine sulfate 1 part in 800 parts of water and a cubic inch of soap per gallon of spray. Later, nicotine sulfate dusts are quite effective. It is not very often that treatment is necessary.

The third important apple aphid is the **woolly apple aphid** (*Eriosoma lanigerum* Hausm.), a European insect now widely distributed in this

country. This aphid secretes white, woolly, waxen threads over its body, practically concealing it. In most cases at least, the winter is spent in the egg stage in crevices in the bark of the elm. These eggs hatch in the spring and the nymphs pass to the buds and feed on the sap of the leaves as they develop, causing them to become deformed, curled and clustered together, forming "rosettes." Two generations participate in this.

During the later spring months winged migrants are produced which pass to the apple, hawthorn and a few other related trees, where they locate on the underside of the leaves and produce young which crawl to thin places, wounds or water shoots and there locate and reproduce during the summer and fall (Fig. 122) until cold weather comes on, when migrating forms are produced which return to the elm where the eggs are laid.

FIG. 122.—Apple twig showing woolly apple aphids (*Eriosoma lanigerum* Hausm.) and swellings of the twig produced by their attacks; about twice natural size.

This life history is complicated by the fact that during the summer some of the aphids migrate from the branches of the apple tree to its roots and feed there, producing knots and swellings which interfere with the nutrition of the plant and, if sufficiently abundant, may cause its death. These aphids are believed to remain on the roots the year around, generation after generation, but with their ranks recruited from time to time by migrants from the aerial members. Some of the latter also are believed to remain on the apple all winter as hibernating nymphs.

The amount of injury which this insect does to the apple above ground is not very great, except perhaps on nursery trees. Woolly spots at scars and wounds on the branches, noticeable chiefly in the fall, are not abundant enough to affect the trees much, usually. The root form, however, is sometimes quite injurious, particularly south of the latitude of Washington, and young orchards may suffer severely.

*Control.*—The waxy, "woolly" threads covering the bodies of these insects make control more difficult by spraying than would otherwise be the case, as the threads repel the spray. Nicotine sulfate, 40 per cent, standard formula, or kerosene emulsion one part to nine of water, driven with much force, are about the only treatments for the aerial forms which have given much success. It is evident that elms growing near apple trees directly favor the successful migration of this pest, and as far as possible, therefore, no elms should be allowed to grow near apple orchards.

For the root form, when sufficiently injurious to make it pay, removing the earth to a depth of six or eight inches over the root area and pouring kerosene emulsion or nicotine sulfate, diluted as indicated, over this exposed surface, using enough to wet the ground thoroughly, has given fair results.

Nursery stock affected can be dipped in the lime-sulfur wash or in these materials, when dug either for transplanting or sale. As the Northern Spy seems to be rather free from this pest, using trees grown on stocks of that variety is desirable.

**The grape phylloxera** (*Phylloxera vitifoliæ* Fitch).—This aphid is a native of America and attacks the grape. Native American vines, however, are resistant to its work to a considerable degree, so that injury to them is not serious. The European grape (*Vitis*

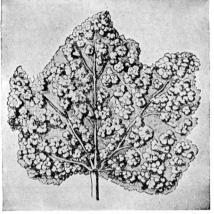

Fig. 123.—Under surface of grape leaf showing galls produced by the grape phylloxera (*Phylloxera vitifoliæ* Fitch); somewhat reduced from natural size. (*From Riley, U. S. Dept. Agr.*)

*vinifera*) on the other hand, is very susceptible to its attacks and, when the phylloxera reached Europe about 1860, it became very destructive, causing the loss of over two million acres of vineyards before any successful checks to the insect were discovered. In this country it reached California, where the European grape is also grown, about 1874 and has been the cause of great injury there also.

The insect lays its eggs, one per female, on old wood of the grape in the fall, and these eggs hatch the following spring into tiny lice which locate on the upper surface of the young leaves and begin to suck the sap. This causes the leaf to become depressed at each place where a louse is at work, so that galls (Fig. 123) projecting from the under surface are soon produced, in which the insects live. Upon becoming full-grown these aphids lay eggs in the galls and the young which hatch from them pass to other parts of the leaves and produce galls of their own. This process continues through the summer but in the fall the young desert the leaves and work down to the roots and rest until the following spring. Then they attack the roots, forming swellings (Fig. 124a), which on young rootlets stop their growth and on the larger ones cause decay which spreads around the root and kills it beyond that point.

During the latter part of this second season some winged forms are produced which make their way up to the surface of the ground and migrate to other vines where they lay eggs. These produce both male and female aphids and each female lays a single fertilized egg which winters over.

This two-year life and the production of leaf galls are not always necessary to the continued existence of the insect, however. The root form generally goes on,

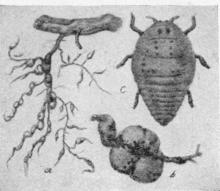

Fig. 124.—Grape phylloxera; *a*, galls on grape roots; *b*, galls enlarged, showing the insects; *c*, phylloxera from a root gall; *b* and *c* enlarged. (*From Sanderson and Jackson, Insects Injurious to Farm, Garden and Orchard, 2d. ed., after Marlatt, U. S. Dept. Agr.*)

brood after brood, particularly on the European grape, without the formation of leaf galls; and although young from the leaves may probably pass to the roots at any time during the summer, the migration of root forms to the leaves is unknown. Apparently, then, the life history just outlined applies to American varieties of the vine, but in the case of the European species, although the aphids may pass to the roots, they do not usually, at least, seem to migrate in the reverse direction, the insects which come from fertilized eggs passing directly to the roots. Root forms may spread to other plants through the soil.

*Control.*—The leaf-gall-making form is the common one in the eastern United States, particularly abundant on the wild grapes, but the root-gall-making form is seldom found. The former does not seem to injure the plant very much in that region, probably because the insect is native there and the plants have become resistant. Accordingly, where European varieties are raised, they are generally grafted on the roots of eastern United States varieties.

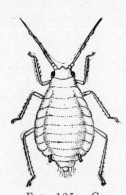

Fig. 125.—Corn root aphid (*Aphis maidi-radicis* Forbes); wingless, viviparous female; greatly enlarged. (*From U. S. Dept. Agr. Bur. Ent. Bul.* 85, Part VI.)

**The corn root aphid** (*Anuraphis maidi-radicis* Forbes). This insect, though it can hardly be regarded as universally distributed throughout the United States, is both a serious pest of corn over a large area and, because of its remarkable relation with ants, an interesting species. It appears to occur throughout the eastern United States as far west as South Dakota and Colorado and south to South Carolina, Louisiana and Texas, but its destructive work mainly covers the territory from New Jersey to South Carolina and west to the Mississippi River.

The eggs of this aphid hatch early in spring and from ten to twenty-two generations (Figs. 125 and 126) are produced during the season. As cool fall weather appears, a generation of sexual individuals (Fig. 127) appears and these lay eggs which pass the winter. During this season these may be found in the ground in nests of several kinds of ants but most frequently in those of the

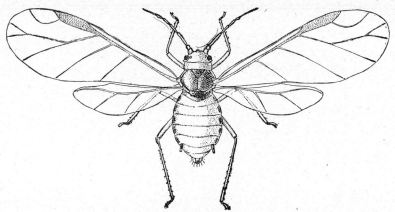

FIG. 126.—Winged, viviparous female of the corn root aphid; greatly enlarged. (*From U. S. Dept. Agr. Bur. Ent. Bul. 85, Part VI.*)

cornfield ant (*Lasius niger americanus*). They are oval, black and glistening, and are sometimes found in small piles in the nests of the ants. In cold weather the ants carry the eggs down below the frost and on warm days bring them up to warmer levels. In spring, when various weeds, such as smartweed, begin to grow, the ants tunnel along the roots of these weeds and place the young aphids, as they hatch, on them to feed. Later, when corn roots become available, the ants transfer the aphids to them, where they and their descendants feed during the rest of the season. Winged migrants are produced after a generation or two and these individuals, spreading, are taken to corn roots by ants which may find them. All summer and fall the ants care for the aphids, taking them from one plant to another and collecting from them the honeydew upon which the ants feed. In the fall when the eggs are laid, these are gathered by the ants and stored in their nests over winter.

FIG. 127.—Oviparous female of the corn root aphid; greatly enlarged. (*From U. S. Dept. Agr. Bur. Ent. Bul.* 110.)

Where the corn root aphid is abundant it becomes a serious corn pest, dwarfing the corn and turning the leaves yellow or reddish and sometimes destroying the plants, particularly when weather conditions are also unfavorable.

*Control.*—Rotation of crops is of much value as a control, for, as the aphids cannot migrate until their second generation, corn planted on land where they are not already present will get well started. Fertilization and frequent cultivation to produce vigorous growth will aid in this. The worst injuries are usually where corn is planted to follow corn and therefore where this pest is already present in the field from the preceding year.  Any method that will destroy the nests of the ants which care for the aphids will also be helpful, and deep plowing and harrowing in both late fall and early spring have proved of value for this purpose.

Among the many enemies of aphids[1] is one group of tiny insects which makes a specialty of attacking them.   An insect of this group will select

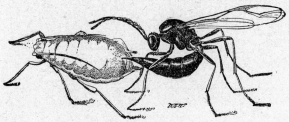

Fig. 128.—Aphid parasite (*Lysiphlebus testaceipes* Cress.) ovipositing in the body of an aphid; greatly enlarged.   (*From U. S. Dept. Agr. Bur. Ent. Bul.* 110.)

an aphid (Fig. 128) and, facing it, will thrust its abdomen forward beneath its body and drive its ovipositor into the insect.  The young parasite hatching from an egg thus deposited will feed upon the aphid whose body becomes distended and generally changes color after a time, and finally dies, adhering to the plant on which it was.   When the

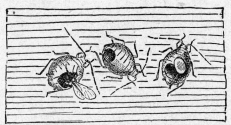

Fig. 129.—Aphids killed by parasites.   Right-hand figure shows the circular piece of chitin cut by the parasite in escaping, but still attached.   Left-hand figure shows the parasite just escaping; much enlarged.   (*From U. S. Dept. Agr. Bur. Ent. Bul.* 110.)

parasite has completed its development within the body of the aphid, it escapes by cutting a circular, lid-like opening through the skin (Fig. 129). Aphids attacked and killed in this way are often very plentiful during and particularly toward the end of a period of destructive abundance of these insects (see page 341).

*Family* **ALEYRODIDÆ.**—The adults of the insects belonging in this family (Fig. 130) are very small and have four wings which are broadly rounded and covered with a white dust; this has led to calling the group the whiteflies.   Occasionally the wings have dark spots or streaks.   The

[1] See also Coccinellidæ (p. 198); one of the Miridæ (p. 127); Chrysopidæ (p. 219); Syrphidæ (p. 314).

eyes are often constricted in the middle or even divided into two parts. The body is generally yellowish, though in some species it may be of other colors.

The nymph, on hatching, crawls around for a short time before settling down on a leaf, then inserts its rostrum in the tissues and begins to feed.

Fig. 130.—Citrus whitefly (*Dialeurodes citri* Riley & Howard): adults and eggs on leaf slightly enlarged. (*From Florida Agr. Expt. Sta. Bul.* 183.)

After molting the insect becomes quiet, with its legs and antennae much reduced, and thereafter does not move from its location until it becomes adult, and wax, which may have been produced before the first molt, now becomes more noticeable. This wax may take the form of a fringe around the sides and may more or less cover the body. The animal after

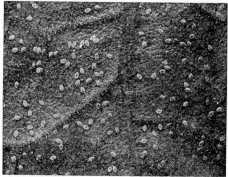

Fig. 131.—Nymphs of a whitefly on underside of a leaf; enlarged twice. (*From Britton, Second Rept. Ent. Conn. Agr. Expt. Sta.* 1902.)

its third molt differs so from its former appearance that this stage is often called a pupa, and as the following molt produces the adult there is evidently quite a metamorphosis to justify the use of this term in the group. Honeydew is produced by these insects.

Whiteflies are essentially tropical, though a few species live in the northern United States. In greenhouses everywhere the **greenhouse whitefly** (*Trialeurodes vaporariorum* Westw.) is too often a serious pest, for it multiplies rapidly and the tiny nymphs (Fig. 131) are not generally noticed in time to check their increase before the plants have suffered greatly. When they are abundant, fumigation for three hours at night, using between one-fifth and one-sixth ounce of sodium cyanide to each thousand cubic feet of space in the greenhouse, should kill all but the eggs and some of the pupae, and repeating this treatment twice afterwards at intervals of two weeks should destroy the others in the stages to which they will have then progressed.

Calcium cyanide dust containing 40 to 50 per cent calcium cyanide two-fifths to one-third ounce per thousand cubic feet of space, is now also extensively employed. In a greenhouse with mixed plants of varying degrees of sensitiveness this strength may possibly injure the most sensitive ones so the treatment should be experimental at first to learn the strength it is safe to use for the plants and how strong it must be to kill the whitefly. As these insects are not killed equally easily in all stages, the treatment may need to be repeated as with the sodium cyanide.

In the southern states and in California, whiteflies attack citrus fruits and cause much injury. Several species are more or less concerned, the most important one being the **citrus whitefly** (*Dialeurodes citri* Ashm.). These insects usually check the growth of the tree and fruit, reducing the yield and size, and by the production of honeydew provide an opportunity in this for the growth of a fungus that covers the leaves and stems and sometimes the fruit. In Florida certain species of fungi attack the whiteflies and are very effective enemies in many seasons.

The citrus whitefly and the purple scale (see page 159) are controlled in Florida at the same time, usually by oil emulsion at about 1 per cent actual oil. However when rust mite is also present, lime-sulfur is applied instead, often with the addition of wettable sulfur to reduce possible lime-sulfur injury without lowering the sulfur content. Sprays of oil and lime-sulfur must not be applied within two weeks of each other.

*Family* **COCCIDÆ** (scale insects).—These are remarkable insects, having been much modified and changed in appearance from the more ordinary forms. Without attempting an accurate classification, they may be grouped under three heads: the armored scales, the soft scales and the mealybugs.

The mealybugs are the least degenerate of the three groups. In them the females preserve their body segments, eyes, antennae and legs and can move about. They secrete a waxy material, usually as long cottony threads or plates, more or less covering their bodies and sometimes forming a large egg sac at the hinder end. In the female soft scales the antennae and legs are not lost but become reduced to such an extent that, though the adult can move about somewhat, it seldom does so. Wax, when secreted, is usually to form a sac at the hinder end of the body enclosing the eggs, and the skeleton on the back of the insect becomes very much thickened, forming a scale, often very convex, strong and protective, though seemingly softer than in the armored scales. In the armored scales the female loses antennae, eyes and legs and secretes a waxy scale, with which the molted skins from the body are felted together, forming generally a rather flat and very tough scale.

The metamorphosis in the females of all three groups is incomplete; in some cases they grow remarkably after being fertilized.

The males develop much as do the females, at first, though not losing any of their parts by degeneration. After reaching full size, however, they pupate and emerge from the pupa as very tiny insects with only one pair of wings and no mouth parts. Thus in the scale insects we have the remarkable fact that, whereas in the males there is a complete metamorphosis, in the females it is incomplete. Whether the former was the original condition in the group and the females through the degeneration connected with their mode of life have changed to an incomplete metamorphosis, or this was the primitive condition and complete metamorphosis has been developed in the males, is unknown, though the other Homoptera all have an incomplete metamorphosis.

About two thousand species of scale insects are known, attacking nearly all kinds of trees and shrubs, and sometimes other plants as well. Many have an almost incredible rapidity of increase, which, under favorable conditions, results in the death of the plant they are on. A few are beneficial to man. Thus the bodies of a scale feeding upon cactus, when dried and prepared, furnish the dye known as cochineal. Shellac is obtained from the excretions produced by another scale, and China wax, used as furniture polish, comes from a third species. Most scale insects, however, are injurious and fail to compensate for the injury they cause by producing anything of value.

Among so many serious pests, only a few can be considered in detail here.

### ARMORED SCALES

There are a number of serious pests in this group of scales.

**The oystershell scale** (*Lepidosaphes ulmi* L.).—This insect, native to Europe, has been so long in this country that it is now very generally

Fig. 132.—Female scales of the oystershell scale (*Lepidosaphes ulmi* L.) on a twig; about twice natural size.

distributed. It is chiefly an enemy of the apple, pear, poplar, willow, ash and lilac but is often found on other plants. It feeds on all parts covered by bark, and the male scales are also often found on the leaves. The full-grown female scale (Fig. 132) is about one-eighth of an inch long and has much the form of an oyster shell, one end narrowly rounded, the other rather more broadly so, and the shell as a whole usually bent somewhat to one side. It is brown to gray in color, varying with age and, to some extent, the plant it is on. During the winter, examination of the scale will show beneath it, at the narrower end, the dead body of the insect, and behind it from fifteen to one hundred tiny whitish eggs. These hatch the following May or June, according to the advancement of the season, into very small whitish nymphs or "crawling young," which are extremely delicate and with no scale. These young crawl out from beneath the parent scale and wander about for a few hours or even a day or so, seeking for places where they may settle; then each thrusts its beak through the bark and begins feeding, and degeneration of eyes, antennae and limbs and the secretion of wax over the body begin. To this secretion the molted skin is added at each molt, making a very tough, hard, covering scale. The insect beneath this becomes adult after a time and following the laying of its eggs, dies. In the northern states the eggs are laid in August or September, but in the middle states and farther south, the earlier seasons permit hatching enough earlier in the season for the adult condition to be reached and the eggs laid by midsummer, and these eggs soon hatch and produce egg-laying adults before the following winter. Thus this insect, though having but one generation each year in the more northern states, has two from about the latitude of New Jersey southward, except at such altitudes as to produce northern conditions.

Many of the male crawling young go to the leaves to settle and the scales they form are smaller and somewhat different in shape from those of the females. Beneath them they attain their growth, then pupate, still under their scales, and at the end of this process emerge as very small two-winged adults without any mouths or mouth parts, having undergone a complete metamorphosis. Some entomologists consider the scale found on the elm and other shade trees a different species from that on the apple.

*Control.*—These insects are least protected while crawling young and, as they are sucking forms, a contact insecticide should be applied while they are moving about or at least before they have had time to produce scales covering themselves. The usual treatment therefore is to spray with a miscible oil or with nicotine sulfate 1 part, water 800 to 1,000 parts, as soon as the young, whitish "crawlers" appear. As this time varies with the latitude, a watch for them should be kept, beginning May 1 or earlier in the south and by June 1 in the north. As the young do not all hatch quite at the same time, a second treatment about ten days after the first is desirable. Dormant sprays of 3 to 5 per cent coal-tar distillate emulsions, recently recommended, have given good control.

The **scurfy scale** (*Chionaspis furfura* Fitch).—This insect, a native of North America, is present nearly everywhere except on the Pacific coast and perhaps in the most southerly portions of the country but is usually less abundant in the more northern states. It attacks the apple, pear, mountain ash, currant, gooseberry, hawthorn, Japanese quince and other plants. The full-grown female scale (Fig. 133) is shorter and broader than the oystershell scale and, when perfect in outline, rather pear-shaped and dirty white in color. Its life and habits are much the same as those of the oystershell scale, but the eggs are fewer in number and

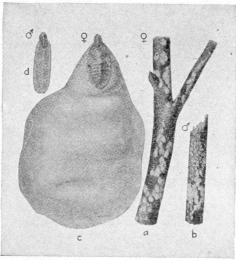

Fig. 133.—Scurfy scale (*Chinoaspis furfura* Fitch): *a*, female and *b*, male scales, natural size; *c*, female and *d*, male scales; greatly enlarged. (*From Sanderson and Peairs, Insect Pests of Farm, Garden and Orchard.*)

dark purple in color, as are also the crawling young which usually hatch a few days later in the season than the other species. Control methods are the same as for the oystershell scale.

The **San José scale** (*Aspidiotus perniciosus* Comst.).—This is one of the most serious pests among the scale insects. Its original home was probably China, but it appears to have reached California about 1870 and since then has spread practically all over this country. It has a wide range of food plants, on many of which it thrives sufficiently to kill them quickly. The plants that suffer most from its attacks are the fruit trees and currants, the dogwoods, thorns, poplars, ornamental cherries and plums, hardy roses, willows, lilacs and lindens; even maples and elms are sometimes attacked, the total list of plants upon which it has been found numbering over a hundred. It feeds on all parts of the plant above ground, even including the fruit.

The full-grown female scale (Fig. 134) is about the size of a pinhead, nearly circular in outline and rather flat, sloping gradually upward from its edge to near the center, where a slight circular depression surrounds the raised center or "nipple" itself. It is brownish gray in color when adult but in earlier stages may vary from this. The adult male scale is somewhat smaller, more oval in outline, and with the nipple not centrally placed but nearer one end.

At the beginning of the winter season specimens of this scale of practically all ages occur, but probably only those from about one-third to one-half or two-thirds grown survive the winter. In the spring these individuals resume their feeding on the sap and after a time the males appear. In the northern states this condition is hardly reached before the middle of May, but at Washington, D. C., it may come as early as April, and farther south still earlier. After mating, the females continue to grow and about a month later the first young appear. These do not, in the San José scale, hatch from eggs laid by the parent but the young are born alive; *i.e.*, this insect is ovoviviparous. These young are produced, a few every day or two, and the parent lives for a month or

FIG. 134.—San Jose scale (*Aspidiotus perniciosus* Comst.). Adult female scales enlarged about five times. (*From Houser, Ohio Agr. Expt. Sta. Bul.* 332.)

more, producing an average total of about four hundred young. These resemble the crawling young of the scales already considered, except that they are lemon yellow in color, and they crawl about and settle down to feed in the same way. The scale now begins to appear, at first as white, waxy threads over the back, which soon mat together to form a pure white covering. As the nymph beneath molts, the molted skins are added to this and variations in color of the scale appear. Sometimes the scale of the partly grown insect may show white, black and gray, varying in arrangement according to the completeness with which the different parts have combined, but before maturity it becomes a quite uniform brownish gray. The young become adult in a little over a month and then themselves begin to produce young. In the northern states there are usually at least three generations in a season, and in the south there are four or even more. The generations overlap, the earliest young produced by the second generation, for example, sometimes appearing before the last born of the preceding one, which results in the almost constant presence of crawling young on an infested tree, from the time the first one appears until reproduction is stopped by cold weather. Assuming the production of four full generations in a season, equally divided between the sexes, and with no loss in number from death by accident or other causes to reduce the number produced, we have a total of 3,216,080,400 individuals as the descendants during one season from a single pair. Fortunately, many never reach maturity, or an infested tree would often be sucked dry before winter.

The San José scale has a number of parasites which are sometimes quite effective, destroying a large percentage of the scales in some localities; but with such an enormous power of increase of the pest, even a high degree of parasitism fails to give the relief needed. A few predaceous insects are also known which feed upon the scale. Most noticeable among these is the twice-stabbed ladybeetle (*Chilocorus stigma* Say), a small black beetle (Fig. 135) with two red spots. It is nearly circular in outline, very convex and is about one-eighth of an inch long. A fungous disease also attacks the scale, particularly in the south, but parasites, predaceous foes and diseases together generally fail to hold it entirely in check.

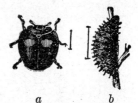

*a*          *b*

Fig. 135.—Twice-stabbed ladybeetle (*Chilocorus stigma* Say). *a,* Adult; *b,* larva enlarged: real length shown by the hair lines. (*From Sanderson and Jackson, Elementary Entomology: after Riley.*)

A ladybeetle closely resembling the twice-stabbed ladybeetle is an enemy of the scale in China, the native home of the pest; this insect has been brought to the United States with the hope that it might do effective work here, but it has failed to accomplish much.

*Control.*—Spraying as for the oystershell scale is useless, for that treatment is based upon the destruction of the delicate, crawling young, by one or at most two applications. With the San José scale, however, the young do not all appear at about the same time but are present practically from May or June according to the latitude of the locality, until winter. To use this method successfully, therefore, would require spraying about every two weeks or so for a period of at least five months— a treatment manifestly impracticable.

Stronger sprays are therefore used during the dormant season of the trees when they are less liable to injury and more thorough applications can be given, the leaves having fallen. For years lime-sulfur was made use of (see page 50 for strength) with excellent results in the more northern states, especially when applied just before the buds open. But about 1920 in several parts of the Mississippi Valley this treatment seemed to become less effective. Commercial oil emulsions are now the most satisfactory if used according to the manufacturer's directions. They can be used whenever the trees are dormant and the temperature above freezing, though here, too, spring applications seem to give the best results.

There is some evidence that strains of the scale more resistant to treatment than others are gradually being developed, particularly in the west.

Fumigation with hydrocyanic acid gas is the most effective treatment for the San José scale, but the cost of tents large enough to cover all but the smallest trees is so great that this method is made use of only for fumigating nursery stock after it has been dug, in houses built for that purpose.

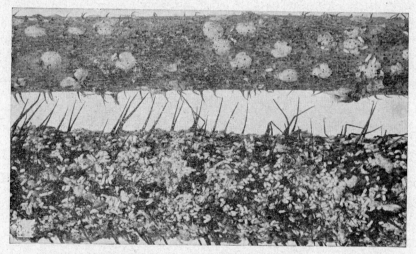

Fig. 136.—Rose scales (*Aulacaspis rosæ* Bouché): *a*, female scales; *b*, male scales; considerably enlarged. (*From Houser, Ohio Agr. Expt. Sta. Bul.* 332.)

**The rose scale** (*Aulacaspis rosæ* Bouché).—This insect is generally distributed in the United States on raspberry, blackberry, dewberry, rose, pear and some other plants; female scales (Fig. 136*a*) white with more or less yellow at margin, nearly circular and about one-tenth of an inch in diameter; male scales white, narrow, very small. Plants thickly infested appear as though sprayed with whitewash. It winters in various stages, so all may be present at almost any time; two or three generations per year. Control is effected by cutting out the worst infested stems during the winter, and spraying with lime-sulfur or oil

Fig. 137.—Pine needle scale (*Chionaspis pinifoliæ* Fitch). Female scales on pine leaf; about twice natural size.

emulsion as for the San José scale. Fish-oil soap, one pound in one gallon of water, may be used for greenhouse plants.

**The pine needle scale** (*Chionaspis pinifoliæ* Fitch).—This scale occurs generally in the United States on leaves of pine and sometimes other evergreens; female scale (Fig. 137) white, narrower than scurfy scale but varying to fit the width of the leaf; male scale much smaller. When abundant, whole branches may appear as though their leaves had been sprayed with whitewash. Two generations a year, purplish crawling young appearing in the northern states about the middle of May and the first of September, at which times spray with a miscible oil or with nicotine sulfate as for the oystershell scale, but take care, in the case of the oil, to use one prepared for application to evergreens, as these are more sensitive to oils than deciduous trees. Dormant applications of lime sulfur one part, water nine parts are also effective.

Fig. 138.—Purple scale (*Lepidosaphes beckii* Newm.); about natural size. (*Modified from Cal. Agr. Expt. Sta. Bul.* 226.)

The purple scale (*Lepidosaphes beckii* Newm.).— In Florida and in the southern part of California near the coast, this scale is of serious importance, attacking twigs, leaves and fruit of citrus trees (Fig. 138). There are usually about three generations each year.

The most common treatment for this scale in Florida is oil emulsion. Although commercially prepared emulsions are usually more satisfactory, the following cold-mixed formula may be used:

Fish-oil soap...................................... 8 lb. or 1 gal.
Lubricating oil, 24 to 28°Bé...................... 2 gal.
Soft water.......................................... 1 gal.

Dilute the soft water to make 100 gallons of spray. Lime-sulfur sprays are used

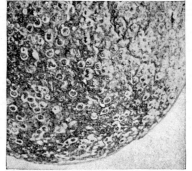

Fig. 139.—California red scale (*Aonidiella aurantii* Mask.) on a portion of a grapefruit; about natural size. (*From Cal. Agr. Expt. Sta. Bul.* 214.)

when rust mite must be controlled at the same time (see citrus whitefly, p. 152). On the Pacific coast fumigation with hydrocyanic acid gas during the colder months is the usual control method.

The California red scale (*Aonidiella aurantii* Mask.).—A serious pest of citrus trees in California. The female scale resembles the San José scale in outline but averages larger (Fig. 139) and the scale is transparent enough to allow the red body (yellow in a variety) of the insect to show through. The male scales are smaller and rather elongate. The life history is similar to that of the San José scale, the young being born alive during the summer months. Control on citrus trees is mostly by fumigation with hydrocyanic acid gas, but oil emulsions are also effective. Recently it has been recommended to spray with the emulsion before fumigation to obtain greater control.

Occasionally the lenticels or breathing pores through the bark of plant twigs resemble armored scales, particularly the more circular ones. To determine in any case whether a debatable structure on bark is a scale or only a lenticel, it may be scraped with the fingernail. If it can be removed without breaking the bark (it may leave a whitish mark), the object is a scale; but if the bark is necessarily torn or broken to get it off, it may be assumed that it is a lenticel.

## SOFT SCALES

As a group the soft scales are less injurious than the armored scales. Their rate of increase is less, their covering less protective and their

Fig. 140.—Tuliptree scale (*Toumeyella liriodendri* Gmel.); about natural size; slightly reduced.

larger size renders them more certain to be reached by sprays. The largest one found in the United States is the tuliptree scale, the adult female scale being about one-third of an inch in diameter (Fig. 140). An African soft scale is known which is about an inch long.

Fig. 141. Black scale (*Saisettia oleœ* Bern.); about natural size. (*From Cal. Agr. Expt. Sta.Bul..223.*)

The black scale (*Saissetia oleœ* Bern.).—This scale is found in nearly all parts of the world. It has a long list of food plants but is chiefly a pest on citrus trees and the olive, oleander, apricot and prune. In the United States it is therefore chiefly important in the south and west. The adult female scale is from one-eighth to one-fourth of an inch in diameter and almost hemispherical in form, black in color and with ridges forming an H on the back (Fig. 141). The male scales are much smaller, long, narrow and flat. The eggs, from 50 to 3,000, are for the most part laid in May, June and early July, and the adult condition is reached early the next year, though variation from this is frequent. The young scales attack the leaves generally but later pass to the twigs. The injury they cause by removing the sap from the tree is increased by the honey-dew they secrete, which, falling in large amounts on fruit and leaves, forms an excellent material in which a sooty fungus grows and more or less cuts off light from the leaf surface, thus affecting the growth; it may also clog the stomata or breathing pores on the leaves, besides causing the fruit to look objectionable and need cleaning before its sale. Control of this pest was formerly by hydrocyanic acid fumigation, but in many places it seems to have become more resistant to this treatment and oil sprays now give better results.

The terrapin scale (*Lecanium nigrofasciatum* Perg.).—This is a native insect attacking various shade and fruit trees. The scale of the female is nearly hemispherical in form, about one-sixth of an inch in diameter, reddish, mottled and streaked with black (Fig. 142). This insect is ovoviviparous, the young appearing in June and July and becoming adult the following spring. The young spend

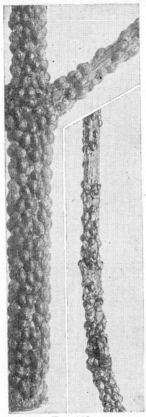

Fig. 142.                    Fig. 143.

Fig. 142.—Terrapin scale (*Lecanium nigrofasciatum* Perg.); reduced somewhat (right-hand figure), and somewhat enlarged (left-hand figure). (*From Houser, Ohio Agr. Expt. Sta. Bul.* 332.)

Fig. 143.—Cottony maple scale (*Pulvinaria vitis* L.); about half natural size. (*Modified from Felt, N. Y. State Mus. Mem.* 8.)

a part of their life on the leaves before migrating to the stems. Control, when necessary, is by spraying just before the buds open in spring with a 2 per cent oil emulsion stock, or with miscible oil.

The cottony maple scale (*Pulvinaria vitis* L.).—This insect attacks maple, linden and other shade trees and plants. The scale of the adult female is rather flat, about one-fourth of an inch in diameter, and by midsummer generally lifted at one end from the twig it is on by a projecting mass of cotton-like threads which surround 2,000 to 3,000 eggs (Fig. 143). These soon hatch and the young crawl to the leaves and cover themselves with a thin waxy coating. In fall they migrate to the twigs for the winter and become adult the following spring. When abundant, the large, white, cotton-like masses make this a very noticeable insect. Control is the same as for the terrapin scale.

**The hemispherical scale** (*Saissetia hemisphærica* Targ.).—This scale is usually found in greenhouses and on house plants, such as ferns, palms and ornamental asparagus, and also out of doors in the south. It is very convex but more oval than hemispherical, about one-eighth of an inch long, brown in color. The partly grown young are very flat and have a notch at the hinder end. The eggs are laid during about a three-month period in late spring, thus resulting in the appearance of young during a long time. Control is by the use of oil-emulsion stocks or by dipping the plant in fish-oil soap, one pound, water two gallons, and after an hour rinsing the plant by dipping it in water.

## MEALYBUGS

Mealybugs move about more or less freely during their life, as their limbs are not lost to any extent by degeneration. Nor is a scale present, the body being generally well covered by long, waxy threads, though in some cases waxy secretions forming plates connected with the body are produced.

The insects are inhabitants of warm climates and in the north are found only in greenhouses and on house plants.

**The citrus mealybug** (*Pseudococcus citri* Risso).—This insect attacks many plants and is a serious pest on citrus plants, feeding on the stems, leaves and fruit, gathering in large clusters on the last. It produces a large amount of honeydew, on which the sooty fungus already referred to grows. The adult females, pale

FIG. 144.—Citrus mealy-bug (*Pseudococcus citri* Risso); enlarged.

yellow in color and well covered by a thick waxy secretion (Fig. 144), are one-fourth of an inch long. The 300 to 400 eggs are laid in loose, white cotton-like masses, chiefly during fall and winter, and young and adults move about freely, the former becoming adult in from six to ten weeks. Control in California is mainly by means of ladybeetles artificially reared and liberated. Oil emulsions are helpful but not entirely satisfactory. For greenhouse plants some of the synthetic contact insecticides are the most effective. A number of natural enemies are of some value against this insect.

**The long-tailed mealybug** (*Pseudococcus adonidum* L.).—This is often found in greenhouses, attacking many kinds of plants. The bodies of adult females vary from yellow to gray, and the young are born alive, there being apparently several generations each year. Hydrocyanic acid fumigation seems to be the most successful treatment for these insects. Nicotine sulfate may also be used.

Not one of the mealybugs, but related to them is the **cottony-cushion scale** (*Icerya purchasi* Mask.). This serious pest of citrus and many other plants apparently reached California from Australia about 1868 and by 1880 had spread all over the citrus-growing regions of the state and was threatening the destruction of the entire citrus-fruit industry.

Investigation showed that in Australia it had an enemy known as the vedalia (*Rodolia cardinalis* Muls.), a ladybeetle, and these were finally brought to California and colonized in the orange groves, where they attacked the scales so effectively that in the course of a few years these were brought under control, and now only an occasional local outbreak makes the scale of importance. When this happens, the introduction of the ladybeetles to that region is soon sufficient to check

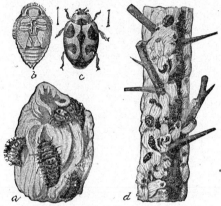

Fig. 145.—Cottony-cushion scale (*Icerya purchasi* Mask.) and its ladybeetle enemy, the Vedalia (*Rodolia cardinalis* Muls.): *a*, larvæ of the Vedalia feeding on a scale; *b*, pupa of the Vedalia; *c*, adult Vedalia; *d*, twig with the scales and ladybeetles. *a* greatly enlarged; real length of *b* and *c* shown by hair lines; *d* about natural size. (*From Sanderson and Jackson, Elementary Entomology; after Marlatt, U. S. Dept. Agr.*)

all injury. In later years the scale has appeared in Portugal, South Africa and elsewhere; when the introduction of the vedalia into those regions has successfully followed, the scale has soon become relatively unimportant.

The female scale has a red, yellow or brown body. It lays its 400 to 1,000 eggs in a large cottony mass formed at the hinder end of the body, the upper surface of the mass being grooved or fluted (Fig. 145). There are several generations in a season.

Several of the scale insects treated in this chapter furnish good illustrations of the way in which nature works to preserve a balance in the insect world. In the first place, it should be noticed that our native scales are often found with tiny circular holes in them showing where parasites, after having fed on the insect beneath, have made their escape. Other scales, long in this country, such as the oystershell scale, now have numerous parasites, some of which are also enemies of other kinds of scales and in fact may be considered as scale enemies in general, or at least of most scales of the same section.  New parasites also appear from time to time as enemies of scales.  But when a new scale or other insect native elsewhere establishes itself in this country, one of the factors at least in its success here must be that none of its parasites in the locality whence it came accompanied it in its transfer.  If, under these circumstances, climatic and other conditions prove satisfactory, we have a case of an insect set free from all restraint to work its destruction with no check, at least until some insect already present shall select it as a new and satisfactory food.  In the meantime, however, years of destruction may elapse before any such check will appear, and the possibility of obtaining its special enemies from its native country appears to offer much in the way of quick relief.  This bug vs. bug idea, as it has been called, has a strong appeal to those suffering losses from the attacks of a newly introduced pest, and it has therefore been widely exploited.

Probably the first attempt to carry out this idea was the introduction of the vedalia for the cottony-cushion scale, and in this case an unqualified success resulted.  On the other hand, the attempt to establish the Chinese ladybeetle in this country to control the San José scale has thus far been a failure, and the introduction of the parasite *Scutellista cyanea* Motsch to work on the black scale cannot be regarded as more than partially effective.

All in all, the bug vs. bug idea, though always having many possibilities of success, is also one that will often fail and therefore cannot be relied upon as a certain panacea for troubles caused by introduced pests.

# CHAPTER XXV

## ORDER COLEOPTERA

The Coleoptera, or beetles, is the largest group of insects and members of it are familiar to everyone. Over 240,000 kinds are already known, and more are discovered every year. Beetles usually have wings, though in some cases they are very small and never used. The front pair are hard and horny and are called elytra (pronounced el'y-tra). They are not used in flight but when closed lie flat on the back, covering and protecting the hind wings and the rather soft external skeleton of the upper side of

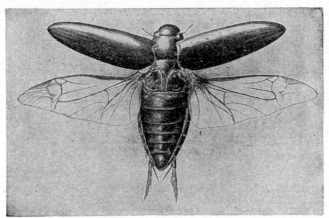

FIG. 146.—Water beetle with wings spread. (*From Folsom.*)

the abdomen. In some groups they do not reach the end of the body, and in those insects the unprotected portion of the abdomen is generally of its usual thickness. The hind wings are usually quite large and fold in an irregular peculiar way to reduce their size and bring them under the elytra when they are not in use (Fig. 146).

The external skeleton of the beetles is usually harder and thicker than in most of the other groups. The mouth parts are for chewing, both as larvae and adults, and the jaws are often very powerful. The early stages are entirely unlike the adult condition, the members of this group undergoing a complete metamorphosis.

The distinctive characters of the group are

*Insects which as adults nearly always have four wings, the front pair entirely thickened and horny, the hind pair membranous; mouth parts for chewing; body usually rather stout. Metamorphosis is complete.*

165

There is a great diversity in the structure of the antennae in different beetles, and also in the form of the legs and number of tarsal segments. The arrangement of the skeletal plates around the articulation of the fore coxae to the body is also variable and of importance in classification.

Eggs of the Coleoptera are laid in many kinds of places—on leaves, in branches, in decaying matter, water, etc. The larvae that hatch are usually called grubs except when they bore in wood. Then, as with larvae of any order found under such conditions, they are termed borers. They usually have the three pairs of legs which become those of the adult, though these are sometimes wanting. Some feed upon other animals, some on leaves or wood, some on carrion and others on various substances. After full larval growth has been attained, they pupate. The pupal shell or skeleton generally covers the surface of the body closely, but the wings and legs though lying close to it are covered separately as projecting appendages and not sheathed by the shell enclosing the body proper. Such a pupa is called a pupa libera, or free pupa (Fig. 35b). In some Coleoptera this condition does not obtain, the pupa shell enclosing wings, limbs and body with no projecting appendage sheaths, and such a case is called a pupa obtecta (Fig. 35a).

The beetles are generally divided as a matter of convenience into the true Coleoptera (Coleoptera genuina or Coleoptera vera) and the snout beetles (Rhynchophora), though it is at least doubtful if the latter is a natural group. The insects in this section are easily recognized, in most cases, by having the front of the head prolonged into a snout which may be long and slender—in some cases even longer than the body—or short and stout, being sometimes so short as to be hardly noticeable. The antennae arise from the sides of the snout and in most cases have a bend like an elbow near the middle. The mouth parts are at the end of the snout but may be differently modified in different species. The insects of this group are even more firm bodied than most other Coleoptera.

The true beetles (Coleoptera vera) have no snout. The mouth parts are all present and as a group its members average larger than the Rhynchophora—indeed the largest bodied insects known belong here.

### THE TRUE COLEOPTERA (Coleoptera vera)

This is by far the larger section of the beetles, more than seventy-five of the eighty odd families belonging here. They vary greatly in structure, habits and food. Many of the families are of little or no economic importance and have few members; others include a very large number of species, many of which are very destructive.

*Family* **LAMPYRIDÆ** (fireflies, etc.).—In several ways the insects belonging here appear to be among the simplest of the beetles (Fig. 147). Their bodies are quite soft as compared with others; the abdomen has been little reduced, seven or eight segments being perceptible, and the larvae are quite simple and feed on small insects and other animals such as snails, either living or dead.

Only a few members of the group are often noticed except by entomologists, but those which attract attention are familiar by the light they produce at night; this has given them the name fireflies, lightning bugs, etc. The light is produced by specialized areas of the body, frequently at least on the underside of the abdomen near its tip. The light itself is not persistent but comes in flashes and is distinctly yellow in most cases. It is believed to be produced by the oxidation of granules in the outer layer of the luminous organ, the oxygen being sup-

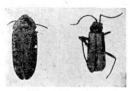

Fig. 147.—Examples of common lampyrid beetles; about natural size.

plied by the tracheae, and under control of the nervous system. In some species the adult female is wingless so that its light appears as it crawls on the ground; such individuals are often called glowworms.

Other insects and animals also have luminous organs, but the lights they produce are probably less frequently seen than those made by lampyrids, these being widely distributed and very abundant insects.

*Family* **CARABIDÆ** (ground beetles).—These insects are active, running quickly over the ground, and the group is a large one containing many different species, over twelve hundred of which are found in the United States (Fig. 148). They feed mainly at night, hiding by day, and the majority are dark colored or black, though a few have bright colors. They are predaceous, both as larvae and

Fig. 148.                              Fig. 149.

Fig. 148.—Common ground beetle (*Harpalus caliginosus* Fab.); natural size.

Fig. 149.—European Calosoma beetle (*Calosoma sycophanta* L.) and its larva; natural size.

adults in most cases, though a few have been known to depart from their usual habits and feed on berries and seeds. One species (*Calosoma sycophanta* L.) has been brought to this country from Europe as it feeds to quite an extent on the caterpillars of the gypsy moth, even climbing trees in search of its prey, and it is now fairly common in most of the New England states (Fig. 149). As a whole, the group is distinctly a beneficial one, feeding on injurious insects both above ground and as these enter the ground to pupate.

*Family* **CICINDELIDÆ** (tiger beetles).—The active flight and bright colors of many of the tiger beetles, though most of them are small insects, only about half an inch long, make the members of this family quite noticeable (Fig. 150). They are sun-loving forms, most common along roadsides and in sandy places. When flushed, they fly quickly a few yards, then alight and often turn, facing the intruder as though watching his movements. Both they and their larvae feed on other insects, the larva living in a burrow in the ground and placing itself at the mouth of the burrow ready to grasp any unwary insect that may come near. The elytra of the adult are usually metallic brown with light-colored marks suggestive of musical characters or perhaps hieroglyphics, though in some cases bright green, purple or other colors dominate. In the west the largest insect belonging to this family (*Amblychila cylindriformis* Say) does its hunting at night, as is also the case with certain related forms of the Pacific coast.

Fig. 150.　　　　　　Fig. 151.

Fig. 150.—Tiger beetle (*Cicindela*); slightly enlarged.
Fig. 151.—Dytiscid beetle (*Dytiscus verticalis* Say); natural size.

*Family* **DYTISCIDÆ** (carnivorous diving beetles).—Members of this family are present in almost every quiet stream and pond. They are oval, rather flat beetles, usually black, and good swimmers, the hinder pair of legs being broad and somewhat oar-like and heavily fringed with hairs (Fig. 151). The antennae are thread-like. Whenever they need air, they float up to the surface of the water and allow the hinder end of the body to project a little out of the water. Then, lifting the elytra slightly, the air enters the space under them and is retained there aided by hairs present. The insect can now stay under water until this air supply has been exhausted. The larvae, often called water tigers because they are such voracious creatures, feed, like the adults, on various water insects and other animals, even attacking small fish. Some of this family may be at least an inch and a half long.

*Family* **GYRINIDÆ** (whirligig beetles).—These insects swim on the surface of quiet water, generally in groups, and go around and around in a "whirligig" sort of fashion. They are usually bluish black, oval in form, and the compound eyes are so divided that one part of each is directed upward and the other downward (Fig. 152). They feed on small insects that come within their reach. The larvae, living in the water, breathe by abdominal tracheal gills and are also carnivorous. The group does not include many species, but their habit of swimming in companies and their peculiar "gyrating" over the surface attract attention, nearly everybody having noticed them on this account.

FIG. 152.  FIG. 153.

FIG. 152.—Gyrinid or whirligig beetle (*Dineutes*); natural size.
FIG. 153.—Water-scavenger beetle (*Hydrous triangularis* Say); natural size.

*Family* **HYDROPHILIDÆ** (water-scavenger beetles).—The water-scavenger beetles occur in the same types of stream and pond as the carnivorous diving beetles, which they greatly resemble (Fig. 153). The outline, however, is usually a little more elongately oval; the antennae are club-shaped, and in addition to other structural differences they obtain air by raising the head slightly above the surface and collecting a film of it over the under surface of the body, where it is retained by a close coating (pubescence) of fine hairs. They feed on decaying animal and plant material for the most part, though sometimes taking to living plants and insects. Some species may be about two inches in length. They are of little economic importance.

*Family* **STAPHYLINIDÆ** (rove beetles).—This large family in some regards is suggestive of the fireflies as the body of the insect in this group is not so hard and firm as in most beetles and seven or eight abdominal segments are present (Fig. 154). In other ways, however, it differs greatly from the lampyrids, the body being slender for its length, and the elytra short, not nearly covering the top of the abdomen, the segments of which are very movable. The insects run rapidly, often lifting up the end of the abdomen in a menacing way. Most of the thousand or more species found in this country are small, the larger kinds seldom being more than an inch long. They are land forms, feeding on decaying vegetable and animal materials near which—or under stones and wood—they are found. They must be considered as beneficial insects, acting as scavengers.

FIG. 154.—
R o v e  beetle;
s l i g h t l y  e n -
larged.

*Family* **SILPHIDÆ** (carrion beetles).—Most of the members of this family are of good size, ranging from half an inch to three times that length. Two rather distinct types of insect are common in the group, one (*Silpha*, Fig. 155) having a broad, rather flat body and with the sides of the prothorax very thin. These insects average less than an inch in length and the elytra are usually black. In the other type (*Necrophorus*, Fig. 156) the insect is larger, stout, with a body more cylindrical, and the elytra generally have dull-red markings and are frequently shorter than the abdomen. Both types feed on dead animals in most cases, and their larvae have the same food, so that the group may therefore be regarded as beneficial. It is not a very large family, in the United States at least.

FIG. 155.                 FIG. 156.

FIG. 155.—Carrion beetle (*Silpha americana* L.); about natural size.

FIG. 156.—Carrion beetle (*Necrophorus marginatus* Fab.); enlarged one-half. (*From Kellogg's "American Insects."*)

*Family* **DERMESTIDÆ** (dermestids).—These insects are small, the largest common species in this country being only about one-third of an inch long. Most of them are rather short, thickset beetles, covered with very small scales which give them a gray or brown color, with occasional black, white or red scaly areas in some cases, producing spots or bands of these colors. They feed on decaying substances, but those most important as pests attack wool, furs, feathers and meat, cheese and fats. In some cases the adults feed on pollen.

**The larder beetle** (*Dermestes lardarius* L.).—This common insect is frequently found in pantries on foods, particularly of a fatty nature. The adult (Fig. 157) is dark brown, with a pale-yellowish band across the elytra near their bases, in which are a few black dots. The larva (Fig. 158) is longer and more slender than the adult, with numerous, rather long, black hairs; it is brown in color and attacks ham, cheese, beeswax, feathers and almost any material oily or fatty in its nature.

*Control.*—Little can be done in the way of controlling this pest, except by cleanliness and close watch of all fatty substances kept in stock, removing and destroying the insects whenever they are discovered. Tightly closed receptacles, giving no opportunity for the insects to enter, should be used in which to keep such substances. Infested storerooms or pantries may be heated to 125° for three hours or fumigated with ethylene dichloride after removing any meat. Infested meat should be thoroughly cleaned and the trimmings burned.

**The buffalo carpet beetle** (*Anthrenus scrophulariæ* L.).—This is one of several related household pests which attack woolen goods, carpets, feathers, furs, hair, silk, leather and other animal and sometimes plant products. This and the black carpet beetle (*Attagenus piceus* Oliv.) are European insects.

The buffalo carpet beetle is a tiny beetle, mottled black and white, with a red line having side branches along the middle of the back (Fig. 159). Its eggs are laid on the material upon which the larvae feed. Adults are often noticed on house windows along with ladybeetles and in the early summer they feed on the pollen of flowers, the *Spiræa* being a favorite.

The length of life of a generation probably varies according to the temperature and abundance of food. One generation may possibly be completed in less than a year in the south, but under unfavorable conditions it may take more than twice that time. The larva is shiny brownish, covered with tufts of black hairs giving it the appearance of a tiny black shoebrush.

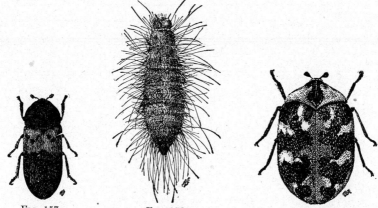

FIG. 157.          FIG. 158.                    FIG. 159.

FIG. 157.—Adult larder beetle (*Dermestes lardarius* L.); four times natural size. (*From Herrick's Insects Injurious to the Household. By permission of The Macmillan Company, publishers.*)

FIG. 158.—Larva of the larder beetle; three times natural size. (*From Herrick's Insects Injurious to the Household. By permission of The Macmillan Company, publishers.*)

FIG. 159.—Adult carpet beetle (*Anthrenus scrophulariæ* L.); nine times natural size. (*From Herrick's Insects Injurious to the Household. By permission of The Macmillan Company, publishers.*)

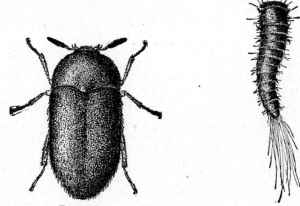

FIG. 160.                              FIG. 161.

FIG. 160.—Adult black carpet beetle (*Attagenus piceus* Oliv.); enlarged nine times. (*From Herrick's Insects Injurious to the Household. By permission of The Macmillan Company, publishers.*)

FIG. 161.—Larva of the black carpet beetle; five times natural size. (*From Herrick's Insects Injurious to the Household. By permission of The Macmillan Company, publishers.*)

The black carpet beetle (*Attagenus piceus* Oliv., Fig. 160) has somewhat similar habits, but the larva (Fig. 161) is longer and more slender, reddish brown, and has a tuft of long hairs at the end of its body.

*Control of carpet beetles.*—Woolens and other materials liable to attack by carpet beetles may, when free from these pests, be protected from infestation by being stored in tight containers or even in carefully sealed paper garment bags. Fabrics freshly washed, dry-cleaned or fumigated will be free from insects. Liberal amounts (one pound to each ten to fifty cubic feet of space) of moth crystals, either paradichlorobenzene or naphthalene, should be kept in storage bags or boxes for repellent and killing value. Cedar chests furnish no more protection than any other tight box after the cedar oil evaporates from the wood. After the woolen lint has been cleaned from cracks in floors and around baseboards these cracks should be treated with liberal applications of a pyrethrum or similar fly spray, or even kerosene. Badly infested buildings may be fumigated, but some carpet beetles hidden in cracks will often survive, especially when they are located near outside walls in buildings of poor construction.

Fig. 162.—Adult flatheaded apple tree borer (*Chrysobothris femorata* Oliv.); enlarged three and one-half times. (*From U. S. Dept. Agr. Farmers' Bul.* 1065.)

**Family BUPRESTIDÆ** (flatheaded borers).— This group of beetles contains many forms that injure trees by boring in their trunks. Others attack berry canes which often show swellings as a result. A few are leaf miners or gall makers. The adults are generally stout, robust beetles with heads set into the thorax, rather flat backs, and in general dark colored but with a metallic luster, though a few are bright green or of other colors. The larvae, which bore in trees, are white except for a small yellowish head and have a large flattened prothorax and no legs. They burrow at first just under the bark in the sapwood and later in the heartwood. The average life history requires about a year for its completion, but if the tree is vigorous the larva is liable either to die or be delayed in its development. The adults are fond of the sun and fly freely in the daytime. They are often found on flowers. Several hundred species are known in this country, all of them injurious, the damage they do being largely dependent upon the importance of the tree or plant they attack.

**The flatheaded apple tree borer** (*Chrysobothris femorata* Oliv.).—This is probably the most injurious of the buprestids. It attacks more than thirty kinds of trees and shrubs, generally selecting individuals that are not in a healthy condition or are otherwise favorable for their larvae. The beetle (Fig. 162) is about half an inch long, rather broad, dark brown, faintly marked with bands and indefinite spots of gray, and having a brassy metallic reflection at certain angles. The underside is bronze, and under the wings the abdomen is a metallic greenish blue. It occurs almost everywhere in the United States and in southern Canada and is a serious enemy of fruit trees.

The beetles appear soon after apple-blossom time and live for several weeks. They frequent the sunny side of the trunks and limbs of trees. Here the eggs are laid in fine cracks or under small scales of the bark. They hatch in from two to three weeks and the tiny larva (Fig. 163) bores into the inner bark, feeding on this and on the sapwood, and grows rapidly unless the tree is vigorous, in which case such an outpouring of sap may occur at the wound as to kill (drown?) the larva or drive it into the outer layers of bark where it may live for a time, later working back into the sapwood if the flow becomes small enough to permit it. If the larva can feed in the sapwood, it will grow to full size, about an inch long, by fall, at this time burrowing into the wood to form a pupal cavity in which the winter is spent, pupation itself taking place there the following spring and continuing several (three to four) weeks, after which the adult beetle escapes.

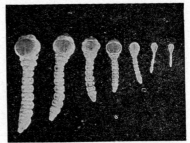

FIG. 163.—Flatheaded apple tree borers (larvae) of various ages; natural size. (*From U. S. Dept. Agr. Farmers' Bul.* 1065.)

*Control.*—Vigorous, healthy trees are not generally liable to attack, and cultural methods which will ensure this condition are important. Trees headed low will shade their trunks and the sun-loving beetles will go to those exposed to sunlight. Shading trunks exposed to the sunlight, by boards cutting off this light, is a protection, as are also poles set in the orchard and covered with sticky material to catch and hold the beetles visiting them in search of places to lay their eggs. Wrapping the young trees with paper the first year they are set out will prevent egg laying. This should be done before mid-May and allowed to remain through the second year. Birds and insect enemies aid in controlling this pest.

The Pacific flatheaded borer (*Chrysobothris mali* Horn) is found in the west. It is smaller than the last and rather dark coppery in color. The adults are found in spring and summer. The borers attack many kinds of trees and bushes and there is only one generation a year. Control measures are the same as for the last species.

*Family* **ELATERIDÆ** (snapping beetles; click beetles; skipjacks).— These insects somewhat resemble the buprestids when adult but are usually more slender, with their sides more nearly parallel; the economic species also lack a metallic reflection. The hinder corners of the pronotum are elongated, forming sharp points in the majority of the group. The insects are usually some shade of brown or black, though the pronotum and elytra sometimes differ in color and the latter are spotted in some cases, mottled black and white in our largest common species, and some have rather bright colors or markings (Fig. 166). When these insects fall on their backs, they are able to throw themselves into the air by a sudden snap of the body for the purpose of getting onto their feet as they alight again, and if this fails the first time the snapping is repeated. The larvae (Figs. 164, 165), commonly called wireworms, are nearly all slender, yellow or brown, with very hard shells, often glistening; one subfamily where they are soft-bodied and white forms a notable exception to this. The outline of the

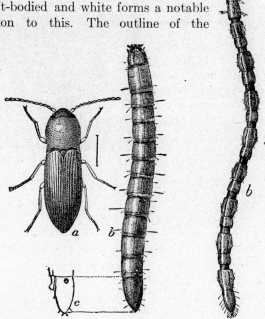

FIG. 164.                    FIG. 165.

FIG. 164.—Wheat wireworm (*Agriotes mancus* Say); *a*, adult; enlarged about five times; *b*, full-grown larva (wireworm); enlarged about three times; *c*, side view of last segment of larva.  (*From U. S. Dept. Agr. Bul.* 156.)

FIG. 165.—Sand wireworm (*Horistonotus uhlerii* Horn): *a*, adult, enlarged about ten times; *b*, full-grown larva (wireworm); enlarged over four times.  (*From U. S. Dept. Agr. Bul.* 156.)

hinder end is often made use of in distinguishing the different kinds of wireworms.  Their food habits have a wide range: some feed on decaying wood under bark or elsewhere; others on fungi; several groups are carnivorous; and still others feed on roots or seeds in the ground.

One of the largest insects of this family found in the United States is the eyed click beetle (*Alaus oculatus* L.), which is about an inch and a half long; the elytra black, finely marked with white dots; and with a pair of large, oval, velvety-black spots rimmed with white on the pronotum (Fig. 166). The larvae of this insect feed on insects in decaying wood, often that of the apple, but are of little economic importance.

In the far south and also in the West Indies and Mexico are species of elaterids (*Pyrophorus* spp.) which have an oval, yellowish spot near each hinder corner of the pronotum (Fig. 167), and also an area on the underside of the abdomen close to, and partially concealed by, the metathorax, which is luminous, producing an intermittent, greenish-yellow, quite brilliant light, making the insects very noticeable at night. They are beneficial, the larvae feeding on white grubs.

The injurious members of this family are those wireworms which feed on seeds and the roots of plants, and there are many kinds that have this habit. Some attack wheat; others corn; and still others feed on cotton, grass, potatoes, sugar beets and other crops, doing much damage. Some are most abundant in heavy soils containing much vegetable matter, and others prefer high, sandy land. So many species of wireworms are

Fig. 166.—Adult eyed click beetle (*Alaus oculatus* L.); about natural size. (*From Linville and Kelly, General Zoölogy, Ginn and Company, publishers.*)

injurious and so unlike are their habits in different parts of the country that each kind seems to require treatment especially adapted to it.

Fig. 167.—A luminous elaterid (*Pyrophorus* sp.) showing luminous spots on sides of pronotum; natural size.

*Control.*—Some general factors in control may, however, be suggested. When wireworms are abundant in low, poorly drained land, drainage will be of much assistance. When they attack grass roots in great numbers, it is desirable in cultivating such places to substitute field peas, buckwheat or some crop not closely related to grass for the first crop, if possible, even though this does violence to the general ideas of crop rotation. When sod land is to be planted, plowing it in July and cultivating often and deeply the rest of the summer will destroy many of the insects. In the south and in arid regions, however, the insects go deeply into the ground, during hot or dry weather, beyond reach by cultivation. In such cases planting early in the season and forcing the plants ahead by fertilizers and frequent cultivation are helpful. As the underground feeding period of these insects is from three to six years, proper treatment for a single season will at best give only partial relief; to obtain the most successful control the special habits of the particular species concerned should be ascertained, and control measures to correspond be adopted. Various methods for the protection of planted seed have been tried but the results have not agreed in all cases and further studies along this line are needed.

The Elateridæ is one of the most important groups of beetles from an economic standpoint, and injurious species occur practically everywhere in the United States. Several hundred kinds are known in this country.

FIG. 168.—Egyptian carving of a Scarabæus.

*Family* **SCARABÆIDÆ** (lamellicorn beetles).— This is a very large and important family of beetles, containing many pests. The antennae in this group have several of the terminal segments large, flattened, and broader on one side, movable but generally carried close together (see Fig. 13, right-hand drawing). The insects are stout and rather short in most cases, and the elytra usually do not cover the entire abdomen.

Based on their habits, two sections of the family can be distinguished: the scavengers, which as both larvae and adults feed on decaying matter; and the leaf chafers, which as adults generally consume leaves or flowers, and whose larvae occur in the ground feeding on roots or in decaying wood.

The scavengers, though they may be considered as beneficial, are not of great importance, but some species because of their peculiar habits have attracted attention for centuries. The habit referred to is that shown by some of the so-called tumblebugs in connection with egg laying. A pair of these beetles will together form a little dung into a ball which they then begin to roll over the ground, often for a long distance. Finally they bury it in the ground after an egg has been laid upon it, thus providing partially decomposed food for the larva. The sacred beetle or Scarabæus of the Egyptians was one of the insects of this group (Fig. 168) and has been preserved in their drawings and carvings as a symbolic record of their beliefs. The leaf chafers form the larger part of the family. Among them are a number of serious pests.

**The May beetles or June bugs** (*Phyllophaga* and other genera).—This is a group of beetles quite uniform in both appearance and habits. The adults are generally dark brown and rather glossy above, from half an inch to an inch long, and very stout (Fig. 169). They appear during the spring months, earlier in the south than in the north, flying at night and attracted by lights, to which they fly in a clumsy, erratic way. They feed at night on the leaves of various trees, often entirely stripping them. Different kinds of June bugs appear to prefer different kinds of trees for their food. Some species seem to select the oak, others the ash, still others the pine. Small birches have been completely stripped of their foliage in a single night. In the south two species appear to prefer the longleaf pine. Whatever the species, large areas of timber may be defoliated when the beetles are abundant, though this seldom appears to be the case in New England. On the Pacific coast too, though June bugs occur, they do not seem to be so important as in the interior of the

Fig. 169.—Adult "June bugs," female and male, natural size. (*From U. S. Dept. Agr. Farmers' Bul.* 940.)

country, particularly in the Mississippi Valley and as far north as the Great Lakes.

The eggs of the June bugs are laid in the ground and hatch in a few weeks into tiny "white grubs" with brown heads and legs, and soft white bodies which increase in size toward the hinder end. The grub (Fig. 170) as usually found when dug up is curled through the greater part of a circle; this is very characteristic, only a few other beetle larvae (and those belong to the same family) greatly resembling it. The grubs feed during the summer on decaying vegetation and living plants close to the surface of the ground but on the approach of cold weather go deeper into the ground to pass the winter. The following spring they come up near the surface again and feed on the plant roots, causing in this, their second season, the largest injury. In the fall of the second season they again go deep into the ground to pass the winter, coming up the third spring to feed on plant roots

Fig. 170.—Full-grown larva (white grub) of "June bug"; about natural size. (*By courtesy of A. A. Granovsky, Minn. Agr. Expt. Sta.*)

until June or July, when they go down a little, though not usually much if any below where they may be reached by deep plowing. Here they transform to pupae which become adult after a month or two, but the beetles remain in these underground pupal cells until the next (fourth) spring, when they emerge. The length of a generation as thus outlined therefore is three years, but living in parts of four calendar years.

This life history holds for most of the injurious species of June bugs in the central states, through the country east of the Rocky Mountains. In the north, however, the life history, in some cases at least, requires four years; in the southern states two years appears to be the normal period. Some appear every year though, indicating the existence of three broods in those regions where the three-year life history exists, but the size of these broods is markedly different and the injury done varies correspondingly. Every third year (the second year of feeding of the brood) the most abundant brood will be destructive; in the years between, the other two broods, being fewer in numbers, will destroy less. If conditions very unfavorable for the large brood or unusually favorable for either or both of the smaller ones should develop and continue long enough, it might be that the relative importance of the broods would change.

Though white grubs have many natural enemies, including numerous mammals, birds and insects, and also several diseases, both bacterial and fungous, they are not sufficient checks to prevent considerable injury.

*Control.*—Upon the activities of white grubs depend the various measures that may be taken for their control. (1) Since the adult June beetles prefer to oviposit in a loose grassy sod or weedy land and the larvae prefer to feed upon corn, grains, potatoes and strawberries, and seem to dislike legumes, especially the sweet clovers, the rotation of crops should be arranged so as not to plant crops likely to be injured by white grubs on grub-infested sod. Such crops should, if possible, be planted after sweet clover, after a good stand of other legumes or after the cultivated crops. (2) In the years preceding heavy beetle flights, clovers should be planted as much as possible. During the year of heavy flight cultivated crops should be kept free of weeds to avoid heavy grub infestation. Pastures with dense stands of leguminous plants will also be avoided by June beetles and will hardly be injured by the grubs. It is well to plant the crops susceptible to grub injury on such land the following year. Areas known to be infested should be planted to legumes, buckwheat and other crops resistant to grub injury.

Fall plowing will not control white grubs, but frequent and thorough late summer cultivation. disking and harrowing, will tend to reduce the number of grubs.

Where adult beetles are stripping the foliage of shade trees these may be sprayed with lead arsenate two pounds, water fifty gallons, if conditions are such as to make this practicable.

When sod in lawns is injured by white grubs, or even in valuable pasture land, lead arsenate may be added to the top dressing at the rate of from five to fifteen pounds per thousand square feet. One heavy application may protect a lawn for several years. Grub-infested pasture can be renovated by harrowing and then seeding with some suitable mixture containing legumes, especially sweet clover and alfalfa.

The rose chafer (*Macrodactylus subspinosus* Fab.).—This insect occurs all over the eastern United States as far south as Virginia and Tennessee and west to Colorado, being particularly abundant and destructive in sandy localities. The adult beetle is about a third of an inch long, rather stout, though less so in proportion to its length than are the June bugs, dull yellow, with pale red legs which are long and slender. It appears about the time roses begin to bloom, *i.e.*, in May in the south and in June in the more northern part of its range, and attacks a large number of plants. It seems originally to have been a rose feeder; later

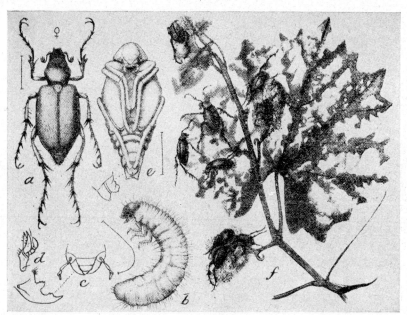

Fig. 171.—Rose chafer (*Macrodactylus subspinosus* Fab.): *a*, adult beetle; *b*, larva (grub); *e*, pupa; *f*, injury to leaves and blossoms of grape with beetles at work. Fine lines beside *a*, *b*, and *e*, show the true length; *f*, somewhat reduced. (*From U. S. Dept. Agr. Farmers' Bul.* 721.)

it became a serious pest of the grape and is now destructive to many fruit and shade trees and shrubs, and even to garden fruits and vegetables when abundant, eating blossoms, leaves and any fruit that may be available during its adult condition (Fig. 171).

The eggs are laid a little below the surface of the ground, preferably in sandy soil, and in two to three weeks hatch into small white grubs which feed on plant roots until late in the fall; then each works deeper into the ground and forms an earthen cell in which to winter. Pupation occurs in the spring and after two to four weeks the adult beetle digs its way to the surface. There is only one generation each year.

*Control.*—Stomach poisons fail to kill quickly enough to save the plants from much injury in most cases and they mar the appearance of the blossoms of ornamental plants. On grapes and other fruits, lead arsenate three pounds and cheap molasses one gallon in fifty gallons of water should be applied thoroughly as soon as the beetles appear and once in ten days thereafter until the insects are gone. Care must be taken not to spray during blossoming and not to apply more sprays to fruit than necessary because of poisonous residues at harvest.

Hand-picking, although tedious, is effective in small gardens if done every day to get the adults that come from other plants. Choice flowers and clusters of grapes can be bagged with cheesecloth. Harrowing the breeding grounds of the insect near vineyards to a depth of three or four inches, during the pupal period, *i.e.*, the latter part of May for the central part of its range, destroys many of the pupae which appear to be easily killed by any disturbance. The difficulty is to locate the areas where breeding is most abundant. Light, sandy ground will generally prove to be the place for such treatment.

**The Japanese beetle** (*Popillia japonica* Newm.), a native of Japan, was discovered in New Jersey in 1916. The beetles (Fig. 172) attack

the foliage and fruit of many kinds of plants, including fruit trees, small fruits, garden crops and ornamental trees and shrubs; the larvae feed on the roots of grasses and other plants.

This insect has now become continuously distributed from southwestern Connecticut through lower New York, New Jersey, Delaware, southeastern Pennsylvania and most of Maryland and at least single specimens have been taken from Maine to Florida and in nearly every state east of the Mississippi River. There is every prospect that in time this pest will occur everywhere in this country except where climatic conditions hold it in check. Several parasites have been introduced

Fig. 172.—Adult Japanese beetles (*Popillia japonica* Newm.); slightly enlarged. (*By courtesy of Ray Hutson, Michigan State College.*)

from Asia and are beginning to do good work, but they cannot exterminate the insect. It has recently been found in Ontario as well.

The adults are about half an inch long, the head and thorax bronze-green, the elytra brownish; there are two white spots at the tip of the abdomen. They begin to appear in June but are most abundant in July and August. They lay their forty to fifty eggs in the ground, and the grubs, on hatching, feed on decaying vegetation and living plant roots but on the approach of cold weather go more deeply into the ground. Here they stay until April when they come up and resume feeding until pupation in June, followed by the emergence of the adults. There is but one generation a year.

*Control.*—Lead arsenate spray, 3 pounds in fifty gallons of water with an added sticker such as flour (two pounds) will protect foliage from injury by the adult beetles although it repels rather than kills them. In no case should fruit be sprayed unless the residue is removed naturally or artificially. Individual plants, especially ornamentals, may sometimes be advantageously protected with cloth netting. Special traps designed by the U. S. Bureau of Entomology and baited with geraniol are often used in residential districts where the infestation is not great and are also utilized to determine the extent and relative density of infestations. Many beetles may be collected by jarring them onto sheets spread under the trees and shrubs in the cool of the morning, then killed by putting them in a pail of water covered with kerosene.

Grubs in the ground are controlled with lead arsenate five to fifteen pounds per thousand square feet for the season, applied with top dressing. Carbon disulfide emulsion is sometimes used for this purpose also; directions for its preparation and application are too complicated, however, to be described here. A bacterial "milky disease" which attacks and kills the grubs is now being cultivated and spread, apparently with considerable success, being scattered by the grubs themselves.

**The Asiatic garden beetle** (*Autoserica castanea* Arrow).—Discovered in New Jersey in 1922, this insect has been found in a number of states near the Atlantic coast beyond its center of continuous distribution in New York and New Jersey. The adult beetle resembles the May beetle but is less than half an inch long, cinnamon brown, has small, narrow grooves along its elytra and is covered by a fine pubescence. The beetles appear in June and July and lay an average of sixty eggs in the ground. These hatch in about ten days and the larvae (grubs) feed on the roots of plants and by the middle of October go deeper in the ground to winter. About the middle of April they come up and resume feeding until into June, then pupate in the ground and escape as the adults one to two weeks later. The beetles feed at night on the leaves of plants and are attracted to lights, but hide in the ground during the day. Though the beetle feeds on the leaves of many kinds of trees, shrubs, vegetable and garden plants and weeds, the rose, carrot, turnip, aster, chrysanthemum, sunflower and ragweed seem to be preferred. The larvae feed on the roots of grass, sometimes ruining lawns, and on many of the common vegetables and flowers, but potatoes are not attacked. Long continued dry periods kill many of them.

*Control.*—Plants can generally be protected from the adults by spraying with lead arsenate six pounds, wheat flour four pounds, in 100 gallons of water. This spray should be repeated often enough to keep the plants covered as long as the adults are feeding. Bait traps are also useful as for the Japanese beetle. For the grubs in lawns the lead arsenate treatment for the Japanese beetle can be used.

Many other scarabaeids are occasionally injuriously abundant in different parts of the country but can hardly be considered as of nation-wide importance. The largest bodied beetles found in the United States also belong here and are called rhinoceros beetles. One species, *Dynastes tityus* L. (Fig. 173), about two and one-half inches long, is greenish gray with black spots on the elytra. The male has a long horn on the head, projecting forward and upward, and another projecting forward from the pronotum. The female has only a small tubercle on the head. It occurs in the southern states. In another species found in the west the prothoracic horn is much longer.

Fig. 173.—Rhinoceros beetle (*Dynastes tityus* L.); about natural size.

*Family* **CHRYSOMELIDÆ** (leaf beetles).—This is the largest family of beetles but its members are small, not often being over half an inch long. Most of them are leaf feeders, though the larvae of a few are worm-like and attack underground stems or roots. Many are serious pests and, though almost none is found throughout the entire country, allied species working in similar ways occur.

In the group as a whole, yellowish elytra with black lines or spots seem to be the prevailing color pattern, though, of course, with many exceptions. Together with the next two families, from which other characters separate this one, the third segment of the tarsus is generally broad, being drawn out into a lobe on each side, and is covered beneath with minute, closely set hairs (pubescent). The antennae are at most of only average length.

**The Colorado potato beetle** (*Leptinotarsa decemlineata* Say).— This well-known insect was discovered about 1823 by Long's exploring expedition to the Rocky Mountains, in the region of the upper Missouri River. Its food there was the buffalo bur (*Solanum rostratum* Dunal) and the insect was apparently not very abundant, and certainly of no economic importance, nor did it become so until civilization, and with this the potato, reached that territory. Then a new and satisfactory food plant, abundant enough to provide all the insects with food, became available and the potato beetle increased in numbers and began to spread to the east. At first its rate of spread was only about fifty miles a year but after crossing the Mississippi River this became more rapid and it reached the Atlantic coast about 1874. Since then it has spread both northward and southward until it is now found practically everywhere east of the Rocky Mountains where the potato is grown and it has also reached the Pacific coast. It apparently does not thrive in the hot climate of the more southerly states. In Europe it has appeared at various times and places and now seems to be present rather generally in northwestern Europe except in England where it has several times been eradicated.

The adult beetle (Fig. 174*b*) is somewhat less than half an inch long and about two-thirds this width, its back rather high and rounded. It is clay yellow and has ten longitudinal black lines on its elytra. The head has a black spot above, and the pronotum has a number of irregular spots. Winter is spent as the adult in the ground but the insects come out quite early in the spring. As soon as the potatoes are up, they begin to feed and soon lay their eggs, placing these on the under surface of the leaves in small clusters, an individual laying 500 or more in all. They are small yellow eggs which hatch in four days to a week or more, according to the temperature. The grubs, or slugs as they are often called (Fig. 174*a*), are dull brick red, soft and with fat bodies. They feed from two to three weeks, then go into the ground where they pupate for a week or two, after which the adults emerge and lay eggs for a second generation, the adults of which appear early in the fall. This second generation of beetles feeds for a time, then in September or October enters the ground to pass the winter.

*a        b*
Fig. 174.—Colorado potato beetle (*Leptinotarsa decemlineata* Say): *a*, full-grown larva (grub); *b*, adult beetle; slightly enlarged. (*From Berlese. After U. S. Bur. Ent. Circ. 87.*)

As the eggs of this insect are not all laid at one time, different ages, and different stages even, may be found together in the same field. And as the adults feed in the spring during their egg-laying period, as do the two generations of adults produced during the season, in addition to the two generations of grubs which also consume the leaves, the plants are being attacked much of the time.

Although the potato appears to be the preferred food of this insect, other members of the nightshade family are sometimes attacked, particularly the tomato and eggplant.

*Control.*—This pest is easily controlled by spraying with any of the stomach poisons and, as the potato is quite resistant to poisons, the strength of the mixture can with safety be somewhat increased above that of the standard formula. The chief difficulty in control is that, as the beetles attack the rapidly growing plant as soon as it appears above ground, the spray should be applied then; a week later a large amount of new growth which has no poison on it will have developed, upon which the insects can feed. To avoid this, spraying during the period of rapid growth needs to be done more frequently than is the case with most plants. Two or three treatments, however, will generally be sufficient, and a combination with Bordeaux mixture is advantageous where lead arsenate is the stomach poison used.

On small areas, dry Paris green, mixed with ten to twenty parts of some inert material dusted over the plants, preferably while the dew is on them, is a fair treatment.  This poison can also be used as a spray.  Lead arsenate and calcium arsenate are now the preferred poisons for this pest, however, though zinc arsenite or cryolite may be used.

Various birds, skunks, snakes and toads feed on the Colorado potato beetle to some extent, and it also has numerous insect enemies.

The history of the development of the Colorado potato beetle, from an unimportant, even probably a rather uncommon, insect, feeding upon a plant of no value to man, into one of the most abundant and widely distributed of our pests, attacking and seriously injuring an important crop, is a suggestive one.  In a division of the insects of the United States into those which are injurious as regards man and his various interests; those which are beneficial; and those which are of little or no economic importance either way, we shall find that the last group is by no means a small one.  How many species in this group are there which are potential pests?  It is true that the making available of a new food plant to which the Colorado potato beetle could turn was probably the chief factor in this particular case, but any insect which for some reason changes from an unimportant food plant to a crop plant may at once become a pest.  Thus another chrysomelid only a little smaller than the Colorado potato beetle and closely related to it, the three-spotted doryphora (*Doryphora clivicollis* Kirby), which feeds on milkweed, is now of practically no importance.  But if it should change its food to some valuable crop plant, it would at once become an important addition to the list of insect foes man has to combat.  Several such cases are already known.  How many others may appear as the changing conditions which always accompany an increasing population and the consequent changes in plant population take place, no one can predict.  Some species of plants once common are rapidly disappearing.  As they go, will the insects feeding on them go too, or will they be able to find another food plant, and will this one be of value to man?  The appearance of new pests in such ways may come at any time, and the fact that an insect is not now a pest should not lead to its being ignored, for it may have great potential importance.  The murky ground beetle (*Harpalus caliginosus* Fab.) is now mainly a carnivorous beetle but sometimes, though rarely, attacks the strawberry.  If it should turn to this latter plant entirely for its food, another important pest would be added to our list and lost from among our friends.

Such facts call for as complete a knowledge as possible of the life and habits of all insects whether now beneficial or only of no economic importance, in order that we may have the knowledge of them and their ways which is necessary in case they should become injurious.

**The striped cucumber beetle** (*Diabrotica vittata* Fab.).—The common cucumber beetle is found everywhere in this country (of which it is a native) east of the Rocky Mountains. It is a small beetle about a fifth of an inch long, with a black head, yellow pronotum and three black stripes along its yellow elytra (Fig. 175). The insect passes the winter as the adult beetle in protected places, probably among dense weed growth. It leaves its winter quarters early in the spring, before any of its cultivated food plants are available, and feeds on blossoms of various kinds until cucumbers, squashes and the other cucurbits which are its favorite food plants are available. It then attacks these and may also seriously injure peas, beans, apples and, later in the season, corn. It lays its eggs either singly or in clusters, in the ground near the stems and roots of the cucurbits, often in crevices of the soil, the total number of eggs per beetle varying from a few hundred to over a thousand. The eggs hatch in a week or two, according to the temperature at that time, and the grubs feed on the stems and roots. They are tiny, white, slender, and resemble maggots more than the usual forms of beetle larvae, and when

FIG. 175.—Adult striped cucumber beetle (*Diabrotica vittata* Fab.); enlarged about six times (see hair line for true length). (*From U. S. Dept. Agr. Farmers' Bul.* 1038.)

full grown, after two to five or more weeks, according to the temperature, are only about three-tenths of an inch long. They then soon change to pupae, still in the ground, in which stage they remain for about a week before the beetles emerge. The life cycle therefore varies in length according to the temperature, it being perhaps not over four weeks in the south and eight in the more northern states. This gives time for several generations each season; and though in the north there is apparently but one, this number increases farther south until in Texas there may be four.

The destruction caused by these insects when they are abundant is often very great. Their first attacks come just when the young plants are struggling to establish themselves and the feeding of the adult beetles is often sufficient to kill them. Later in the season the beetles continue feeding on the leaves and stems, reducing the vigor of the plant and its productiveness, and they may also feed on the outer surface of the fruit, making it more or less unsalable. They also frequently enter greenhouses and attack cucurbits there. The larvae affect the vitality of the plant by attacking the underground stems and roots but are less injurious than the adults.

The beetles are also injurious by carrying the "bacterial wilt" disease and "cucurbit mosaic" disease, the former not only from plant to plant but also from one season to the next. As these diseases are serious ones, often destroying plants, this adds to the importance of the insect as a pest.

On the Pacific coast is a slightly larger species, known as the western striped cucumber beetle (*Diabrotica trivittata* Mann.), which has much the same habits as the eastern form. In the more southerly portion of this region the adults are more or less active during the cold months. There appear to be at least two generations a year. The following methods for the control of the eastern species also apply for this one.

*Control.*—This is a difficult insect to control, particularly where large areas are planted to any of the cucurbits and small garden methods will not pay. Protective methods, practicable in gardens, enable the plants to get well started, after which they are able to grow and produce the crop to quite an extent, despite the insect. Screening the plants before they come up, using fine-mesh wire or thin cheesecloth stretched over a frame, works well for this purpose, provided the edge of the frame fits tightly into the earth everywhere, so that the beetles cannot burrow under it. Sometimes an excess of seed is planted with the idea of giving the insects enough food so that few or none of the plants will be too thickly infested to be able to live, and the poorest ones can be thinned out later. Gathering all but a few of the plants as soon as the crop has been harvested, and burning them will leave the others for the beetles to gather on. These can then be sprayed with a strong stomach poison or a strong contact insecticide. Early cucurbits, such as gourds, can be planted near later cucumbers and will act as trap plants, attracting the beetles.

Dusting with mixtures containing calcium arsenate, cryolite, or rotenone are the most common chemical controls. Calcium arsenate, 1 part, is mixed with 9 parts of dusting gypsum; cryolite with 3 parts of gypsum. Rotenone dusts should contain about 1 per cent of the toxic agent. Dusting must be thorough and done frequently enough to keep the new growth well covered. Spraying with nicotine sulfate 1 to 600 with an added spreading agent may be substituted for dusting. Whatever material is used, give the first treatment as soon as the plants show above ground.

**The corn rootworms.**—There are several species of the genus *Diabrotica* which as larvae appear to make a specialty of feeding upon either the base of the stem or the roots of corn.

The southern corn rootworm or spotted cucumber beetle (*Diabrotica duodecimpunctata* Fab.) is found practically everywhere in the United States east of the Rocky Mountains, but is usually a serious pest only from Maryland to Florida and as far west as southern Ohio, Indiana and Illinois, Alabama, Louisiana and Texas. The insect generally winters as the adult beetle (Fig. 176) under rubbish or in other protected places, except in the far south where it is more or less active during this period. In spring it lays its eggs just below ground, on or near the young corn plants, and the tiny grubs that hatch attack the corn, feeding on the roots and drilling into the stem just above them, boring out the crown and killing the bud (Fig. 177). From this habit the insect is often called the budworm or drillworm. Small plants injured in this way break off at the crowns when pulled, and larger ones become dwarfed and yellowish. Other

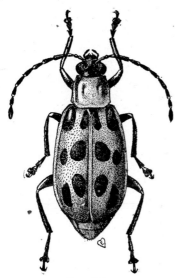 

Fig. 176.                    Fig. 177.

Fig. 176.—Adult spotted cucumber beetle (*Diabrotica duodecimpunctata* Fab.); enlarged about eight times. (*From U. S. Dept. Agr. Farmers' Bul.* 950.)

Fig. 177.—Grub of spotted cucumber beetle and its burrow in corn; much enlarged. (*From U. S. Dept. Agr. Farmers' Bul.* 950.)

plants such as wheat, millet and alfalfa are also attacked by the larvae. The adult beetle is about a quarter of an inch long, yellowish green with black head and legs and twelve black spots on its back. It feeds on squashes, cucumbers and many other plants. The number of generations appears to vary from one in the north to three and a partial fourth in the south, but most of the injury is caused by the first generation. Burning over waste places, where there is rubbish, during the cold months will destroy many of the beetles seeking protection.

*Control.*—It is desirable to avoid following a legume crop with corn. Late planting of corn on ground plowed in the fall or early spring, and then kept thoroughly cultivated and free from grass and weeds for about a month, appears to be the most important control method. The insect is most serious in wet seasons and on low land. Corn is often more thickly planted on low places on this account, to increase the chance of getting a stand. Fertilization and cultivation increase the vigor and resistance of the plants to attack. In the far south corn planted during April is more likely to be injured than that planted before this time or after the tenth of May.

Another species (*Diabrotica vergifera* Lec.) having similar habits and similarly controlled is often destructively abundant in Colorado.

West of the Rocky Mountains the western spotted cucumber beetle (*Diabrotica soror* Lec.) largely replaces the spotted cucumber beetle. It appears to have the same general habits as its eastern relatives, but observations thus far indicate that the grubs are injurious mainly to alfalfa, beet and pea roots; the adults sometimes appear in enormous numbers and feed on the foliage of nearly

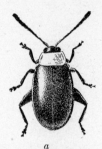

*a*　　　　　*b*　　　*c*

Fig. 178.—Adult flea beetles: *a*, spinach flea beetle; enlarged nearly five times; *b*,potato flea beetle; enlarged about seven times; *c*, eggplant flea beetle; enlarged about seven times. (*From U. S. Dept. Agr. bulletins.*)

all kinds of plants except that of conifers. The winter appears to be spent in the adult stage and the eggs are laid from March to May in different latitudes. There are probably two generations each year. The adult is one-fifth to one-fourth of an inch long. The head, antennae, legs and body are black; the pronotum and elytra green or yellowish, the latter with twelve black spots often partly fused. Control is directed mainly against the beetles, using when possible the same dusts or sprays as for the striped cucumber beetle.

**Flea beetles.**—Many tiny beetles belonging in the Chrysomelidæ are known as flea beetles because when disturbed they hop away like fleas. The economic forms vary in size from about a fifth to a fifteenth of an inch in length (Fig. 178). Most of them are blackish or steel blue, though some have portions of the body yellow, whitish, red or of other colors. The hind femora are very large, enabling the insects to make vigorous leaps. The adults feed on the leaves, eating tiny holes; in most cases the larvae are root feeders, generally on the same plants which their adults attack, though in some cases they also attack the leaves. Many attack garden crops such as the potato, turnip, beet, spinach, rhubarb and radish, and other species feed on the strawberry, grape, tobacco, hop, clover, apple, Virginia creeper, willow, alder, etc. In most cases there are two generations a year, the first appearing early in the season and the second in midsummer or early fall, though some species have but one generation and some have several.

*Control.*—Treatment is directed against the adults because the larvae are usually inaccessible. Dusting with cryolite or barium fluosilicate gives the most favorable results, although the insects are repelled by repeated sprays of Bordeaux mixture or Bordeaux combined with lead or calcium arsenate at 1½ to 2 pounds in 50 gallons of water. Plants in seedbeds may be protected by screening the beds with cheesecloth. The plants may be dipped in the poisoned Bordeaux or in lead arsenate ½ pound in 10 gallons of water before being set out.

The tiny holes made in leaves by the feeding of flea beetles provide excellent opportunities for the entry of disease organisms. The corn flea beetle (*Chætoc-*

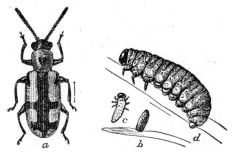

FIG. 179.—Asparagus beetle (*Crioceris asparagi* L.): *a*, adult; *b*, egg; *c*, larva, just hatched; *d*, full-grown larva. Greatly enlarged; hair lines beside *a* and *b* show real length. (*From U. S. Dept. Agr. Farmers' Bul. 837.*)

*nema pulicaria* Melsh.) is known to carry over winter the bacteria that cause bacterial wilt of corn and to transmit them from plant to plant.

**The asparagus beetle** (*Crioceris asparagi* L.).—This insect reached this country from Europe about 1856 and is now present nearly everywhere where asparagus is grown.

The adult beetle (Fig. 179*a*) is a little less than a quarter of an inch long. It is dark blue or bluish black, with a red thorax, and its elytra are dark blue and yellow, the former present as a band along the middle, with two lateral extensions toward the sides into the yellow, while the outer border is reddish. The distribution and amount of the blue and yellow vary considerably according to the locality, the blue often so encroaching on the yellow as to leave only six spots of the latter color.

The insect winters in the beetle stage in any protected place it can find and, as the asparagus plants begin to come up in spring, leaves its winter quarters to feed and lay its eggs (Fig. 179*b*). The beetles at this time feed on the stems and when abundant do considerable harm. The eggs are laid on the stems, singly or in rows, attached by one end, are dark brown in color and hatch in three to seven days according to the temperature. The grubs (Fig. 179*d*), often called slugs, are gray with black heads. They feed from ten days to two weeks, gnawing the stems, and thus aid the adults in making the asparagus unfit for sale. Then they enter the ground and pupate for about a week, after which the adults emerge.    The life cycle therefore is from about four weeks in hot weather to six or seven weeks in spring or fall.    There are at least two generations in the north and probably three or four in the south each year.

The later generations feed on the leafy growth and in the case of young plants may seriously weaken them.    Eggs when abundant on the stems cut for market are objectionable, and a black fluid, poured out by the grubs when disturbed, often stains the stems also.    Fortunately, exces-

sive heat appears to kill many of the grubs, and the alternation of severe cold with much warmer periods in winter has a similar effect on hibernating adults.    Several parasites and other enemies also reduce the numbers of this pest.

*Control.*—During the cutting season injury to the young asparagus shoots by the larvae may be prevented by cutting the crop every three to five days, before most of the eggs have had time to hatch.    In case of heavy infestations the shoots may be protected with derris dusts applied while the dew is on the plants.    After the cutting season is ended, spray with a mixture of lead or calcium arsenate three pounds, dried skimmed milk or a similar spreader three pounds, water fifty gallons, or dust

Fig. 180.—Eggs, larvae and adults of common asparagus beetle on the plant; natural size. (*From U. S. Dept. Agr. Farmers' Bul. 837.*)

with a mixture of one part of the arsenical and eight to ten parts of hydrated lime. Dusts containing rotenone are also effective. The spraying or dusting should be repeated

during the summer as often as necessary to keep the insects under control.    Poultry feed freely on the insects and should therefore be allowed to run through the asparagus beds.

**The spotted asparagus beetle** (*Crioceris duodecimpunctata* L.).—This insect arrived in this country from Europe about 1881 and was first discovered near Baltimore, Md.    Though beginning its work here more than twenty years later than the other species, it is now widely distributed.

The adult beetle (Fig. 181) is slightly larger and broader in proportion to its length than the asparagus beetle.    It is orange-red or brick red above except for twelve black dots on the elytra.    The life history and habits do not seem to differ much from those of the other species except in the following features: The beetle appears to depend upon flight rather than upon dodging around the stems to escape its enemies; the egg is not attached by one end, but by a side, to the plant; the larva feeds inside the berries and is orange to yellowish in color.    The hibernating insects feed on the young plants like the other species but the beetles of later generations feed on the berries. Control is similar to that for the common asparagus beetle except that the larvae are not reached by insecticides.

**The grape rootworm** (*Fidia viticida* Walsh).—The grape rootworm appears to be a native of this country and is found from New York to North Carolina and west to Dakota, Missouri and Texas. There is also a California record for it but it appears to be largely replaced there by the California grape rootworm (*Bromius obscurus* L.). The insect passes the winter as the nearly grown or fullgrown larva a number of inches deep in the ground, but in spring it comes nearer the surface and feeds on the roots of the grape until full grown. Pupation usually occurs two or three inches below the surface and the adult beetles begin to emerge about the time blossoming of the grape ends, most of them appearing during a period of four or five weeks. The beetles (Fig. 182) are brown, covered with whitish hairs, are rather stout, about a quarter of an inch long, and have long legs. They feed on the grape leaves, making irregular holes, often so connected as to form narrow crooked slits. The eggs are laid, several hundred in all, placed in clusters of about thirty or forty, mainly under loose strips of bark. These hatch in about ten days and the tiny grubs drop to the ground and work down to the roots, consuming the smaller ones entirely and burrowing in the larger ones, until winter, when they are full grown or nearly so.

Fig. 181.—Adult spotted asparagus beetle (*Crioceris duodecimpunctata* L.). Nearly six times natural size. (*From U. S. Dept. Agr. Farmers' Bul.* 837.)

When these insects are abundant, the grapevines may be killed in a year or two but the usual result of their presence is so to check the growth of the plants that little or no crop is obtained. The grape-raising territory of western New York, Pennsylvania and Ohio appears to suffer most from the attacks of this pest.

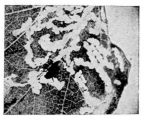

Fig. 182.—Adult grape root-worm (*Fidia viticida* Walsh) about natural size, and its work on a grape leaf. (*Modified from Cornell Expt. Sta. Bul.* 208.)

*Control.*—The adult beetles can be killed by spraying the leaves with lead arsenate or cryolite, using 1½ to 2 pounds in 50 gallons of Bordeaux mixture, just before or as soon as the first signs of feeding appear, and again after ten days. Great care must be taken, however, to do this work thoroughly, as the beetles avoid sprayed foliage. The beetles may also be jarred off the vines, particularly on warm days, on to sticky boards, flypaper or sheets or some other type of catcher placed beneath the plants, whence they can be gathered and destroyed. The pupae are located within a few inches of the top of the ground and are mostly within two or three feet of the vine. In this state of their existence they are easily destroyed by any thorough breaking up of the soil where they are, and this is taken advantage of by throwing up the earth on each side of the vines in the fall to form a ridge. Most of the larvae work up into this to pupate the following spring and, while the insects are in the pupa stage there, this ridge should be hoed away by a horse hoe and by hand, or by the latter alone for small areas. Later cultivation will reach some of those escaping the first treatment, which in the grape belt named is usually about the middle of June.

The Californian species is a little smaller than the one just described, and jet black or brown. Its habits and methods for controlling it are about the same as with the eastern pest.

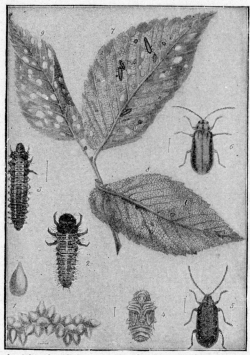

Fig. 183.—Elm leaf beetle (*Galerucella xanthomelæna* Schr.): 1, egg cluster; 1a, single egg greatly enlarged; 2, recently hatched larva (grub); 3, full-grown larva; 4, pupa; 5, beetles after wintering over; 6, freshly emerged beetle; 7, under surface of leaf showing grubs, their work, and a few holes eaten by adult beetles; 8, leaf nearly skeletonized by the larvae; 9, leaf eaten by adults. Figures 1 and 1a enlarged; 2 to 6 about twice natural size; 7, 8 and 9 reduced. (*From Felt; Manual of Tree and Shrub Insects. By permission of The Macmillan Company, publishers.*)

The elm leaf beetle (*Galerucella xanthomelæna* Schr.).—This European insect appears to have reached this country at Baltimore about 1834 and has now spread through most of the New England and Middle Atlantic states and scatteringly westward to the Mississippi River, though not everywhere present within these limits. It is also found on the Pacific coast.

The adult beetle (Fig. 183, 6) is about a quarter of an inch long, dull yellow in color, with black spots on the head and pronotum, a black band near the outside of each elytron, and a short streak at the base of each, nearer the middle. The beetles winter over in protected places and in the spring the dull yellow has changed to an olive green (Fig. 183, 5). They fly to the elm trees when the foliage develops and feed, eating irregular holes in the leaves and from time to time laying yellow eggs on the underside of the leaves, usually about twenty-five in number and nearly always in two rows, side by side (Fig. 183, 1). The eggs hatch after about a week and the tiny yellow and black grubs feed for about three weeks, working on the under surface and leaving the upper epidermis of the leaf unbroken. When full-grown (Fig. 183, 3) and about half an inch long, they crawl down the tree to the trunk and pupate for from one to over three weeks according to the temperature, either in crevices of the bark on the lower part of the trunk or on the ground near the foot of the tree (Fig. 183, 4). In the more northerly states the larvae feed during June. Farther south they begin in May and a second generation feeds during the late summer or early fall. The European elms are most severely injured by this insect but other species often suffer greatly.

*Control.*—Spraying the trees about the time the eggs are laid, *i.e.*, soon after the leaves are fully grown, with lead arsenate is the usual method of control. The strength of the arsenical should be 2½ to 3 pounds in 50 gallons of water; a sticker should be added to obtain good results. It should be kept in mind that as the grubs do not feed on or reach the upper surface of the leaves, the spray should be directed as far as possible to the under surfaces.

Destroying the descending larvae and the pupae on the lower part of the trunk and on the ground with a strong kerosene emulsion spray is an auxiliary treatment; but as these individuals have completed their feeding, this affects only the abundance of the next generation. Power sprayers are a necessity for spraying tall trees in the way here described.

F I G .  1 8 4 .— Tortoise beetle (*Deloyala clavata* Fab.); about two and one-half times natural size.

The tortoise beetles are interesting members of the Chrysomelidæ (Fig. 184) because of their resemblance in form to tortoises. In most cases they have a golden color, which is lost after death. Some species attack the sweet potato but are not usually serious pests. They are small insects, usually not over a quarter of an inch long, nearly as wide, and often with black markings. If they become injuriously abundant, spraying the leaves, on which the larvae feed, with lead arsenate will control them.

*Family* **BRUCHIDÆ** (pea and bean weevils).—In this group of small beetles the head is extended downward into a broad but short snout. The elytra are shorter than the body, leaving the hinder end of the abdomen exposed above. The larvae feed in the seeds of leguminous plants such as peas and beans and frequently cause a great amount of damage. Several kinds are abundant in the United States, the pea weevil and the common bean weevil being perhaps the most important.

**The pea weevil** (*Bruchus pisorum* L.).—This pest of field and garden peas winters as the adult beetle (Fig. 185a) either in peas or in protected places and, after the pea pods begin to form, lays its eggs on them. It is about one-fifth of an inch long, brownish, with black and white spots. The larvae (Fig. 185b) bore their way into the peas, the holes they make either closing up or being too small to be noticed, and feed on the contents of the pea until full-grown. They then pupate (Fig. 185c) and, upon the production of the adult, those in the south leave the peas; in the north they remain in them over winter. Only one weevil usually feeds in a pea and the insect cannot reproduce in dried peas. There is there-

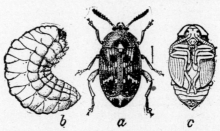

FIG. 185.—Pea weevil (*Bruchus pisorum* L.): *a*, adult beetle; *b*, larva (grub); *c*, pupa; greatly enlarged. (*From U. S. Dept. Agr. Farmers' Bul.* 983.)

fore only one generation a year except where spring and fall crops of peas are grown.

**The bean weevil** (*Acanthoscelides obtectus* Say).—This insect is now found in nearly all parts of the world. The beetle is smaller than the pea weevil and is brownish gray in color, its elytra slightly mottled (Fig. 186). The beetle lays its eggs on or in the pods of the beans growing in the field, either in holes it makes or in cracks caused by splitting of the pods. In the case of shelled beans the eggs are scattered loosely among the beans. The larvae gnaw their way to and into the beans, and unlike the pea weevil a number may enter the same seed and feed upon its substance. Development from

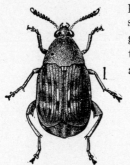

FIG. 186.                                        FIG. 187.

FIG. 186.—Adult bean weevil (*Acanthoscelides obtectus* Say); greatly enlarged; hair line at right shows real length. (*From U. S. Dept. Agr. Farmers' Bul.* 983.)

FIG. 187.—Work of bean weevils; natural size.

the egg to the adult occurs within the bean and the adult finally escapes through a circular hole it has cut in the skin after having spent from three weeks to nearly three months there, according to the temperature where the beans are kept. When infested beans gathered in the field are brought in, their infestation may not be apparent but, after they are kept a while, the adult beetles will escape and lay their eggs for another generation which will develop in the same seeds if these are kept where it is fairly warm (Fig. 187), and thus by spring there may be practically no beans left to plant.  Six generations may be produced in a year in the south and, if the beans are kept where it is warm during the colder months, as many may occur in northern localities, though in the field it is doubtful if there are more than one or two.

Another species, the cowpea weevil (*Callosobruchus maculatus* Fab.), which feeds on the cowpea and other peas and beans, is more abundant in the south, and a fourth, the four-spotted bean or cowpea weevil (*Bruchus quadrimaculatus* Fab.) has a wide distribution, probably wherever cowpeas are grown.  Both of these species breed generation after generation in stored cowpeas, and in warm temperatures there may be a number of generations each year.

The broadbean weevil (*Bruchus rufimanus* Boh.) in its life and habits more nearly resembles the pea weevil than the other species just considered.  It is injurious in Europe and northern Africa and has now established itself in California.  The beetles resemble the pea weevil but seem to prefer broad beans or horse beans.  They appear in the fields in March and lay numbers of eggs on the bean pods; the grubs on hatching make their way to the young beans, several often entering one bean.  Feeding is completed by early August and the adults are produced later in the fall.  They generally winter in the beans but do not breed in dried beans, there being therefore only one generation a year.

*Injuries.*—The damage caused by the attacks of pea and bean weevils is of two kinds: injury by consuming the bulk of the seed and leaving the remainder unfit for food; and injury by so reducing the stored material or the germ itself that the seed cannot germinate and grow.

*Control of pea and bean weevils.*—When these insects lay their eggs on the growing plants, as is the case exclusively for the pea weevil, control is difficult.  To dispose of pea straw will destroy many of the insects that winter over out of doors.  Derris dusts (0.75 per cent rotenone), applied soon after blooming and then at frequent intervals while necessary, will kill the adults when they attempt to lay their eggs.

Infestation in stored peas and beans may be stopped by fumigation or heating.  Treatment in tight bins, metal drums, or other gastight containers with ethylene dichloride mixture, two to three quarts per hundred bushels is effective.  If proper precautions are taken to prevent explosion, carbon disulfide, one quart per one hundred bushels, may be used, continuing for one or (better) two days.  The fumigant can be poured directly on the seeds just before covering them tightly.  Heat will kill the weevils but it is necessary to heat throughout and yet not injure the seeds; so, with this treatment, spread out the seeds well, raise their temperature to 130°F. and hold it there for an hour.  After the seeds have been either fumigated or heated pack them in closely woven bags and keep in a clean tight room, as cool as possible.  No development of the weevils will occur at temperatures of 45° and lower. Uninfested seeds may also be protected by packing either in hydrated or air-slaked lime at the rate of one part by weight of lime to two or three parts of seed. Even where the peas or beans are intended for food this method can be used if the seed is thoroughly washed before cooking.

The shorter seasons and cold winters of the north give the pea and bean weevils less opportunity to increase through a number of generations than in the south, and many of the adults are killed by the cold. Northern climates for these reasons are therefore better for the extensive production of seeds of these plants.

*Family* **CERAMBYCIDÆ** (roundheaded borers or longicorn beetles). The insects of this family are for the most part of fair size, a number being several inches in length. Their antennae are usually long—sometimes longer than the body—and the beetles are frequently bright-colored and strikingly marked (Fig. 188).

The larvae are chiefly wood borers, living in burrows in the trunks or roots of trees or the pith of plant stems and are termed roundheaded borers because the thoracic segments are circular in outline and the tunnels they produce are therefore also of this shape. The larvae themselves are soft, whitish or yellowish grubs,

Fig. 188.—Cerambycid (*Monochamus*); natural size, showing long antennae.

with strong jaws, and most of them have no legs. The eggs are usually laid on the bark of the tree and the larvae live on the wood they tunnel out, for a varying period, usually two or three years, and pupate in the tunnels just beneath the bark, through which the emerging beetle finally gnaws its way and escapes. Some species cut the stem in which they live nearly through and, when it breaks off, fall with it to the ground, thus pruning the tree. Those which tunnel in the heartwood of timber trees often greatly reduce the value of the timber by their holes. Some species attack sound wood and apparently vigorous trees, while others seem to prefer trees already unhealthy, for their food. The family is a large one and contains many forms injurious to shade and forest trees.

**The roundheaded apple tree borer** (*Saperda candida* Fab.).—This serious enemy of the apple tree is found practically everywhere in the eastern United States except in the extreme south, and westward into Minnesota, Iowa, New Mexico and Texas. It also attacks the service tree, pear, quince, thorns, mountain ash and a few other Rosaceæ. The adult beetle (Fig. 189) is a little less than an inch long, pale brown above, with a pair of white stripes extending backward from the head across the pronotum and along the elytra to their tips at the hinder end of the body. Beneath, it is silvery white. It appears during the late spring and summer months and lays its eggs singly here and there in small slits it cuts in the bark near the base of the tree, laying about fifteen to thirty in all. On hatching, two to three weeks later, the larva burrows through the bark to the sapwood and there makes broad, rather shallow galleries just under the bark and in general working downward. The bark over these galleries frequently dries and cracks, or the borer makes holes in it,

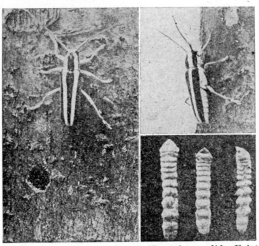

Fig. 189.—Roundheaded apple tree borer (*Saperda candida* Fab.); back and side views of adult beetle on bark and exit hole; full-grown larvae (borers). (*After Rumsey and Brooks.*)

letting out the borings and castings, often called sawdust which shows the location of the burrows. After hibernating during the winter the borer (Fig. 189) resumes its work the following spring, still feeding on the sapwood; if the tree is small or if several borers are present, girdling may result. After a second winter in hibernation the borer turns its attention to the heartwood, boring into this, and finally, as it approaches full growth, working its way out toward the surface, being now about three-quarters of an inch long. After a third winter of rest the larva pupates in its tunnel in the spring, having previously carried the tunnel out to the bark, and the adult beetle emerges after about three weeks. One generation accordingly requires three years in which to complete its life history but this comes in parts of four calendar years. In the southern part of its range this is shortened to two years and in intermediate regions some may require two and some three years.

Small trees suffer most severely by the attacks of this pest, a single borer often entirely girdling a tree; large ones are weakened and become unhealthy and if strongly infested may also be killed.

*Control.*—Various methods of control have some value. "Worming" the trees, *i.e.*, cutting out the young borers, early in the fall is a good practice if it is thoroughly done and if the cutting is carried on carefully. Litter should be carefully scraped away from the trunk to expose any sawdust present, and from this the burrows can be located and the dead

a            b            c            d

Fig. 190.—Examples of ladybeetles: *a*, twice-stabbed ladybeetle (*Chilocorus stigma* Say); *b*, two-spotted ladybeetle (*Adalia bipunctata* L.); *c*, nine-spotted ladybeetle (*Coccinella novemnotata* Hbst.); *d*, spotted ladybeetle (*Ceratomegilla fuscilabris* Muls.); all about twice natural size. (*From Conn. Agr. Expt. Sta. Bul.* 181.)

bark cut out and the borer killed, either in place under the bark or by running a flexible wire into its burrow if it has gone deeper into the tree. In cases where the borer cannot be reached by the wire, a little carbon disulfide on cotton placed in the burrow, the opening then being closed

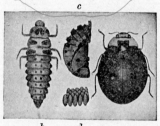

b    d    a

Fig. 191.—Different stages of the nine-spotted ladybeetle: *a*, adult; *b*, larva; *c*, pupa; *d*, eggs; all much enlarged. (*Modified from Palmer, Ann. Ent. Soc. Am., vii*, 1914.)

with mud, will serve the same purpose. Worming should be done in early fall; the work should be thorough, and host trees of every kind within several hundred feet of the orchard should be worked at the same time, for the beetles do not usually fly far and, if the immediate neighborhood is cleared of them, reinfestation from a distance does not occur very frequently.

As the beetle feeds somewhat on twigs and leaves, the usual sprayings with a stomach poison for other apple pests are liable to kill some of the beetles also. Woodpeckers feed freely on the borers.

*Family* **COCCINELLIDÆ** (ladybeetles, ladybugs, or ladybirds).—The ladybeetles are nearly all carnivorous, feeding as both larvae and adults on scale insects, plant lice and other important pests. They are generally small beetles, nearly circular or oval in outline, strongly convex, often resembling in size and form a split pea. Their colors are usually black and red or reddish yellow, sometimes the spots or markings being black on a red ground, sometimes the reverse. In a number of species the beetle is entirely black (Figs. 190 and 191).

The larvae (Fig. 191*b*) are active and crawl around over leaves, twigs, etc., searching for their food. They are dark colored but frequently have a few spots of yellow or blue on the side of the body, and their general appearance has suggested to some persons a resemblance to alligators.

The family is quite a large one, and its species are abundant and well distributed over this country. Among the more useful or noticeable of the family is the two-spotted ladybeetle (*Adalia bipunctata* L.), one of the smaller species averaging about a sixth of an inch in length (Fig. 190*b*). The head is black, sometimes with two yellow spots; the pronotum black with yellow side margins, and the elytra are red with a black dot in the center of each. This insect frequently winters in houses and may be found on the windows in spring trying to escape. It is often mistaken for some injurious household pest on this account. This species feeds mainly on plant lice, but to some extent also on the pear psylla. Another species of about the same size is known as the twice-stabbed ladybeetle (*Chilocorus stigma* Say) (Fig. 190*a*). Here the head and pronotum are black, as are also the elytra, except for a red spot in the center of each, thus just reversing the elytral color pattern of the previously described species. It feeds on scale insects and also on aphids and the Colorado potato beetle.

Other common species are the nine-spotted ladybeetle (*Coccinella* 9-*notata* Hbst.) with nine black spots on its red elytra; the fifteen-spotted ladybeetle (*Anatis* 15-*punctata* Oliv.), the largest species in the northeastern states, which has fifteen black spots on its red elytra; the pitiful ladybeetle (*Pentilia misella* Lec.), a very tiny black species which feeds on scale insects and aphids; and the spotted ladybeetle (*Ceratomegilla fuscilabris* Muls.) about a fifth of an inch long, usually bright pink with black spots and with its body rather oval in outline, somewhat pointed behind. This species feeds on many kinds of plant lice and other small insects and tends to hibernate in clusters, often several hundred together, under leaves at the bases of tree trunks.

The convergent ladybeetle (*Hippodamia convergens* Guer.) is about a quarter of an inch long, with two converging yellow marks on the pronotum and six black spots on each elytron. This widely distributed species has been found feeding on a number of kinds of plant lice and, in addition, on asparagus beetle larvae, eggs of the Colorado potato beetle and of the grape rootworm, red spiders, the bean thrips, alfalfa weevil and chinch bug. On the Pacific coast they gather in enormous numbers in the high mountains to hibernate; while thus collected in quantities they are gathered and in the spring distributed through the truck-growing regions to attack the plant lice, about 30,000 being regarded as enough to protect the plants growing on ten acres. Several tons are often collected for distribution for this purpose. It takes nearly 1,500 of these beetles to weigh an ounce.

Because of their efficiency as feeders on insect pests, a number of kinds have been introduced into this country to attack the special insects of their native lands which have reached the United States and have become pests here. Among these are the vedalia (*Rodolia cardinalis* Muls.) (see Fig. 145c), imported from Australia to attack the cottony-cushion or fluted scale; the mealybug destroyer (*Cryptolæmus montrouzieri* Muls.), brought also from Australia to attack several kinds of mealybugs found in California; the steel-blue ladybeetle (*Orcus chalybeus* Bdv.) which feeds on a number of kinds of armored scales; the black ladybeetle (*Rhizobius ventralis* Er.) which is an active enemy of the black scale (*Saissetia oleæ* Bern.); besides numerous other species. Many of these imported forms have done valiant work in their attacks upon their ancient foes in the country to which both have come, but in some cases this attempt to aid nature in the control of insect pests has been less successful, and it is evident that the success of each experiment of this kind can rarely be determined beforehand (see cottony-cushion scale, Chap. XXIV).

Fig. 192.—Mexican bean beetle (*Epilachna varivestis* Muls.). Three adult beetles and a larva on the underside of a bean leaf showing the injury they cause; somewhat enlarged. (*Modified from U. S. Dept. Agr. Farmers' Bul.* 1624.)

The Mexican bean beetle (*Epilachna varivestis* Muls.) is an exception to most of the members of this family, being a serious pest. It has been known for many years as present in Mexico, western Texas, New Mexico, Arizona, Utah, Wyoming, Colorado and western Nebraska and has been quite injurious to beans. Apparently its activities in the semiarid and arid regions were restricted, but about 1918 it reached Alabama, probably in shipments of alfalfa hay from Colorado and New Mexico. Here, under new conditions, it increased rapidly and has now been found in every state east of the Mississippi River (except Wisconsin?) and in Ontario (Fig. 192).

The beetles winter as adults in any protected places. In spring they feed on the growing bean plants, eating the under surface of the leaves and frequently through them, making holes. After about ten days they begin laying their orange-yellow eggs in clusters of about fifty on the underside of the leaves. The eggs hatch in ten to fourteen days in the early spring, but later in about six days. The early hatched grubs may take five weeks to become fully grown, but later ones need only about twenty days and pupation averages about a week, making the time from egg to beetle slightly over a month in summer. These beetles begin egg-laying within two weeks after their emergence and in the south three, or even four, generations are produced during a year, though in the north only one or one and a partial second are produced. The number of eggs laid averages nearly 500 per female.

The beetles begin to leave the fields for their winter quarters late in the summer and by the time of the first frosts they are practically all gone.

Common edible beans are the preferred food, but the insect will often feed on beggarweed (beggar-tick) and can live on cowpeas and soybeans. A number of predaceous and parasitic enemies are known but are not very effective.

*Control.*—Several dusts and sprays are recommended for application to bean plants every ten days as soon as the beetles or their eggs are found on them. The dusts are (1) cryolite one part, dusting gypsum or other inert carrier three parts; (2) magnesium arsenate one part, hydrated lime four parts; (3) powdered derris or cube containing 4 per cent rotenone one part, talc seven parts. Calcium arsenate may be applied as a spray at 1½ pounds in 50 gallons of Bordeaux mixture, being careful to direct the spray at both sides of the leaves. For pod or green beans only the derris or cube dust can be used after the pods begin to form, as the other insecticides are poisonous to man.

After the crop has been gathered, plow the plants as far under as possible, or burn them.

*Family* **TENEBRIONIDÆ** (darkling beetles).—This rather large family of beetles contains many forms found on the ground and superficially resembling the Carabidæ. They are usually rather slow of movement, however, feed on vegetable instead of animal food, and, whereas their fore and middle tarsi are each composed of five segments as in the carabids, their hind tarsi each have only four. They are particularly abundant in the southwest and west, though a number are present practically everywhere.

Fig. 193.—Yellow mealworm (*Tenebrio molitor* L.); somewhat enlarged. (*From Minn. Agr. Expt. Sta.*)

The yellow mealworm (*Tenebrio molitor* L.), about three-quarters of an inch long (Fig. 193), is often found around stores of grain, in pantries, stables, etc., and its larva, which closely resembles a wireworm, feeds upon meal and similar materials. It is often raised as food for cage birds. Where abundant, a thorough cleaning out of infested places, followed by sprinkling air-slaked lime around, or fumigation of the infested material with a liquid fumigant is all that is necessary.

*Family* **MELOIDÆ** (blister beetles).—The insects of this family also have but four segments to each hind tarsus. The body is quite cylindrical and rather soft, and the head joins the thorax by a distinct neck (Fig. 194). Many of the members of this family contain a substance called cantharidin, which when applied to the skin produces blisters. The bodies of these species, powdered, formerly were used extensively in medicine under the name of cantharides or spanish flies, for blistering purposes.

A dozen or twenty kinds of blister beetles, averaging from half an inch to over an inch in length are more or less serious pests as adults, feeding during the summer or fall on foliage and blossoms, various vegetables and ornamental plants being attacked. Vegetable crops are sometimes seriously affected. The larvae, on the other hand, feed on the eggs of various species of grasshoppers and are therefore beneficial. The adults are not easily controlled as they are either resistant to, or repelled by, arsenicals. Dusting either with cryolite or barium fluosilicate one part, talc or dusting gypsum three parts, gives satisfactory control

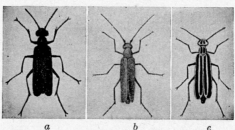

a           b           c

Fig. 194.—Adult blister beetles: *a*, black blister beetle (*Epicauta pennsylvanica* De G.); *b*, ash-gray blister beetle (*Macrobasis fabricii* Lec.); *c*, striped blister beetle (*Epicauta vittata* Fab.); all about natural size. (*Modified from U. S. Dept. Agr. bulletins.*)

where application of these poisons is safe and practicable. On a small scale, hand-picking and screening valuable plants with netting may be resorted to.

RHYNCHOPHORA (snout beetles)

The snout beetles are included in several families. Some are called curculios, weevils and billbugs, and those of one family, the larvae of which work in the bark and wood of trees, are called engraver beetles and also bark borers. Over 25,000 species of Rhynchophora are known (Fig. 195).

Except for the engraver beetles most snout beetles feed on fruits, nuts, etc., though a few attack stems and leaves. The white, nearly always footless larvae also feed for the most part on such materials, and a number are very destructive and therefore important pests.

Fig. 195.—Examples of adult snout beetles showing differences in the development of the snout; about twice natural size.

**The plum curculio** (*Conotrachelus nenuphar* Hbst.).—This insect is a native of the United States and formerly fed upon the wild plum and thorn fruits but now also attacks cultivated plums, prunes, cherries, nectarines, apricots, apples and peaches. It is found practically everywhere east of the Rocky Mountains, though in the western portion of this area it seems to be of less importance than elsewhere. The adult beetle (Fig. 196) is small, being only about a fifth of an inch long, dark colored as a whole but mottled with gray and brown. Its elytra are rough and on each is a black, shining hump a little behind the middle. This pest spends the winter or the colder months in the south, hiding

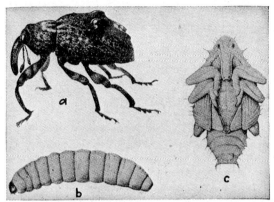

Fig. 196.—Plum curculio (*Conotrachelus nenuphar* Hbst.): *a*, side view of adult, enlarged about six times; *b*, larva, much enlarged; *c*, pupa, much enlarged. (*From Metcalf and Flint, Destructive and Useful Insects.*)

in any protected place it can find, particularly in the woods, in stone walls or under leaves. It appears about the time the plum buds open in spring and feeds more or less on the developing leaves. When the fruit begins to develop, the beetles turn their attention to it, feeding by cutting a circular hole through the skin and consuming the flesh beneath to a depth about equal to the length of the snout of the insect. They also begin now to lay their eggs in the young plums, cutting a hole in the skin and then running the snout obliquely into the flesh beneath. In this cavity is placed the egg which is then pushed farther in by the snout. The beetle next cuts a crescent-shaped slit through the skin close to the egg (Fig. 197) and carries this down through the flesh beneath the egg which thus comes to lie in a sort of flap which wilts and remains soft, and the crushing of the

Fig. 197.—Egg puncture and feeding puncture of the plum curculio in young plums. (*From U. S. Dept. Agr. Farmers' Bul.* 908.)

egg by the growth of firm tissue there is prevented. Several hundred eggs are laid in this way and the "spot and crescent" marks of the insect on small plums are familiar to plum growers. The fruit often pours out gum at these places, probably in an attempt to repair the injury.

The eggs hatch in a week or less and the tiny whitish grub bores through the flesh and in stone fruits passes to the stone, around which it feeds for about two weeks or until full grown.  It then leaves the fruit, and, as this in most cases has fallen before this time because of the injury, the larva finds itself on escaping on the ground.  Into this it now burrows an inch or two and pupates.  Three to four weeks later the adult beetle emerges, comes to the surface of the ground and attacks fruit for food.  Egg laying rarely if ever takes place at this season.  When cold weather comes on, it locates in some protected place for the winter.  There is but one generation a year in the north.  In the

Fig. 198.—Apple showing injury by plum curculio in fall.　(*Modified from Ill. Agr. Expt. Sta. Bul.* 98.)

south, however, some of the beetles appearing in the summer will lay eggs, thus producing a partial second generation.

This insect, by both its feeding and egg-laying punctures, affects the value of the fruit not entirely destroyed, not only in appearance but by the opportunity these cuts afford for the entrance of the spores of disease-producing fungi, and the destruction in the United States which it causes has been estimated at over 8 million dollars annually.  When the insect attacks small apples, its punctures cause dropping of the fruit or its malformation and the production of hard, woody places in the pulp.  In the fall its feeding holes in apples also cause much injury (Fig. 198).

*Control on plums and cherries.*—Spray with lead arsenate, standard formula, just before the blossoms open; again as soon as their covering ("shuck") has fallen, and again about two weeks later.  When the insects are very abundant a fourth application about three weeks after the last may be necessary. A sulfur fungicide is generally added to control brown rot of the plum.

*Control on apples.*—Spray as for the codling moth (page 238) with lead arsenate, standard formula, as soon as most of the petals have fallen, or at least within a week thereafter. Repeat this a week later and again after two weeks more. Dusting with fifteen pounds of the arsenate in a hundred pounds of some inert dust, instead of spraying, is often done, particularly where there is little time available. Cryolite is sometimes used instead of the arsenical.

*Control on peaches.*—In general, spray as the shucks (calyxes) are being shed (about ten days after the petals have fallen) with lead arsenate two pounds, hydrated lime eight pounds. Two weeks after this treatment, spray with lead arsenate two pounds, wettable sulfur as advised on the label by the manufacturer. A month before the variety is due to be ripe, spray with wettable sulfur, strength advised on the manufacturer's label, and if the insect is still particularly abundant add lead arsenate as before. Dusting with lead arsenate, five to ten pounds, mixed with gypsum to make a hundred pounds at the time the sprays would come has given good results and has been used from an airplane successfully.

*General control.*—(1) Clean up all areas near the orchard that could provide places where the beetle might winter. (2) Disk under the trees to break up and kill the pupae in the ground, this to be done weekly from the middle of May to the end of June in the southern states and later, farther north. (3) Jarring the trees, in early morning while the beetles are present, onto sheets spread under the trees will cause many to drop where they can be gathered and destroyed. (4) Gather and destroy the drops under the trees while the larvae are in them. This is one of our worst pests of fruit.

**The boll weevil** (*Anthonomus grandis* Boh.).—This is one of the most serious insect pests of cotton. Recent estimates place the destruction of cotton by this insect at about 4 million bales a year, a loss of about 200 million dollars, besides all the indirect loss to all lines of business connected with the crop.

The boll weevil is a native of tropical America, whence it spread northward and entered Texas about 1892. Since then it has continued its spread and is now present practically everywhere in the cotton belt.

The adult boll weevil (Fig. 199) varies considerably in size but averages about a quarter of an inch in length. When it first emerges from the pupa it is light brown, but it soon becomes gray or almost black. It winters as the adult, hiding under rubbish, in cracks in the ground, in Spanish moss growing on the trees or in fact in any protected place, though those which winter in the cotton fields appear to be least protected and hence least liable to survive, while those in wooded areas winter more successfully.

In spring—March till into June—the weevils leave their winter quarters and eat holes in the blossom buds ("squares."), feeding there. The females lay their eggs, one in a hole, but generally do not lay an egg

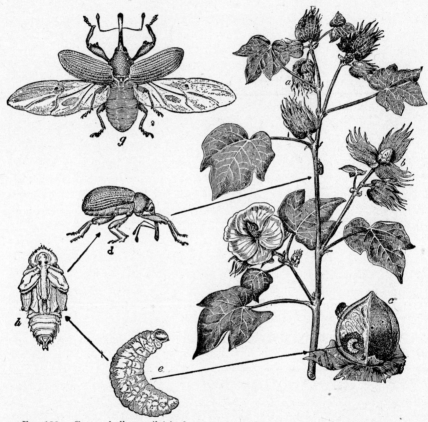

FIG. 199.—Cotton boll weevil (*Anthonomus grandis* Boh.). On the right a cotton plant attacked, showing at *a* a hanging, dry, infested square; at *b* a flared square showing beetle punctures; at *c* a boll sectioned to show a weevil attacking and a larva in the boll; *e*, a larva; *h*, a pupa; *d* and *g*, adult beetles; *c*, *d*, *e*, *g* and *h* greatly enlarged. (*From Metcalf and Flint, Destructive and Useful Insects; rearranged from U. S. Dept. Agr.*)

in a square where one is already present. Later they attack the developing seed cases ("bolls") in the same way. The eggs generally hatch in about three days and the larva, white, legless and with a brown head, eats out the inside of the square or boll, so the seeds, if they develop at all, will have only little cottony fibers, this taking a week to twelve days. It then changes to a pupa where it fed and remains in this stage three to five days before the adult beetle emerges. Climatic conditions affect it, but the average length of time from egg to adult is two to three weeks. Thus there is time in a season for from two or three to eight or ten generations. Late in the fall when unattacked bolls have become scarce, the beetles will lay eggs in those already infested, but the squares are preferred to deposit in. Infested squares open widely ("flare") and drop off or hang down, wilted.

During August and September the weevils fly freely and this is the time when the spread of the insect has chiefly occurred. After frosts come they go into winter quarters.

*Control.*—(1) In the fall, badly infested plants should have what cotton they bear gathered if worth the cost and the plants plowed up and buried deeply or burned, thus destroying the abundant late weevils in them, which would otherwise winter over. (2) Fall plowing as soon as the crop has been picked will remove many hibernating places for the beetles. (3) Rotate crops where this is practicable. (4) Hasten crop production by planting early-maturing varieties as early as possible and fertilizing well. (5) Dust with calcium arsenate dust of at least 40 per cent arsenic pentoxide, not over 0.75 per cent of which is water soluble, and bulking 80 to 100 cubic inches to a pound. Dust this at night or on calm, damp days by ground machines, three or four times, 4 or 5 days apart, using about 6 pounds per acre. Begin this when 1 or 2 out of every 10 squares are punctured. Dusting by airplane in the daytime is now carried on extensively, covering 400 to 500 acres per hour, and the dust stays on the plants better than when ground machines are used. (6) Sometimes when the early infestation is very heavy, calcium arsenate dust can be placed on the tips of the plants. (7) "Florida method." Remove all buds or squares the first week in June. This does not seem to reduce the crop, more buds forming. Then dust with calcium arsenate as above, or apply a poisoned sirup made by mixing 2 pounds of calcium arsenate in ½ gallon of water and adding 1 gallon of sirup. This is mopped into the buds of the plants. In wet seasons this is better than dusting.

**The white-pine weevil** (*Pissodes strobi* Peck).—This native enemy of the pine occurs practically wherever the white pine is found, *viz.*, from New Brunswick and Canada west to Minnesota, and south to North Carolina. It also attacks our other native pines and the spruces somewhat.

The adults (Fig. 200) pass the winter in protected places, possibly in the ground, and in spring gather on the terminal shoots (leaders) of the pines, generally on the trunk leader in preference to those of the branches. Here, near the tip, they feed on the bark and soon cut tiny holes in it, placing their eggs in the holes. The borers which hatch from these eggs tunnel downward through the leader (Fig. 201) and by August have finished feeding and pupate in the tunnels. After transformation to the beetle has been completed, these escape to the outside by making round holes through the stems they are in.   Later they hibernate for the winter.

The adult beetle is about a quarter of an inch long, reddish brown or somewhat darker, with a white spot on each elytron not far from its outer end, which when the elytra are closed brings these spots not far from the end of the body.   There are also several irregular areas on the elytra somewhat lighter than the ground color.

*Control.*—Spraying the leaders before the beetles gather on them in the spring, with lead arsenate 2 pounds, water 50 gallons is practicable on a small scale.   Collecting the beetles after they have begun to gather on the leaders is also practiced, jarring them off into a net held beneath, as they generally drop instead of flying when disturbed then.   This treatment should be repeated

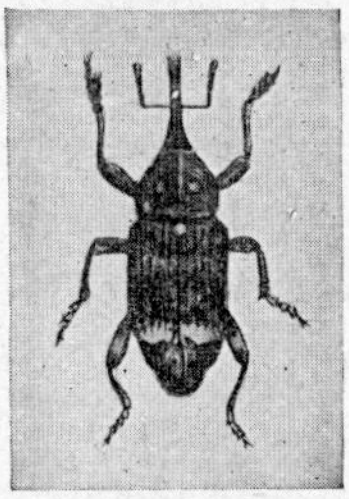

Fig. 200.                                    Fig. 201.

Fig. 200.—Adult white-pine weevil (*Pissodes strobi* Peck); enlarged nearly three times. (*After Felt, N. Y. State Mus. Mem.* 8.)

Fig. 201.—Work of white-pine weevil in terminal twigs of pine.   (*After Felt, N. Y. State Mus. Mem.* 8.)

several times at four- or five-day intervals.   It can hardly be done except on small trees.   White pine may best be protected from the weevil by growing it in mixed stands.

The injury caused by these insects, aside from their feeding, is the killing of the leader, which stunts the growth of the tree.   Usually a side branch grows up to replace the lost leader, which makes the tree deformed, or when two do this, a fork is produced.   In either case the value of the tree either for timber or as an ornament is largely lost.   The work of the weevil is most serious and also most frequent on young trees, making its injuries more important on this account.

**The alfalfa weevil** (*Hypera postica* Gyll.).—This European beetle was found in Utah in 1904 and has now spread into parts of Montana, Idaho, Wyoming, western Nebraska, Colorado, Nevada, California and Oregon.   The adult (Fig. 202) is a snout beetle only about three-sixteenths of an inch long, brown when fresh but almost black after a time.   It winters as the adult close to the ground or in crevices there, and in some cases under rubbish, and in severe winters many are killed by the cold.   In the spring the weevils become active and fly, often many miles, in search of food.   They puncture the stems of the alfalfa plants and sometimes lay as many as forty eggs in a puncture and an average of perhaps 700 eggs in all. The eggs hatch in about ten days and the larvae (Fig 203) feed at first on the leaf buds, stopping the growth of the plant, and later on the leaves and, when many are present, stripping the plants. After feeding about two months they drop to the ground and spin a loose, silken network cocoon (Fig. 204) in which they remain about ten days before emerging as adults. Late in summer these adults make a flight, looking for places in which to winter, and may go quite long distances. There is only one generation a year. It is the most serious pest of alfalfa we now have, and as it also feeds on other legumes to some extent it would seem to have dangerous possibilities.

  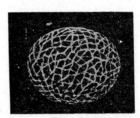

Fig. 202.  Fig. 203.  Fig. 204.

Fig. 202.—Adult alfalfa weevil (*Hypera postica* Gyll.); much enlarged. (*From U. S. Dept. Agr. Bur. Ent. Bul.* 112.)

Fig. 203.—Side view of larva of alfalfa weevil; greatly enlarged. (*From U. S. Dept. Agr. Bur. Ent. Bul.* 112.)

Fig. 204.—Cocoon of the alfalfa weevil; greatly enlarged. (*From U. S. Dept. Agr. Bur. Ent. Bul.* 112.)

*Control.*—(1) Any treatment, such as disk harrowing, to hasten the growth of the first crop, is desirable, this being the one that suffers most. (2) Harvest this crop as early as possible. (3) Spray with lead arsenate one pound in fifty gallons of water, about two weeks before the first crop is ready for cutting. (4) Rotation of crops every four or five years. Certain introduced and native enemies of this insect and a fungus disease are helpful in control.

**The clover leaf weevil** (*Hypera punctata* F.).—This pest of clover is a native of Europe and was first found in the United States about 1881. It is now present in most of the regions where clover and alfalfa are grown.

The adults are about a quarter of an inch long, stout, brownish to black insects. They appear in May to July and feed on clover, mainly at night, till September, when egg laying begins and continues until into November. The earlier laid eggs hatch the same fall and the young feed during the day, chiefly on the leaves, until cold weather, then hibernate, resuming their feeding in the spring. Late-laid eggs winter in this stage and hatch in the spring. Pupation in cocoons formed as a fine network of silken threads occurs in May and June and the first beetles emerge before the end of the former month. There is but one generation a year.

Injury to clover would be severe were it not for the fact that this insect is attacked by a fungus disease which usually nearly wipes out the insects in a single season and only rarely does it escape long enough to do any great amount of injury. Control measures, then, are not often necessary.

**The strawberry root weevil** (*Brachyrhinus ovatus* L.).—This insect, often also called the strawberry crown girdler, occurs in both Europe and this country where it is widely distributed. The adult beetle is about a quarter of an inch long, almost black, stout, the elytra with parallel longitudinal grooves in which are indentations. The elytra are grown together so the insect cannot fly.

The beetles live about a year and pass the winter both as adults and larvae. The overwintered adults appear early in spring and lay eggs. The overwintered larvae resume their feeding in spring, eating the strawberry roots and doing their greatest injury at this time. When full grown they pupate and the adults from these pupae appear by midsummer. These lay their eggs and the larvae feed until fall, then hibernate during the winter. It is probable that the eggs laid early by wintered-over adults reach the adult stage themselves before winter, thus becoming those which winter over as adults and which probably lay some eggs that fall before hibernating. In the north there seems to be only one generation a year, but in the south it is possible that there are two.

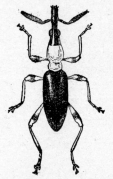

The injury to strawberry plants by these insects is very great; they also attack the roots of small evergreen seedlings in nurseries and when abundant will destroy great numbers of them. The larvae feed on the roots of the strawberry, seedling conifers, red clover and various other plants, and there are usually many larvae around each plant. In addition, strawberry plants may be girdled just above the surface of the ground. A curious fact about this insect is that thus far no males have been found.

FIG. 205.—Adult sweetpotato weevil (*Cylas formicarius elegantulus* Summers); enlarged over five times. (*From U. S. Dept. Agr. Farmers' Bul.* 856.)

*Control.*—(1) Rotation of crops, removing the berry plants after the second crop. (2) Poisoned bait for the adults. One such bait consists of five pounds of raisins or dried apples soaked in five quarts of water for about ten hours. Then mix five pounds of sodium fluosilicate and fifty pounds of shorts and add to the raisins from which the surplus water should have been drained off. Now run this through a butcher's mincer, set coarse, producing a moist, crumbly mash. Drop about a tablespoonful of this in the center of each strawberry plant as soon as the beetles appear, and give another treatment when the beetles coming from the overwintered larvae show themselves later. Apply in dry, warm weather, if possible. This treatment is the most important one and, in nurseries, can also be used quite effectively. (3) Trapping the adults under boards has given fair results. Do not set conifer seedlings where they were the preceding year.

**The sweetpotato weevil** (*Cylas formicarius elegantulus* Summers).—A tropical insect first reported in the United States about 1875 and now present in Florida, Georgia, Alabama, Mississippi, Louisiana and Texas, attacking the sweet potato. The adult (Fig. 205), unlike the other snout beetles here considered, is very slender, about a quarter of an inch long, with a black head, reddish prothorax and legs and dark blue elytra. The prothorax is strongly narrowed, forming a noticeable "waist" for the insect.

The eggs of this pest are laid singly in small holes eaten in the stem or any exposed potato. They hatch in a few days and the grubs in the stems burrow through them down to the potato, then tunnel irregularly about, becoming full-grown in two or three weeks. The grub now forms a cavity and in this it pupates for about a week and then a few days later eats its way out and may leave the potato or may remain there and lay eggs for another generation in the same potato in which it itself developed; this process may continue until the entire potato is destroyed. As long as food is available, one generation after another is thus produced, but when no more can be found the adult insects live along for a considerable time without feeding, attacking the plants and laying their eggs in them whenever more appear. Adult beetles feed on the leaves and stem somewhat.

As soon as tunnels in the potato are formed, the tissues around them change color and decay soon follows, so that an attack quickly ruins the value of the crop.

*Control.*—Sweet potatoes found infested ever so slightly should immediately be destroyed, either by feeding to stock or in some other way. If any area becomes infested, no sweet potatoes should be planted there for several years; as the insect can also breed in the wild morning-glory, all plants of this species should also be destroyed as far as possible within the area. Spraying the plants with lead arsenate or other stomach poison, applied as soon as the beetles appear, has recently given encouraging results. Following sprays at about ten-day intervals may be given if necessary.

*Family* **IPIDÆ** (formerly Scolytidæ) (bark beetles or engraver beetles).—The members of this family are borers and nearly all attack the inner bark or wood of trees. They are small insects, from one twenty-fifth to two-fifths of an inch long, brownish or blackish in color, and usually with cylindrical bodies (Fig. 206). In habits they form two chief groups. In the so-called ambrosia beetles the tunnels extend through the wood and the young develop there; in the true bark beetles the tunnels are formed either in the inner bark or between this and the wood. The adult in either case cuts a tunnel slightly larger

Fig. 206.—Adult bark beetles; greatly enlarged. (*Modified from Felt, N. Y. State Mus. Mem. 8.*)

than itself in to the inner bark or through this, but the ambrosia beetles continue it on into the wood. The bark beetles, having arrived at the desired depth, turn and excavate one or more channels between the bark and the wood, which become the egg tunnels. Along the sides of these the eggs are deposited, singly in little hollows, several together in larger excavations, or many in grooves of the tunnel. The larvae, on hatching, excavate tunnels for themselves, leading away from the egg tunnel (Fig. 207) and becoming larger with the growth of the larvae. Pupation is at the end of the larval tunnel in a somewhat wider portion and after transformation the adult bores its way to the outside. In the case of the ambrosia beetles a fungus used as food by the insects grows on the walls of the tunnels and generally turns these walls black.

Destruction by these insects is mainly of forest and shade trees. As nearly all the bark beetles appear to prefer dying bark in which to live, the refuse of cutting operations, commonly termed slash, will provide much of this, and most of the insects will work there. When slash comes to an end, however, by the ending of operations in that area, the increased number of insects due to abundant slash often forces

them, for lack of other material, to turn to the healthy trees, themselves changing thereby from "secondary" to "primary" foes. Slash should therefore be destroyed before beetles in it can develop to the adult condition. Fire in forests produces many dead and weakened trees also, frequently leading to insect attacks, and epidemics, either local or quite widespread, may thus result. Many trees, when the beetles bore into them, pour out their sap or resin, and some of the insects may easily be drowned in this. If attacked by multitudes, however, the supply of sap becomes so reduced that the insects coming later can accomplish their purpose.

Removing "beetle trees" before the adults escape and removing and burning the bark; floating the logs; or sawing the same winter and burning the slabs and trimmings are some of the measures used for the protection of our forests against these insects.

Fig. 207.—Work of bark beetles on inside of bark; slightly reduced.

One species of ipid, the smaller European elm bark beetle (*Scolytus multistriatus* Marsham), and probably one or two others now present over the northeastern United States, carry the destructive fungus disease called the Dutch elm disease which is a serious enemy of our elms. Another ipid, the clover root borer, tunnels in the main roots of clover. Other species attack fruit trees, usually those not healthy.

**The shot-hole borer or fruit tree bark beetle** (*Scolytus rugulosus* Ratz.).— This European fruit-tree pest has now been in the United States about fifty years and is present nearly everywhere east of and in many localities west of the Mississippi River; it has been reported from California. It breeds in most of the cultivated deciduous fruit trees as well as in several kinds of wild ones. The beetle (Fig. 208) is about a tenth of an inch long, almost black, except the tips of the elytra and the legs, which are dull red.

The beetles emerge from the trees in the spring but soon enter them again and dig out egg channels one or two inches long, about parallel to the grain of the wood, partly in this, partly in the inner bark.  Here, in little niches or hollows along the sides, the eggs are laid.  These hatch in a few days and the grubs burrow, first directly away from the egg channel, then turning in various directions, extend these larval tunnels several inches and pupate at their ends.  When the

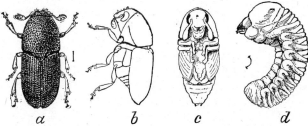

*a*  *b*  *c*  *d*

Fig. 208.—Shot-hole borer (*Scolytus rugulosus* Ratz.): *a*, adult beetle; *b*, side view of same; *c*, pupa; *d*, larva.  Hair lines show true length.  (*From U. S. Dept. Agr. Farmers' Bul.* 763.)

beetles have been formed there, they bore out to the surface of the tree (Fig. 209) and soon begin to tunnel in again, to lay eggs for a second generation which in the north becomes adult before winter, thus giving two generations a year.  In the south with its longer warm season, three or perhaps four generations may be produced each year, the adult beetle, in some cases at least, wintering in the tree, but in others this season may be passed in the egg stage.

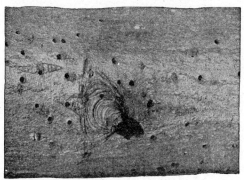

Fig. 209.—Exit holes of the shot-hole borer in bark of a young tree; about natural size. (*From U. S. Dept. Agr. Farmers' Bul.* 763.)

Healthy trees are not often attacked except when the beetles become so abundant that a sufficient supply of weak or dying ones is not available.  In healthy trees the flow of gum sometimes prevents the development of larvae but in time this becomes less and the insects then have a weakened tree to attack.  Trunk, branches and twigs are perhaps equally liable to be injured.  The burrows extending in all directions, partly in the outer surface of the wood, partly in the inner bark, destroy the cambium or growing layer, often entirely girdling the twig, branch or trunk, as the case may be, and causing its death.

*Control.*—This must largely be accomplished by means to keep the trees as vigorous and healthy as possible. Any injured, broken or otherwise affected limbs should be removed or so treated, if possible, as to restore them, and close watch of trees outside the orchard, liable to infestation, should also be given. Infested trees which are still pouring out gum can sometimes be saved by cutting back strongly and then cultivating and fertilizing freely. In some cases a thick coat of whitewash mixed with a little table salt can be applied as a repellent for the beetles. This treatment sometimes needs to be applied three times—once in spring, again in midsummer and once again in the fall. Washes of soap and carbolic acid have occasionally been used with some success, and it is claimed that the larvae can be killed in their burrows by using a carbolineum spray material. This is made by dissolving three pounds of naphtha soap in three gallons of hot water; adding a gallon of carbolineum, stirring thoroughly and then diluting for use at the rate of one part of this to four of water, but this is rather expensive treatment.

These methods should work equally well for any of the bark beetles where the bark is no thicker than at the places where these insects attack the fruit trees.

# CHAPTER XXVI

## ORDER STREPSIPTERA

These tiny insects are seldom seen except by entomologists, and their parasitic habits aid in their concealment. For a long time opinions were divided as to where they belonged, some regarding them as a family of aberrant Coleoptera and others considering them as forming an order. Recent studies seem to confirm the latter view and the group is now generally rated as a separate order, though its closest relations are probably with the beetles.

The Strepsiptera, from the meaning of this name, may be called the twisted-wing parasites, though the words stylops and stylopid are fre-

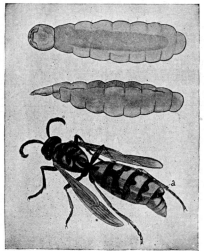

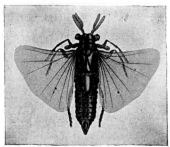

FIG. 210.

FIG. 211.

FIG. 210.—Male strepsipteron (*Xenos vesparum* Rossi); rather more than six times natural size. (*After Pierce.*)

FIG. 211.—Female strepsipteron, top and side views and a stylopized wasp: *a*, end of the parasite projecting between the abdominal segments of the wasp; all greatly enlarged. (*After Leuckart's Wandtafeln.*)

quently used in referring to them. The males, on reaching the adult condition (Fig. 210), become free and can fly. The females, on the other hand, remain partly within the bodies of their host insects and are worm-like or grub-like (Fig. 211) in appearance. The males are very small, soft-bodied animals, ranging from about one to perhaps four twenty-fifths of an inch in length. The eyes are more or less stalked and the antennae have one or more segments elongated on one side. The mouth parts are greatly modified but appear to be of the chewing type, though the adult does not feed. On the mesothorax is a pair of tiny clubs, some-

215

times rather flattened, which represent the front pair of wings. The
metathorax forms nearly half the entire length of the body. It bears
a pair of well-developed wings which are broad and fold lengthwise when
at rest. The abdomen is composed of ten segments. The females are
soft and resemble a rather long sack bearing traces of segmentation, and
at one end is a constriction, beyond which is a sort of knob, believed to be
a combination of the head and thorax; a cephalothorax in fact. This
portion of the body is pushed out between two of the body segments of
the host during the latter part of the metamorphosis, thus becoming
external (Fig. 211) and the body of the host is distorted in this way.

The members of this order may be characterized as follows:

*Tiny insects which from the first larval instar to the adult are internal
parasites in other insects. The male adult has stalked eyes, mouth parts of
the chewing type, but little or not at all developed; antennae with one or more
segments prolonged laterally; pro- and mesothorax small, the latter with a
pair of small clubs corresponding to the forewings of most insects; metathorax long, forming at least half the length of the body and bearing a pair of
broad wings which fold longitudinally. The female adult is worm-like,
without feet, and located within the body of its host except for a cephalothorax
which protrudes between two abdominal plates of the latter. It is enclosed
by its pupa skin. Metamorphosis is complete.*

These insects, often called stylops, are parasitic only in some Orthoptera, Homoptera, Hemiptera and Hymenoptera, as far as known, and
at the present time only Gryllotalpa in the Orthoptera and Chrysocoris
in the Hemiptera are known as hosts in those groups. Most of the
parasitism is of leafhoppers, wasps and the solitary bees, and these are so
disabled by the removal of their body fluids by the parasites that "stylopized" individuals are unable to reproduce and are greatly lacking in
vitality. Their bodies are often distorted also and other changes are
produced.

The eggs of the stylops appear to hatch within the body of the mother
and the young escape by passing from the body out into the space between
this and the pupa case of the parent in which it remains, and then through
an opening in this at the cephalothorax, thus reaching the open-air.
They are now on the body of the parental host and this insect may carry
them to its nest, where, if the host is a colonial form, the stylops may find
young to attack there. It is generally probable, though, that they leave
the parental host at some place (possibly a blossom) where other insects of
the host species will be liable to visit. Transferring on to such individuals
as chance may permit, the stylopids finally arrive where larvae of the
proper species are available and at once attack them. Thus far they
have been active little six-legged larvae, but after burrowing into the
body of their host larvae they change greatly, becoming worm-like and

legless.  The males finally enter a pupa stage, after which the adults escape, but the females remain throughout the rest of their life in the bodies of their hosts.

Where stylopids are abundant and attack injurious species of insects, such as are many, at least, of the Homoptera, the stylopized individuals, being unable to produce, become of lessened importance and their parasites must be considered as beneficial.  Most of the Hymenoptera they attack, however, are beneficial and parasitism in such cases can hardly be considered helpful to man.  The group is not sufficiently abundant, though, to be an important factor under ordinary conditions, as only about a hundred species are known, but these are widely distributed over the globe.

# CHAPTER XXVII

## ORDER NEUROPTERA

### (Megaloptera: Planipennia)

The insects placed in this group, though quite similar in structure, differ markedly in appearance in many cases. They vary much in size, ranging from less than a quarter of an inch to several inches in length, and their wings may be small or large.

The mouth parts are for chewing or biting, and most of the group feed upon insects and other small animals. The wings are four in number, well supplied with both longitudinal and (with a few exceptions) cross veins. The larvae in general are active, moving about in search of their prey. A few, though, live in the egg sacs of spiders, feeding on the young spiders, and in one or two cases fresh-water sponges appear to be their food. There is a quiet pupa stage.

The group may be characterized as

*Insects which when adult have two pairs of wings usually large as compared with the body and with numerous longitudinal and (in most cases) cross veins. Mouth parts for chewing. Metamorphosis is complete.*

So far as is known, none of the Neuroptera are injurious insects and some at least are decidedly beneficial. About half a dozen families are usually recognized some of which are here considered either because of their economic importance or because they are large and common enough frequently to attract attention.

In the family **SIALIDÆ** belongs the largest member of the order (Fig. 212) found in the United States. This is commonly called the dobson fly or hellgrammite (*Corydalis cornuta* L.), which is quite common throughout the country except in arid regions. The mandibles of the male are nearly an inch long, slender and somewhat curved; those of the female are short. The distance from tip to tip of the wings, when these are extended, may be over five inches, and the size of the insect and the long jaws of the male have led to the mistaken belief that this really harmless animal is dangerous. The eggs are laid in large masses on objects which hang over the water, into which the larvae enter on hatching, making their way under stones where they feed for nearly three years on the nymphs of May flies and other insects. Here they are searched for by fishermen to use as bait. When full-grown, the larva makes a cell under some stone close to the stream and pupates for about a month, after which the adult escapes.

Smaller species, some with gray or black wings or black wings spotted with white, belong here. They are often quite common around streams and ponds during the summer months and are frequently called fish flies. The members of the family **CHRYSOPIDÆ** are of great economic importance as the larvae feed freely on injurious insects, particularly aphids, and are so voracious that they are often called aphis lions. The adults (Fig. 213) are rather small, slender-bodied insects, averaging less

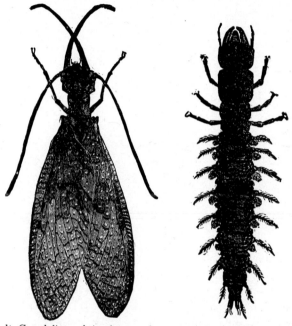

Fig. 212.—Adult Corydalis and its larva; about natural size. (*From Sanderson and Jackson, Elementary Entomology; after Comstock.*)

than an inch long, with long antennae and large, finely veined green wings, which when not in use are carried sloping over the body. These adults are sometimes called goldeneyes because of their shining, golden-yellow eyes, but perhaps more frequently lacewings, from the delicacy and beauty of these structures.

The lacewings are found practically everywhere in this country and are usually quite abundant. They lay their eggs on the stems, branches and leaves of plants, first constructing a slender but quite stiff stalk of silk about half an inch long, to the end of which the egg itself is attached (Fig. 214). These eggs are usually placed in groups and it is believed that, were the eggs not raised on stalks out of reach, the first larva to hatch would at once proceed to eat the eggs as its first meal. These larvae are rather short, somewhat oval in outline, and have long mandibles with which they grasp their prey. The lower side of each mandible is grooved and the maxilla of the same side is. so modified as to fit into this groove and convert it into a tube. An insect attacked by an aphis

lion is seized by the tips of the jaws and its blood is drawn through the tubes into the body of its captor.

Aphis lions are often found in colonies of aphids which have by their feeding caused leaves to curl, and, with an abundant food supply thus provided, the insect is both protected by the leaf and ensured of the food it needs for its development.

FIG. 213.—Adult lacewing (*Chrysopa plorabunda* Fitch); slightly reduced. (*From Folsom.*)

When full-grown, the aphis lion forms around its body a white, shining, spherical silken cocoon in which it pupates. When this process is complete, the adult cuts out a circular piece of the cocoon, forming a hole through which it escapes.

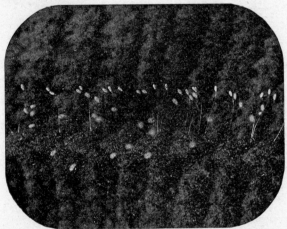

FIG. 214.—Eggs of a lacewing; greatly enlarged. (*From Sanderson and Jackson, Elementary Entomology; after S. J. Hunter.*)

The importance of lacewings as friends of man is such that they should be protected and not destroyed under the impression that being among known pests they must also be for that reason injurious.

In the western states are a few insects belonging to the Neuroptera, and family **RAPHIDIIDÆ.** They are small, less than an inch in length, but with an unusually long prothorax (Fig. 215). The larvae feed on other insects and, among others, on codling moth larvae. They occur chiefly under loose bark in this stage and, although not so abundant as could be desired, do good work by attacking many injurious species.

Another family, the **MANTISPIDÆ,** though few in numbers, has its members quite widely distributed. The mantispas (Fig. 216), as they are called, like the raphidians, have a greatly elongated prothorax and their forelegs are also long and adapted to grasping their prey.   The adults are larger than the raphidians, being about an inch in length and with long wings.   Though feeding on other insects, most of which are likely to be injurious, the mantispas are not numerous enough to be of any great importance.

FIG. 215.                                 FIG. 216.

FIG. 215.—Adult Raphidia (*Agulla admixa* Hagen), about twice natural size.

FIG. 216.—Adult Mantispa (*Climaciella brunnea* Say), showing grasping front legs; somewhat enlarged.

The insects belonging to the family **MYRMELEONTIDÆ** are generally spoken of as the ant lions, though the name doodlebug is sometimes applied to their larvae.   They are widely distributed over the United States, particularly in sandy places, but are most abundant in the south.

FIG. 217.                                 FIG. 218.

FIG. 217.—Adult ant lion; about natural size.

FIG. 218.—Larva of an ant lion; about twice natural size.   (*After Meinert.*)

Many kinds of the adults (Fig. 217) superficially greatly resemble the "damsel fly" section of the dragonflies (Odonata), their long, slender bodies, large, gauzy wings and their general size causing the resemblance. Their antennae, however, instead of being very small and not noticeable, are of fair size and knobbed at the tip, which provides an easy way by which to distinguish the two groups.   Other characters and their life history also prove that the resemblance is only superficial.

The larvae of the ant lions (Fig. 218) greatly resemble those of the lacewings in general form and in the possession of long jaws grooved for sucking the blood of their victims.   They excavate little conical pits in soft, dry, preferably sandy ground, an inch or two across and as deep as possible for the sandy sides to hold.   At the bottom of the pit thus dug, the young ant lion buries itself except for its head and waits for an unwary insect to fall in. Sliding down the slope of loose earth, the victim literally falls into the jaws of the waiting enemy and is killed and devoured. It has been stated that sometimes the insect on its way down the side of the pit is able to check itself and start to climb out, and that then the ant lion shovels a load of sand on to the top of its flat head, with its leg, and snaps the sand up the side of the pit, where, falling, it sweeps the prey down to the bottom within reach of the ant lion!

The process of excavating the pit is also one of extreme interest. The insect first traces out a circle of the desired size, loading its head with sand from inside the circle and snapping it out and, on completing the circle, repeats the process but in the reverse direction, and this is continued until the pit has been completed. In doing this the larva always moves backward.

After becoming full-grown, the ant lion larva forms a spherical cocoon of sand and silk in the ground, within which it transforms to the adult. The ant lions, though feeding on other insects, are of little, if any, economic importance, as the forms they are most liable to capture are not often serious pests. Their habits and manner of life, however, are so interesting that much attention has been given to them and what has been published about them forms one of the most interesting chapters of entomology.

The Neuroptera, though widely distributed over the world, do not constitute a large group. Only about two hundred kinds are known in this country and rather less than four thousand kinds in all have thus far been discovered. Fossil specimens of several of the families have been found.

# CHAPTER XXVIII

## ORDER TRICHOPTERA

The caddice (sometimes spelled caddis) flies, as the members of this order are usually called, are rather soft-bodied insects ranging in size from less than an eighth of an inch to an inch or more in length.

The wings, though much reduced in a few cases, are almost always large and well developed, with numerous longitudinal veins, but few cross veins. They are membranous, the front pair somewhat leathery, and all are more or less densely covered with hairs which in some species are rather scale-like in form. The hind wings are usually broader than the front pair and when not in use are sometimes folded lengthwise. The position of all the wings when at rest is with their hinder margins together over the back of the insect and their costas down at the sides of the body, upper faces sloping downward and outward like a house roof (Fig. 219).

The mouth parts of the adult are poorly developed, though evidently modified from the chewing type, and it is probable that little if any food is taken in this stage. The antennae are generally well developed, and in some species they may be several times as long as the body. The legs are quite long and slender.

The larvae (Fig. 220) somewhat resemble small caterpillars in form. They are nearly all found in water, chiefly that of ponds or slow-running streams; a few inhabit rapid currents. The abdomen is soft, the chitinous skin being delicate, and the larvae therefore construct cases of various materials as a protection for this portion of the body.

The Trichoptera may be defined as

*Insects which as adults have rather soft bodies; four membranous wings with numerous longitudinal and few cross veins, and more or less closely covered by hairs, folded over the body like a house roof when at rest. Mouth parts rather rudimentary. Antennae and legs quite long, the former sometimes exceptionally so. Larvae live in cases, nearly always in the water. Metamorphosis is complete.*

The adult caddice fly, though having well-developed wings, is not a strong flier and these insects are therefore most frequently found near water.

The eggs are, at least usually, laid in clusters in a mass of jelly and are probably dropped into the water. On hatching, the larvae begin the

223

construction of cases in which to live.   The materials of which these are
made differ according to the species of caddice fly concerned and vary
greatly (Fig. 221).   Some take pieces of leaves that have fallen into the
water; others select veins of the leaves and similar sized straws and put
them together crisscross, something like the logs
of a log house; some species use the finest sand
for this purpose, others coarse gravel, and still
others use a mixture of long and short pieces of
plants so that the ends of the longer ones extend
some distance behind the end of the case.

The case itself is usually straight but in some
species it may be curled and resembles a small
snail shell.   Indeed this resemblance is so close
that, in one instance at least, such a case was actually described as that of a shell!   The materials,
whatever they may be, are held together by silk
spun by the larva, coming from silk glands within
the body and poured out through an opening close
to the mouth.   Within the case the larva lives,

Fig. 219.—Caddice flies: adult at rest, above; with wings spread, below.   Larvae showing
three kinds of cases, crawling.   (*From Linville and Kelly, General Zoology.*)

crawling about by extending its head and thorax out of the front end so
that its feet can be used, and dragging the case along.

Some caddice fly larvae make simpler houses than these.   Such species
live in rapid water and there fasten a few tiny stones under rocks by their
silk and between these spin a silken tube in which to live.   Close to this

they spin more or less funnel-shaped webs, the mouth upstream and so arranged that tiny animals swept down by the current within the outer limits of the funnel come within reach of the larva lying in its tube. Although these larvae are carnivorous, in most of the species plant materials are eaten.

The larvae, in most cases, breathe by tracheal gills which are slender filaments, frequently grouped in clusters and attached to the abdominal segments. Other structures present in some species are also suspected of being concerned with respiration.

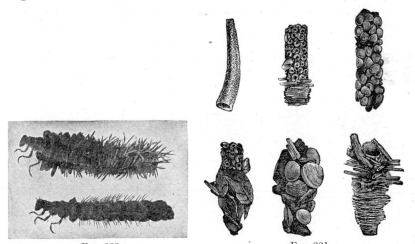

Fig. 220.         Fig. 221.

Fig. 220.—Caddice fly larvae. Larva with head and thorax extended out of its case, above; larva removed from its case, below, showing tracheal gills; about twice natural size. (*Modified from Leuckart's Wandtafeln.*)

Fig. 221.—Examples of different types of cases formed by caddice fly larvae. (*From Sanderson and Jackson, Elementary Entomology; after Furneaux.*)

When full-grown, the caddice worm forms a sort of lid or door grating across the front opening of its case, though not complete enough to prevent water from entering and supplying the insect with the oxygen it needs. After pupation in its case the adult swims to the surface and grasps some object, from which it takes its flight. In some species it is apparently the pupa which, when ready to become the adult, comes to the surface and passes its final molt there.

The Trichoptera comprise quite a large group of insects, representatives of which are found in almost all parts of the world. Twelve to fifteen hundred species have thus far been described, but five or six thousand kinds probably are in existence. Their food is largely decaying vegetable matter in pools and they are therefore of little economic importance. In a few cases, though, they are known to sever the lines by which fishing nets are attached to their floats. Around Lake Erie they accumulate around the edges of the lake in great numbers and many people become allergic to their hairs so abundant there.

The Trichoptera are evidently closely related to the Lepidoptera in many ways and are undoubtedly, with the last named order, divergent descendants from common ancestors. Some Lepidoptera so closely resemble Trichoptera, in fact, that they have been placed in the latter group. They also have many resemblances to the Neuroptera, but their connection with this order is plainly more remote, and sufficient time has elapsed since the divergence of the present Neuroptera and Trichoptera from their common ancestors to permit the development of many differences.

Adults and cases of the larvae have been found as fossils in some abundance.

# CHAPTER XXIX

## ORDER LEPIDOPTERA

The Lepidoptera are the moths and butterflies, which form one of the largest and most noticeable groups of insects. Its members are found in all countries and their large size in many cases, their brilliant colors and the habits of their larvae, as well as the injuries they cause, have attracted much attention.

The adults have four large, membranous wings in most cases (a few have lost their wings), more or less completely covered by overlapping scales, making the wings opaque where these are present. Colors of the wings are due either to the presence of pigments in the scales, to optical colors caused by the surfaces of the scales breaking up the light striking them, or to both factors together.

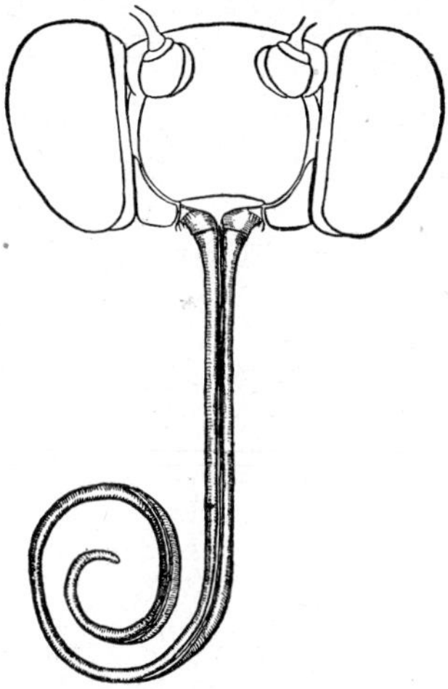

The mouth parts of the adult are greatly modified from those of chewing insects, though enough remains to show that the ancestors of the group must have fed by chewing. The development of the parts varies in different species, some of the lower forms having, as a whole, a much closer resemblance to the condition in chewing insects than is the case with most of them. In one group, the mouth parts are sufficiently of the mandibulate type to enable the insects to feed on pollen.

Fig. 222.—Diagram of head of a lepidopterous insect, showing the tongue; palpi removed. (*From a drawing by M. F. Webster.*)

In general a labrum or front lip is evident, but the mandibles are practically lost. The maxillae are extremely modified, a portion of each contributing its half to the formation of a proboscis or tongue (Fig. 222). This is a flexible organ varying greatly in length, its two halves so interlocking as to form a tube between them, through which, when completely developed, fluids may be drawn into the mouth. The degree of development of the proboscis differs greatly in different Lepidoptera and, whereas it is functional in perhaps the majority of the group, it is only partly developed or even rudimentary and useless in others. Such Lepidoptera evidently do not feed while adult.

227

In some cases the maxillary palpus is developed; in others it is nearly or wholly lacking. The labium or hinder lip is also practically absent except for the labial palpi which are usually large, thickly covered by hairs or scales, and project forward at the sides of the head, often turning upward somewhat, and partially or wholly concealing the proboscis when this is coiled up under the head, the place where it is carried when not in use.

The mouth parts of the larva (or caterpillar as it is usually called) are entirely different. In this stage they are chewing structures, similar to those of a grasshopper in a general way, and no special description is needed. In the center of the end of the labium, however, is a slender projection called the spinneret, which at its tip has the external opening of the duct leading to the silk glands.

The antennae of adult Lepidoptera are usually quite long but vary greatly in their form in different species. In the butterflies they are slender but enlarged near the tip forming a club (Figs. 303 to 311), or with this enlarged part bent into a sort of hook (Fig. 302). These forms of antennae are almost never found in the moths, where they may be simple and thread-like; with small hair-like projections at the side; bristles in place of the hairs; clusters of the bristles; with tooth-like or saw-like side projections; with long projections on one or both sides, in the latter case giving the antennae a feather-like appearance; and other forms also occur (compare Figs. 223–299).

The eyes are large, though in some cases partly concealed by hairs or scales, which as a rule thickly clothe the entire body. Ocelli are also sometimes present. On the top of the prothorax a pair of projections or lobes often occur, called patagia, sometimes very large and capable of some movement, at other times smaller or even reduced to mere traces. On the large mesothorax is a somewhat similar pair of structures, called the tegulae, which extend backward over the point where each forewing articulates with the body. The abdomen may be long or short, stout or slender, connected with the thorax by either a broad or a rather constricted attachment. The legs are quite long and slender.

Members of this group may be distinguished as

*Insects which as adults have (with a few exceptions) four membranous wings more or less completely covered by overlapping scales; mouth parts for sucking. The larvae have chewing mouth parts. Metamorphosis is complete.*

The Lepidoptera form such a large order that great differences in its members are very common. The smallest ones are almost microscopic, and the largest one known may measure about a foot between the tips of its expanded wings. The wings of each side, to obtain their greatest efficiency, are more or less completely coordinated for flight by one of three methods. In the butterflies and some of the moths, the basal portion of the costal region of the hind wing is enlarged, forming a sort of shoulder over which the hind margin of the forewing lies, thus enabling the two to a large extent to function as a single wing. In most moths, however, instead of a shoulder, a rather long, curved bristle or cluster of bristles, called a frenulum, arises near the base of the hind wing and runs forward and outward, passing under a small flap or through a tuft of scales on the underside of the forewing, so that, as the two wings move in flight, this frenulum slides backward and forward in its track under the forewing and holds the two together. A third type of connection, found in only a few moths, is a small lobe near the base of the hind margin of the forewing, which extends backward toward the hind wing. This lobe is called a jugum and is also probably more or less effective in producing coordination in the use of the wings.

The number and arrangement of the wing veins are of great importance in the Lepidoptera, much of the classification in this order being based upon these structures. The main veins (see Fig. 21) are, of course, longitudinal, starting at the point of attachment of the wing to the body and diverging toward its outer margin, some of them branching several times. Cross veins are very few, however, and consequently there are only a few closed cells (see page 13), and some at least (perhaps all) of these are produced by the fusion of branches of longitudinal veins, rather than by true cross veins.

Various ways of designating the veins and their branches have been offered, but these are best comprehended in connection with laboratory work on the insects themselves and are therefore not given here.

The eggs of Lepidoptera vary greatly in form and also in color. They may be elongate, spherical, flattened, scale-like or of other forms, and the shell or chorion may be smooth or sculptured with ridges and reticulations. The eggs may be laid singly or in clusters and may or may not be covered with hairs from the body of the parent moth or with a secretion which conceals them from view. They may hatch in a few days or after longer periods, in some cases many months. The adults have no ovipositor so the eggs are always laid on the surface of the place of deposition; though if the abdomen of the insect is small, this may be in a small crack or other opening.

The larvae produced by the hatching of the eggs are called caterpillars and have no resemblance whatever to the adults they are to become. They are usually rather worm-like animals, with a generally recognizable head and a body consisting of a series of rather similar segments, the first three of which correspond to the thorax of the adult and almost always bear six legs. Some of the following segments will also have legs but these are totally different in structure from the others and are merely temporary in their nature, designed to support this portion of the body (see Fig. 22).

A large majority of the caterpillars are termed naked, having only a few tiny spines or hairs, not large enough to be noticeable. From this condition every grade of density of covering occurs, to species entirely covered by long, thickly placed hairs which give the animal a hairy or "woolly" appearance. Some have large warts or horns on the thorax (Fig. 22) or a sort of horn above, near the hinder end of the body (Fig. 301).

Their colors also vary greatly, some being brightly colored and others—green—either with or without white streaks, appearing to seek concealment by their resemblance to the leaves on which they feed. Those living in protected situations, such as in plant stalks, are nearly white; cutworms which pass the day in the ground are dark as a rule, with rather faint markings.

The internal structures of the caterpillar do not differ greatly in their arrangement from those of an adult insect, except that the reproductive organs are only slightly developed at this time, and that there is present, along each side of the body, a silk gland, large in those which will later need large quantities of silk, but present in all. A duct from each gland runs forward to the mouth where the two unite and open to the exterior through the spinneret already referred to.

Most caterpillars feed on plants or vegetable material. Their work is noticed chiefly by their stripping plants of their leaves, though some bore in stems, roots, fruit, seeds or other parts. A few attack feathers, silk, etc., but this is not the general habit. The larval stage may last only a few days for some species but is generally a month or more, and some feed during the fall, become quiet during the winter and complete their feeding the following spring.

When the caterpillar has become full-grown, it generally leaves the place where it was feeding and in some satisfactory location spins a cocoon around itself, using for this purpose the silk produced by its silk glands. In some species the cocoon is very complete, thick, tough, and entirely conceals the larva within (Fig. 253). On the other hand, there are cocoons where only sufficient silk is used to attach the insect and hold it in place; and between these extremes all degrees of cocoon construction occur. Sometimes leaves, hairs from the body of the caterpillar or dirt when the insect enters the ground at this stage are incorporated in the cocoon.

Within the cocoon the caterpillar molts, leaving its castoff skin at one end. The result of this molt is a pupa, its form showing through its new skin, which is generally brown. The outlines of the adult body and its appendages including the wings are evident, these last, however, being very small as there would be no room for the full-sized wings of the adult within the cocoon. . Internal changes and the completion of such external ones as are necessary now proceed until the adult insect has been entirely formed and is ready to escape. When this happens, another molt releases the insect from the brown outer pupa skin and, either before or after this, an opening in the cocoon is made and the adult emerges. It then crawls up on something and remains quiet for a while; its wings, being free to expand, increase rapidly till of their full size; the surplus fluids in the body are expelled, and after an hour or two the insect is ready for flight.

Although for most Lepidoptera this outline of development is in general correct, in the butterflies we find that cocoon making is limited to attaching the hinder end of the body by silk to the object on which it is to pupate, and in most of the families the formation of a silken loop around its body to hold it up. Such a pupa, producing a butterfly, is usually given the special name chrysalis (see Fig. 35a).

Besides the names butterflies (Rhopalocera) and moths (Heterocera) used to distinguish different sections of the Lepidoptera, we also have the terms Microlepidoptera, or small moths, and Macrolepidoptera, or large ones. These are wholly relative and rather indefinite but are, nevertheless, convenient in spite of the fact that it would be doubtful under which head to designate many species of the order.

The latest list of the insects of this order found in North America places them in about seventy families, but there are more of these divisions in other parts of the world. Some of the families include many species and insects of much economic importance, and others have only a very few. Only the more important families, either in size or because of the pests they contain, are included here. Over 100,000 species of Lepidoptera are known.

### HETEROCERA (moths)

*Family* **COSSIDÆ** (carpenter moths).—The larvae of the moths belonging in this family bore in trees and are sometimes quite injurious. There are several native species, the most common being the carpenter worm or goat moth (*Prionoxystus robiniæ* Peck), which lays its eggs in the crevices of the bark of various trees. The larvae bore in the limbs, injuring or killing them, and the entire life history is believed to take three years. The adults which appear in June and July are quite large, the wings of the female spreading about three, and those of the male about two, inches. The wings are mottled light and dark gray, except the hind wings of the male, which are yellow. The leopard moth (*Zeuzera pyrina* L.), a European pest belonging to this family, reached this country before 1879 and now occurs along the Atlantic coast from New Hampshire to Delaware and a rather short distance inland. The wings of the moths (Fig. 223) spread from one to about two inches and are white with numerous black spots.

FIG. 223.—Adult female (left) and male (right) of the leopard moth (*Zeuzera pyrina* L.); about natural size. (*From Britton, Eleventh Rept. Ent. Conn. Agr. Expt. Sta.*, 1911.)

FIG. 224.—Larva of leopard moth in its burrow. Natural size. (*From Britton, Eleventh Rept. Ent. Conn. Agr. Expt. Sta.*, 1911.)

The thorax has seven black spots above. The moths appear from May till September and lay their eggs on the bark, several hundred in all, but usually only a few at a place. The caterpillars (Fig. 224) are liable to enter the small twigs but may enter elsewhere and bore through the wood. Small twigs are killed and larger ones weakened and in time may also be destroyed by this boring; if the branch becomes too small at any time for the larva, it will leave it for a larger one. Injured limbs are often so weakened as to break off during storms. The borer feeds during parts of three seasons, pupating in its burrow the third spring. It is more abundant in and near cities and towns than in the open country.

The work of borers of this group is often evidenced by fine chips, excrement or frass pushed out of the entrances to the tunnels; by wilted leaves; by tunnels in fallen branches; and by splits and breaks in the bark when the larvae work just beneath it.

Control for the leopard moth and for carpenter moths in general is to locate the entrance holes of the larvae and inject a little carbon disulfide into them, then stopping the opening with putty, mud or wax. Thoroughly infested trees should be cut and burned during the cold months, to destroy the caterpillars in them, as such trees are doomed in any case.

*Family* **TINEIDÆ** (tineids).—The insects belonging in this family are all Microlepidoptera, the distance between the tips of their wings when spread being generally much less than an inch. They are not noticeable insects and only a few are of great importance. Three, however, are serious household pests and cause much injury, being the species commonly called clothes moths, all natives of Europe but for many years now present in this country.

Fig. 225.—Adult of the webbing clothes moth (*Tineola bisselliella* Hum.); four times natural size. (*From Herrick's Insects Injurious to the Household. By permission of The Macmillan Company, publishers.*)

**The webbing clothes moth** (*Tineola bisselliella* Hum.).—Of the three species of moths considered to be pests of stored woolens only the webbing clothes moth is now commonly important over much of the United States. The adult (Fig. 225) has a wing spread of about one-half inch and is a pale cream color or buff with no spots. It flies at night and is not attracted to lights. In fact, if any small moth flies to the lights in a room, that is of itself presumptive evidence that it is not a clothes moth. The eggs are generally laid on woolen goods, including felt, as well as on fur and feathers. Ordinary observers frequently take larval excrement on infested goods to be the eggs. The white larvae appear in about ten days (Fig. 226) and feed under a sort of web of silk which they make. When ready to pupate they form silken cocoons to which are added particles of wool or whatever other material they have been feeding upon. Development is continuous at favorable temperatures as in the warm parts of heated houses, so under such conditions clothes moths may appear at any time of the year, though they are most likely to be seen in summer.

**The casemaking clothes moth** (*Tinea pellionella* L.).—This species was formerly more generally distributed than the webbing clothes moth, but it has now come to be less important; in fact in many parts of the

FIG. 226.—Webbing clothes moth (*Tineola bisselliella* Hum.); larvae, adults and work on surface of a blanket; over twice natural size. (*From Minn. Agr. Expt. Sta.*)

country it is now seldom seen. The adult (Fig. 227) is grayish yellow with several faint spots on the forewings, its hind wings more nearly a silvery gray. It is of about the same size as the preceding species and feeds upon the same materials.

FIG. 227.                    FIG. 228.

FIG. 227.—Adult of casemaking clothes moth (*Tinea pellionella* L.); four times natural size. (*From Herrick's Insects Injurious to the Household. By permission of The Macmillan Company, publishers.*)

FIG. 228.—Adult of the carpet moth (*Trichophaga tapetzella* L.); three times natural size. (*From Herrick's Insects Injurious to the Household. By permission of The Macmillan Company, publishers.*)

**The carpet moth** (*Trichophaga tapetzella* L.).—The carpet moth is not so common as the other two clothes moths and is a larger insect (Fig. 228), spreading about three-quarters of an inch. It seems to prefer to attack heavier and coarser cloths than the other species, as well as felts and skins, and is found in carriage upholstering and similar places as often as in houses. The caterpillar tunnels in its food, lining its galleries somewhat with silk; in these galleries it also pupates.

*Control of clothes moths.*—Most articles made of animal fibers are attacked by these except when in frequent use. If not used for several weeks at a time they should be protected from attack.

Two steps are important in protecting against clothes moth injuries: (1) to make certain that no stages of the moths are already in the goods, and (2) to prevent reinfestation during storage. Several things may be done to remove moths, such as airing and beating thoroughly while the articles hang in the sun, washing, dry-cleaning or fumigating. The latter may be done on a small scale in the house by packing the articles in tight chests or trunks and pouring on cloths, laid over them, a liquid fumigant such as carbon tetrachloride, or ethylene dichloride three parts, mixed with carbon tetrachloride one part, about a cupful to a trunk of average size. After the trunks have been kept tightly closed from two to several days the contents may be sprinkled liberally with naphthalene or paradichlorobenzene flakes and closed for storage. Tight garment bags are helpful for storing heavy coats on hangers. Cedar chests and closets are often used for storage as cedar oil is a repellent; however, the oil disappears after a time and then such storage space is of no more protection than if made of any other kind of wood.

Woolen lint in cracks in clothes closets and under rugs should be removed at intervals and the cracks treated liberally with kerosene. Upholstered furniture and rugs that cannot be cleaned should be fumigated, preferably by commercial fumigators equipped for this type of work. Valuable furnishings may be put into cold storage where they will be kept at or below 45°F. to prevent moth development. When a house becomes heavily infested it is often wise to have a general fumigation, in this case also by a commercial fumigator if one is available. The mothproofing of rugs and other furnishings has now become practicable, certain types of proprietary solutions for this purpose having proved satisfactory in many cases.

*Family* **OLETHREUTIDÆ** or **EUCOSMIDÆ.**—In this family are a number of pests of fruit trees and other plants. All of them are small moths, rarely spreading over three-quarters of an inch.

**The codling moth** (*Carpocapsa pomonella* L.).—This pest of apples, pears and occasionally of other fruits is a native of southeastern Europe but is now found almost everywhere and is present in all the apple-growing sections of this country. In California it is also a serious pest on the English walnut.

The adult moth (Fig. 229) has its forewings brown, crossed by irregular gray and brown lines. It spreads about three-quarters of an inch and is not often seen as it flies only at night and is not attracted by lights.

Winter is passed in the full-grown caterpillar stage in some protected place, usually under a piece of bark of the tree where the insect fed (Fig. 230). Under the bark the caterpillar digs out an oval cavity and lines it with silk in which to winter. In the spring it pupates here and the adult moth escapes a week or two after the petals fall at the blossoming season in the spring. Tiny, white, flattened eggs, fifty to seventy-five in number, are now laid singly on leaves, twigs or the small fruit, but mainly on the leaves. The eggs hatch in about a week and the caterpillars feed a little on the foliage but soon leave this and crawl to the fruit, where most of them enter at the blossom end, often burrowing their way through between the closed calyx lobes or sepals to reach the cup-shaped cavity within. From the bottom of this cavity they tunnel into the fruit to the core, in and around which they feed until full-grown—a period of nearly a month in most cases. The

FIG. 229.                     FIG. 230.

FIG. 229.—Adult codling moth (*Carpocapsa pomonella* L.); twice natural size.

FIG. 230.—Piece of bark showing codling moth cocoons and pupae on its under surface; about one-third less than natural size. (*Modified from Cornell Agr. Expt. Sta. Bul.* 142.)

remainder enter the fruit at any point but appear to prefer a place where a leaf or some other object lies against the fruit.

When its growth has been completed, the caterpillar (Fig. 231) is about three-quarters of an inch long, pinkish or whitish, with its head and a patch above, just behind the head, and another at the hinder end of the body, brown. It now leaves the fruit, generally burrowing out through the side, and makes its way down the tree until it finds some piece of bark loose enough to permit it to gnaw its way under and here it forms an oval cavity as already described.

FIG. 231.—Full-grown larva of codling moth, about twice natural size. (*Modified from Cornell Agr. Expt. Sta. Bul.* 142.)

Over the greater part of the United States there are two generations of the codling moth each year. Where this is the case, the larva pupates in this cavity for about two weeks before it escapes as an adult. Eggs are now laid for the second generation and on hatching the larvae attack the fruit, which is quite well grown by this time, entering it at any point and showing no preference for the blossom end. The feeding of this generation of caterpillars proceeds as with the spring generation but in many cases has not been completed when the fruit is gathered. In this way a number of the larvae may be carried to the bins or barrels in which the fruit is stored. Later, they leave the fruit and make their wintering cases on the sides of the bins or elsewhere.

In the northern states there is only a partial second generation, most of the caterpillars feeding during late June and July failing to transform into moths that season, so that the work of the insects in fruit during the fall may be comparatively unimportant. From southern New England south, however, two complete generations are the rule and in many states with long growing seasons, there may be three generations. In the west, even as far north as Washington, two generations occur. Cold and drought have a considerable effect everywhere, however, late springs

FIG. 232.—Apple blossoms in proper condition for receiving the calyx spray. Adult codling moth; natural size, above. (*From Felt, Twenty-seventh Rept. N. Y. State Ent.,* 1911.)

reducing the number of moths that appear in those seasons. Everywhere, some individuals have only one generation.

The injury caused by this insect places it among our most important pests. Small apples attacked drop in many cases, resulting in the entire loss of some of the fruit early in the season. In years of an abundant crop, this is of less importance, but in "off" years it is a serious matter. Fruit infested which remains upon the tree is reduced in value and thus another loss is produced. The present annual loss to the apple crop in the United States by the ravages of this insect has been estimated at over 13 million dollars.

*Control.*—There are two chief ways in which the habits of this insect may be made use of in control measures. Since the larvae of the first generation enter the fruit largely at the blossom end, poison placed there (the *calyx spray*) kills a large proportion of them as they bore their way through the spray deposit into the apple. Many of the caterpillars hatching later in the season feed for a short time on the leaves before going to the fruit; these are poisoned with general foliage sprays, called *cover sprays*.

Accordingly, spraying with lead arsenate, standard formula, within a week after the petals fall, directing the spray so that as far as possible it will fall into the cup surrounded by the calyx lobes (sepals) is the most usual method of control. In applying this spray, however, it should be

remembered that in the case of the apple these calyx lobes, which at first stand widely open around the edges of the cup, soon draw together and close up the cup mouth, after which no spray can be placed where it is of use (Fig. 232). This closing comes about ten days after the petals fall (Fig. 233) and thus limits the effective spray period to that time. Fortunately, different varieties of apples do not bloom at quite the same time, so that this calyx spray where large orchards are involved should begin with those trees which lose their petals first, taking the later-blooming varieties afterwards. When the sepals close, this helps to hold the poison in the cup ready to be consumed whenever the caterpillars reach it. Where pears are to be sprayed,

Fig. 233.—Small apple showing calyx lobes practically closed. Too late for successful spraying. (*Modified from Cornell Agr. Expt. Sta. Bul.* 142.)

their treatment can be postponed until the work on the apples has been completed, as in the pear the calyx lobes do not close and the spray can be successfully applied more than ten days after the petals fall.

In the northern states a second spray of lead arsenate, about ten days after the petals fall, will place poison on the young leaves where the newly hatched caterpillars feed a little before going to the fruit; a third, about three weeks after the petals have fallen, is also desirable.

To control the second generation is more difficult, as it is harder to fix the time at about which the eggs will hatch, this being largely determined by the temperature. If definite information when to put on this spray cannot be obtained, it may be applied about nine weeks after the petals have fallen and, if the insects are very plenty, another application may be made two weeks later. Where a third generation is present a spray should be put on about the middle of August. All these summer sprays should be of lead arsenate, standard formula, except as modified by the recommendations of the nearest agricultural experiment stations to suit local conditions.

As a result of all this spraying, and especially during dry seasons or where there usually is not a large rainfall, the poison tends to accumulate on the fruit, particularly on the places least exposed to the rain. Such fruit often carries quite an amount of poisonous residue on it when gathered, which has led to the establishment of Federal regulations as to the amount of arsenic and other poisons that may be permitted on the fruit, and in consequence, has resulted in various methods to remove this residue. The use of fluorine compounds instead of lead arsenate has shown that these materials are sometimes also fairly effective against the codling moth, but that the residue may be even less desirable than an arsenical one. Cryolite, however, is sometimes substituted for some of the lead arsenate sprays, as are also nicotine sulfate in oil emulsion, and various combinations of oil with lead arsenate. Weak hydrochloric acid is the most usual wash for removing the spray residue from the fruit, though different kinds of residue require different chemicals, such as sodium silicate, for their removal. Where the residue problem is most acute as in the Pacific northwest nicotine sulfate with summer oil is frequently used for the later cover sprays to avoid an excessive arsenical residue. ·

Minor methods for reducing the numbers of this pest are also used. Some of the caterpillars may escape death from feeding on the poisoned leaves and fruit and, in the first as well as in the second generation, enter the fruit through the side. Such larvae cannot themselves be reached, but the pupae or adults which they become, if destroyed, will reduce the number of the next generation. To do this, all loose bark on the trees should be removed four or five weeks after the petals have fallen and a loose band of cloth, burlap or tar paper placed around the lower part of the trunk. The larvae, on leaving the fruit, seek for a place in which to transform to adults and, finding no loose bark under which to make their cocoons, crawl down the trunk till they find the band, which provides the opportunity they seek and under which they therefore go. Turning over this band frequently during the summer and fall and destroying the insects found under it will thus reduce the number of the next generation. Large numbers are often destroyed in this way. Bands of corrugated paper, treated with beta-naphthol, have been found to kill a large percentage of the larvae which go under them.

Cleaning out bins, barrels and all other places where fruit has been stored, early in the spring, and destroying all the insects found there, is also a good practice and is a desirable treatment for the codling moths located in such places.

**The oriental fruit moth** (*Grapholitha molesta* Busck).—This pest of stone and pome fruits is probably a native of the Orient. Its work was first noticed near Washington, D. C., in 1913 and it is now present in the peach-growing districts in all the states east of the Mississippi River except possibly Wisconsin. It is also found in Ontario, Arkansas and Missouri and is still spreading.

The moth somewhat resembles its close relative, the codling moth. Like that insect it winters as a full-grown larva in its cocoon on the bark or in rubbish near the tree. It pupates in the spring and the adult emerges about the time the peaches are in bloom. After about five days the eggs are laid, singly and, usually at least, on the underside of the leaf in the case of the peach. They hatch in about a week and the tiny larvae attack the young shoots, tunneling down inside them for an inch or more, causing them to die. Several twigs may be attacked, one after another, by the same larva. Feeding lasts from eight to sixteen days, after which the larva pupates. After about a week in this stage the adult moth

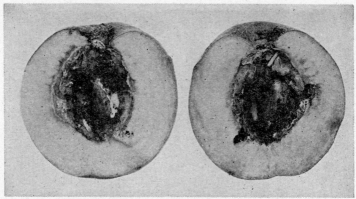

Fig. 234.—Work of oriental fruit moth (*Grapholitha molesta* Busck) showing larvae and injury to peach; about two-thirds natural size. (*From U. S. Dept. Agr. Circ.* 395.)

emerges and lays the eggs for a second generation. The brief period needed to complete a life cycle makes possible one to three or four generations each season in the northern, and five to seven in the southern, part of its range.

In the first generations the injury is mainly by killing young shoots; but after the fruit begins to ripen somewhat, the larvae attack this, tunneling through the flesh and around the stone, sometimes entering by the stem so that the fruit may not show the presence of the larva within (Fig. 234). Larvae coming after most of the fruit is gone attack the shoots.

Injury to apples, pears, quinces, cherries and plums has been reported also, though thus far the insect seems to be primarily a peach pest. It also attacks the Japanese quince and other ornamental plants related to these fruits, injuring both twigs and fruit. A number of parasites attack this insect, including some introduced from abroad.

Control methods have thus far failed to give entirely satisfactory results. The best ones at present seem to be (1) cultivation of the ground as close as possible to the tree shortly before it blossoms; (2) the paradichlorobenzene treatment as for the peach borer, which also kills these insects in their cocoons when they are within reach of the gas; (3) destruction of culls and screening of packing sheds; and (4) application of an oil-impregnated irritant dust at five-day intervals for about three weeks before picking time. The dust may be composed of fine sulfur 60 parts, talc 35 parts, light mineral oil 5 parts, all by weight.

*Family* **ÆGERIIDÆ** (the clear-winged moths).—This family, sometimes called the Sesiidæ, includes a number of moths whose wings are only partially covered by scales. They are not large insects, spreading, on an average, about an inch and are often brilliantly colored. They

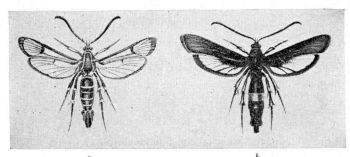

*a*      *b*

Fig. 235.—Adult moths of the peachtree borer (*Sanninoidea exitiosa* Say): *a*, male; *b*, female; twice natural size. (*From Britton, Ninth Rept. Ent. Conn. Agr. Expt. Sta.*, 1909; *after Beutenmuller.*)

fly during the day and particularly during its warmest portion and are very rapid in their flight. The larvae are whitish in color and are all borers, in stems or roots or under bark. They are, therefore, all injurious, their importance to man depending on the value of the plant attacked.

**The peachtree borer** (*Sanninoidea exitiosa* Say).—This insect, which is a native of North America, is a serious pest of the peach wherever these trees occur east of the Rocky Mountains. West of this a very closely related species, the western peach borer (*Sanninoidea opalescens* Hy. Edw.), has a similar life history, habits and control methods.

The adult insect (Fig. 235) is a little larger than the average, usually spreading a little more than an inch. The male has a dark-blue body and its transparent wings are bordered with blue. In the female the forewings are entirely blue, the hind wings transparent, and an orange band crosses the blue body at about the middle of the abdomen. The moths may often be noticed darting about in peach orchards during the middle of the day anywhere between early May and October (even earlier in the Gulf states) but are most abundant during June and July in the southern states, and July and August in the north. The eggs, several hundred in number, are laid singly or a few together on the trunk of the tree near the ground, and the larvae on hatching bore into the sapwood close to the ground and feed in that region until winter, at which time most of them are about one-third grown. In the spring they resume their feeding (Fig. 236) and upon reaching full size work their way to the surface and pupate, forming their cocoons of their excrement and particles of bark and lining them with silk. These cocoons may be at the openings of the burrows but are more frequently fastened to the bark at just about the level of the ground. After three to four weeks in the pupa stage, the transformation to the adult is completed and the pupa breaks its way through the cocoon until it is about halfway out. Then the pupa skin splits and liberates the moth.

FIG. 236.—Larva of peach borer moth and its work on a young peach tree. (*From U. S. Dept. Agr. Farmers' Bul.* 908.)

The injury caused by this insect when it is abundant is often serious. The feeding of the borers is in the cambium layer which is tunneled through in an irregular way, interfering with the growth of the trees; where these are small they are often girdled. The weakened trees also become more liable to injury and destruction by bark borers and other insects.

Where the tunnels are formed, a flow of sap results in the pouring out of gum and this substance on the bark near the ground is usually a good indication of the presence of the borers.

*Control.*—Probably more different materials and methods have been tested for the control of this insect than of any other. Formerly, "worming" and "mounding" were those most often used. Worming is the removal of the borers late in the fall and again in the spring, the date for the spring treatment varying with the locality but before the borers have completed their feeding. In the spring, following the worming, mound up the earth six or eight inches high around the trunk and leave it there until after the moths are done flying, but remove it in time for the bark to harden before winter. This mounding forces the moth to lay its eggs farther up where the bark is tough and harder than at and below the ground level, and fewer of the borers are able to penetrate it to the cambium layer.

Paradichlorobenzene has recently proved to be a very effective material for killing peach borer larvae without injuring the trees they are in, if certain precautions are taken. The pure material, pulverized to the size of coarse salt, is used. Treatment should be given in the fall after all the eggs have hatched but while the temperature of the soil is still above 60°F., to obtain the best results. The ground around the base of the tree is loosened, an inch or two deep; the material is then evenly sprinkled around the trunk to form a band an inch or two wide, but not nearer than one inch to the trunk. Two or three shovels of earth are now placed over this band, care being taken not to move any of the substance closer to the trunk during this process, and then this earth is compacted with the back of the shovel. One ounce of the material may be used for six-year-old trees, and 1¼ ounces for large, old, rough-barked trees. The base of a treated tree should be uncovered a month or so later and left exposed for a day or two before a final recovering with earth, at least in the north.

Recently the use of ethylene dichloride emulsion has replaced that of paradichlorobenzene to a considerable extent. Nine parts by volume of ethylene dichloride are stirred into 1 part of potash fish-oil soap; a stock emulsion is then made by stirring 8 parts of water slowly into this mixture. This stock emulsion is diluted according to the age of the trees to be treated. The soil at the base of each two- or three-year-old tree is sprayed with one-fourth to one-half pint of the emulsion after three parts of the stock have been diluted with seven parts of water; for four- or five-year-old trees the dilution is two parts of stock to three parts of water of which one-half pint is used for each tree; for older trees one-half pint of a half-and-half dilution is used. The base of each tree is mounded as for the paradichlorobenzene treatment. Ethylene dichloride emulsion may be used in weather colder than the other material.

**The squash borer** (*Melittia satyriniformis* Hbn.).—This pest is also a native of the New World and is found from Canada southward to Brazil and west practically to the Rocky Mountains. It attacks the squash and pumpkin and occasionally the gourd, melon and cucumber but does not, usually at least, infest the last two plants when the others are at hand. The adult moth (Fig. 237*a* and *b*) is about the same size as, but a little stouter than, the peach borer. Its forewings are a dark, metallic green, its hind wings transparent, its abdomen orange and black and its hind legs heavily fringed with long, black, orange and a few white hairs, making these legs look very large. It appears about the time the plants are large enough for egg laying and feeding upon—in April or May in the south, in June in the Middle Atlantic states and in July in New England—and lays 150 to 200 eggs (Fig. 237*c*), placing them singly on stem, leaf stalks, leaves or even on the blossoms, but the favorite location seems to be near the base of the main stem. The eggs hatch in one to two weeks and the tiny larvae may bore at once into the plant or may crawl about for a time but finally burrow into the tissues, all working their way toward the main stem.   Through this they make holes to the surface here and there, out of which some of the excrement is expelled. They become full-grown (Fig. 237*d*) in four to six weeks and then go a few inches into the ground to pupate, making dark-colored silken cocoons (Fig. 237*f*) mixed with dirt.   Some may soon pupate (Fig. 237*e*) but most remain over winter as larvae in their cocoons and pupate the following spring for a period of about three weeks.

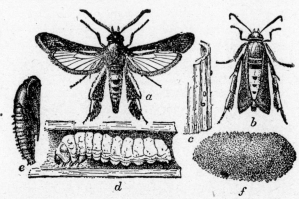

FIG. 237.—Squash borer (*Melitta satyriniformis* Hbn.): *a*, male moth; *b*, female, wings folded; *c*, eggs on a piece of squash stem; *d*, full-grown larva in squash stem; *e*, pupa; *f*, pupal case, found in the ground; all one-third larger than natural size. (*From U. S. Dept. Agr. Farmers' Bul.* 856.)

In the south there are two generations a year of this insect; farther north there is a partial second generation; in the northern part of its range there is only one, winter in any case being passed in the ground.

The injury caused by these insects when they are abundant is serious. The burrows become wet and slimy, hastening decay and thus separating much of the plant from its roots.   The feeding also interferes with the circulation of the sap to some extent.   A sudden wilting of the leaves is generally an indication of the presence of the borers, and coarse yellowish excrement beneath the stems is also evidence of their activity.   In some cases entire fields of the plants have been killed by the work of this pest.

*Control.*—As the winter is spent in the ground of the field where the larvae feed, it is evident that their food plants should not be raised two years in succession on the same land.   Fall plowing to bring up the cocoons and expose them to winter conditions is of value.   Planting some very early varieties of summer squash as a trap crop, on which the insects may lay their eggs before the real crop is available, followed by the destruction of these plants before the larvae in them are full-grown, is helpful.   Free fertilization and frequent cultivation to force the plants ahead often give good results.   Covering the runners with earth about a foot out from the main stem, to induce the formation of secondary roots, "often serves to reduce materially the amount of damage," and cutting out the borers when these are found in the stems, using a sharp knife, splitting the stem lengthwise where the borer is, and killing it, then covering the stem there with earth, is a good treatment.

It has been discovered that spraying the vines four times, at weekly intervals, as soon as egg laying begins, using 1 part of nicotine sulfate, 40 per cent, in 100 parts of water, or nicotine sulfate, 40 per cent, 1 ounce in 2½ gallons of water with ½ ounce of potash fish-oil soap, will kill at least most of the eggs. Fairly good results are obtained with the first formula at 1 part in 250 parts of water when considerable force can be used in spraying. Derris dusts, so applied as to be present on the stems during the egg-laying period, have resulted in higher crop yields.

Many other injurious insects belong in this family, among which the imported currant borer, which bores in currant stems and kills them; the blackberry crown borer, which bores in the roots and crown of the black-berry and raspberry and has a two-year life history; and the maple sesian, which bores in the trunks of maples, may be mentioned.

*Family* **GELECHIIDÆ.**—Some of the small insects that compose this group are leaf miners; others feed on buds; others skeletonize leaves or attack plants in various ways. Many are injurious at times, the amount of injury done depending on their abundance, which varies from year to year.

**The angoumois grain moth** (*Sitotroga cerealella* Oliv.).—This little insect, a native of Europe, where it was named for the French province of Angoumois, is widely distributed in the United States. The larva attacks wheat, barley, corn and other grains, often destroying a large part of the grain. As far north as central Illinois grains may be infested before they are removed from the field. To the north the life cycle is passed entirely in warm places where grain and seeds are stored.

The adult moth (Fig. 238F) is small, spreading about half an inch, yellowish in color, slightly speckled with black. Winter is spent as the caterpillar in the grain wherever it may be stored, and pupation occurs in the spring, also in the grain, followed by the emergence of the adult, which flies to the fields and lays its eggs, about a hundred in all, in the young grain heads. The eggs hatch in about a week and each tiny cater-pillar attacks a kernel, gnawing into it (Fig. 238B) and consuming its contents. After about three weeks the larva becomes full-grown and pupates in the kernel (Fig. 238C) where it fed, escaping a little later as the adult moth. Eggs are now laid on grain ready to harvest and, either in the harvested grain or in corn after it has been husked and is therefore accessible to the insects, there now follow later generations, until cold stops their further development, which is resumed the following spring.

*Control.*—All mills, warehouses and other grain storage places, where these insects have been, should be thoroughly cleaned after removal of the grain and then sprayed with pyrethrum-kerosene or other oil-base contact spray, or in severe infestations, fumigated. If heating facilities are available the temperature of the building may be raised to 125°F. or higher for several hours. Such "superheating" is best done in summer

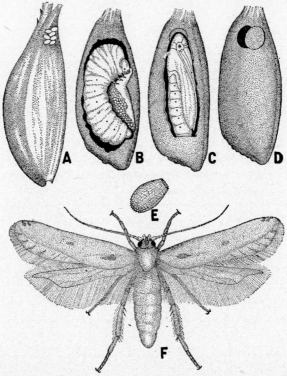

Fig. 238.—Angoumois grain moth (*Sitotroga cerealella* Oliv.). *A*, glume or chaff covering a grain of wheat with a cluster of eggs near its outer end; *B*, larva inside the grain, most of the contents of which it has eaten; *C*, pupa within a grain; *D*, hole made by the moth in escaping; *E*, egg greatly enlarged; *F*, adult moth, greatly enlarged. (*Redrawn after King; From Pennsylvania Bureau of Plant Industry.*)

when the outside temperatures are already high. In the far north it is sometimes possible to open such a building over a week end in subzero weather and kill these cold-susceptible insects. Where there is danger of field infestation, the grain should be threshed and stored in bins as soon as practicable. If it is already infested it should be fumigated with a liquid grain fumigant.

**The pink bollworm** (*Pectinophora gossypiella* Saund.).—Present in nearly all the cotton-growing regions of the world, this insect is rated as one of the dozen most destructive ones known. It reached Mexico from Egypt about 1911 and was found in Texas in 1917. Since then it has been discovered in New Mexico, Arizona, Louisiana, northern Florida, Georgia and Cuba, besides appearing on wild cotton, far from commercial fields, in southern Florida. Extermination in isolated areas and repression for those so near Mexico as to make reinfestation almost certain have been the control methods adopted by the Federal government and at the present time (1942) the insect seems to have been exterminated in northern Florida, Georgia, Louisiana and parts of Texas and destruction of all wild cotton plants in southern Florida is in progress.

The insects pass the colder months of the year as larvae in the ground, in cottonseed stored or in any bolls available, in small cocoons, but most of them are in the bolls or seed. Here, some may remain for many months—even over two years—and the others soon pupate wherever they are located. The moths, which spread about three-fourths of an inch, lay their eggs on any part of the plant, but preferably on the squares or, in later generations, on the bolls; the larvae bore into these and consume the seeds and, later on, the lint after this has begun to form. Feeding continues three to four weeks, after which some transform to adults and lay eggs for the next generation and others may remain quiet for months. There may be four to six generations in a year, but in the case of resting larvae there may be only one generation in from one to more than two years, depending on how long they rest before completing their development.

*Control.*—Cottonseed containing these insects may be safely heated to 145°F. to kill the insects in them. Forcing the crop ahead as fast as possible is helpful, and the destruction of all refuse in the fields and fumigation of every place where cotton has been, such as warehouses and gins, is important. Cotton bales may be fumigated in partial vacuum with hydrocyanic acid gas to destroy any of these insects in them and all cotton bales brought into this country or taken out of quarantined areas are so treated by the Federal government. Barrier zones around infested areas, in which no cotton may be planted for several years, seem to have given good results.

Fig. 239.                    Fig. 240.

Fig. 239.—Adult pterophorid moth showing the cleft wings; nearly twice natural size.
Fig. 240.—Alucitid moth showing the cleft wings; twice natural size.

*Family* **PTEROPHORIDÆ.**—The insects of this family, though rather small, are of much interest, the wings being cleft for a part of the distance in from the outer margin toward the base (Fig. 239). In most cases the forewing is divided into two such parts and the hind wing into three. A single species found in this country and placed in a separate family (Alucitidæ, Fig. 240), has each of its wings divided into six parts.

Most of the Pterophoridæ are not of great economic importance. One species, however, causes some injury to the grape by webbing together the leaves, usually the terminal ones, and feeding within the web. As this frequently involves a cluster of buds which may also be fed upon, the crop may be somewhat reduced in this way. The only control known is to remove the webs by hand and crush the little caterpillars.

*Family* **PYRALIDIDÆ.**—This is a large family but most of the moths belonging here are small. The members of the group have very varied habits. Some

Fig. 241.—Mediterranean flour moth (*Ephestia kuehniella* Zell.): *A*, larvae; *B* and *C*, adults; *D*, side view of adult. Twice natural size. (*From Kans. Agr. Expt. Sta. Bul.* 189.)

fold or roll leaves; some bore in plant stems; some feed on stored cereals or dried fruit; one or two feed on wax and are pests in beehives; others attack foliage, grass or various materials. Many are injurious but few can be rated as serious pests over the entire country.

The little white or brown and white moths which are so numerous in grass fields during the summer months belong here. On alighting on a grass stalk they place their bodies parallel to the stems and fold their wings closely about them. The larvae of some, known as webworms, feed on grass and are sometimes quite injurious, corn and oats suffering severely. Early fall plowing and replowing early the following spring are helpful under such conditions.

Two species are often found in houses, attacking flour, meal, cereals and dried fruits. One species, the Mediterranean flour moth (*Ephestia kuehniella* Zell., Fig. 241), spins a web which causes flour to stick in loose masses, and in mills and storage houses this becomes serious. The other species, the Indian-meal moth (*Plodia interpunctella* Hbn.) is more often found in shelled nuts, dried fruits, etc., and often causes considerable injury. In storage houses and mills fumigation with hydrocyanic acid gas is often used as a control; and if the place can be heated to 125°F. for about six hours, this also has proved effective.

**The wax moth** (*Galleria mellonella* L.) also belongs here (Fig. 242). It is an enemy of the beekeeper, living in the beehives where it feeds on wax and spoils the honey.  Strong colonies of bees can usually protect themselves from this pest, particularly the Italian races.  Where necessary, the bees can be transferred to another hive and the infested one fumigated with carbon disulfide (Fig. 243).

The European corn borer (*Pyrausta nubilalis* Hbn.).—This pest of corn and many other plants was discovered in eastern Massachusetts in 1917, and shortly

Fig. 242.                    Fig. 243.

Fig. 242.—Adult wax moth (*Galleria mellonella* L.); natural size.
Fig. 243.—Cocoons of the wax moth from the inside of a hive; natural size.

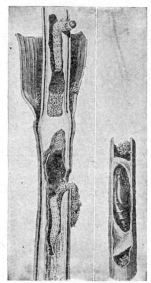

Fig. 244.          Fig. 245.                    Fig. 246.

Fig. 244.—Corn stalk split, showing the larvae of the European corn borer and their tunnels; about natural size.
Fig. 245.—Corn stalk cut to show the pupa of the European corn borer; slightly enlarged.  (*Both figures from drawings by Snodgrass, U. S. Dept. Agr. Bur. Ent.*)
Fig. 246.—Part of a corn plant showing effect on the tassels of the work of the European corn borer (*Pyrausta nubilalis* Hbn.).  (*From a drawing by Snodgrass, U. S. Dept. Agr. Bur. Ent.*)

thereafter near Schenectady, N. Y.  Since then it has spread rapidly and is now (1942) found in all the New England states, west to southern Canada and Wisconsin, and south to Indiana, Kentucky, West Virginia, Virginia and North Carolina.  It is now in the northern part of the great corn-growing region and will probably spread over all of this area, at least.  It is likely to become one of our most serious pests of corn.

It is primarily a borer in plant stems, in which it winters as a practically full-grown larva (Fig. 244), pupating there (Fig. 245) in the spring.  The New

England form has two generations a year; the one found in New York and westward has but one. In New England the moths appear in late May and June (Fig. 247) and lay three to four hundred eggs in small clusters on their food plants, and the larvae tunnel in the stems (Fig. 244), becoming full-grown in about six weeks, the moths from these appearing late in July. Eggs for another generation are now laid and the larvae feed until winter, when they hibernate in their burrows. In the other form, the moths appear during June and July and the caterpillars feed during the following months till winter approaches.

Corn, particularly sweet corn, appears to be a favorite food of this insect, and, where it is abundant, a large part of the crop may be destroyed. Large-stemmed weeds, such as barnyard grass and pigweed, and dahlias, gladioli and other flowering plants are also fed upon, and when the larvae become very abundant many other plants may be attacked.

Fig. 247.—Adult moths of the European corn borer (*Pyrausta nubilalis* Hbn.) enlarged about one and a half times; female moth on the left, male on the right. (*From a photograph by the Conn. Agr. Expt. Sta.*)

*Control.*—Destruction of all infested stalks to below the ground level; ensilage for the cornstalks and late fall plowing of cornfields, to carry the corn stubble as deep into the ground as possible, are of value as control methods. No sprays or dusts appear thus far to be very effective. Parasites from Europe are being imported and bred in enormous numbers by the U. S. Bureau of Entomology, but some years must pass before these can become abundant enough for the results of their work to be evident.

*Family* **LIMACODIDÆ** (slug caterpillars).—The insects belonging to this family are of little importance from an economic standpoint, but their larvae are curious in appearance, having little resemblance to ordinary caterpillars. Instead, they are slug-like, short and rather stout, quite flat beneath, and appear to slide along rather than crawl. Many have spines and rather showy, colored markings, in some cases with soft, fleshy projections sometimes partly or entirely covered with hairs.

*Family* **PSYCHIDÆ** (bagworms).—The caterpillars of a few species of moths in this country construct silken bags around their bodies, partly covered with twigs or other parts of the plant on which they feed. The female is wingless and lays its eggs within the pupa case or skin she vacated on becoming adult. Only one species, the bagworm (*Thyridopteryx ephemeræformis* Haw.) is of much importance; where this is plentiful the plants on which it feeds may suffer considerably (Fig. 248). It occurs from Massachusetts west to Nebraska and south to Florida and Texas. Spraying infested trees as soon as the eggs hatch in the spring, with lead arsenate 2½ pounds in 50 gallons of water with an adhesive added, is usually effective without a later application.

*Family* **GEOMETRIDÆ** (inchworms, spanworms or measuring worms).—This is a large family in this country and the moths vary greatly in size, some being very small, and others spreading nearly two

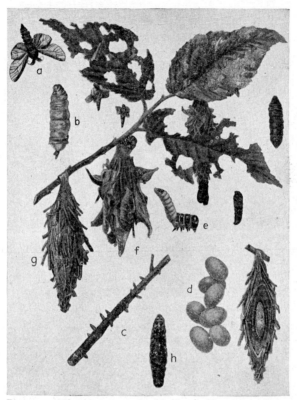

Fig. 248.—Bagworm (*Thyridopteryx ephemeraeformis* Haw.): *a*, adult male moth; *b*, adult female (wingless) moth; *c*, cases of young larvae on a twig; *d*, eggs greatly enlarged; *e*, young larva greatly enlarged; *f*, full-grown larva crawling; *g*, bag as seen in winter; *h*, full-grown larva removed from its case. All but *d* and *e* somewhat reduced. (*From Felt, N.Y. State Mus. Mem.* 8.)

and one-half inches. They nearly all have rather delicate wings and are fragile creatures.

The larvae (Fig. 249) have a peculiar appearance when moving, as the feet which are usually present near the middle of the body in most caterpillars are lacking in this group, leaving only the three regular pairs near the front end and most often two pairs at the hinder end. In consequence, walking is accomplished by bringing the hinder end up as closely as possible to the front end, the body forming at this time a loop. Then the front legs let go their hold and the body is straightened out to find a place where the front legs can grasp and hold on. This striking method of locomotion has led to the common names given to the caterpillars in this family.

Another feature of interest about these larvae is that many of them are colored and formed so as to resemble twigs. When disturbed, the caterpillar releases the grasp of its front feet and straightens out, standing at an oblique angle to the twig it is holding on to, and resembles a dead twig of the plant. Some have markings that make them resemble twigs having buds, leaf scars or scales of the bark, thus increasing their deceptive similarity (Fig. 249).

The food plants of the insects in this family are very numerous. Trees and shrubs of many kinds including fruit trees, currant and gooseberry bushes, cranberries and other plants of value to man suffer from the attacks of these insects, though few are regularly injured, the pests in most cases being destructive only for a year or two, then disappearing, at least for the most part, during quite a period.

**Cankerworms.**—There are two species of geometers which are widely distributed over this country and which at times do serious damage to fruit and shade trees. They are known as cankerworms and, although they differ in certain features, have much in common. In both species the pupal stage is passed in the ground; in both, the female is wingless; in both, the eggs are laid on the twigs of the trees; and in both the caterpillars feed at about the same time in the spring.

**The fall cankerworm** (*Alsophila pometaria* Harr.) occurs in nearly all parts of the northern United States as far west as Wisconsin, and south at least through the Middle Atlantic states. It has also been reported from New Mexico, Colorado and California. It feeds on many kinds of fruit and shade trees. The adult male moth (Fig. 250) spreads about an inch and a quarter, its wings light gray with faint markings. The female (Fig. 251) is light gray and

Fig. 249.—Two "inchworm" larvae, the lower one crawling, the upper one hanging outward like a twig. Compare with real twig just above, on opposite side. (*From Linville and Kelly: General Zoology.*)

wingless. The moths usually appear late in the fall, escaping from their pupae in the ground, and the females crawl up the tree trunks to the twigs where they lay their eggs (Fig. 251) in clusters. These eggs hatch the following spring, as the leaves develop, and the caterpillars (Fig. 252) feed on the foliage until full-grown some time in June in the northern states, and earlier farther south. During this time they often drop from the leaves some distance, spinning a thread

FIG. 250.

FIG. 251.

FIG. 250.—Male fall cankerworm (*Alsophila pometaria* Harr.); about natural size. (*From Britton, Eighth Rept. Ent. Conn. Agr. Expt. Sta.*, 1908.)

FIG. 251.—Adult female fall canker worm on a cluster of eggs; about two and one-half times natural size. (*Houser, Ohio Agr. Expt. Sta. Bul.* 332.)

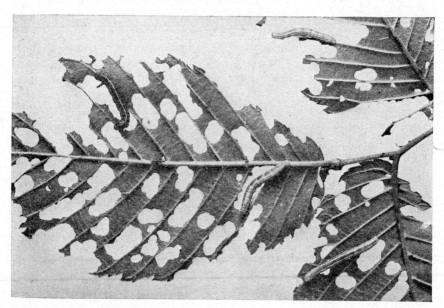

FIG. 252.—Fall cankerworm caterpillars feeding on elm; natural size. (*From Britton, Eighth Rept. Ent. Conn. Agr. Expt. Sta.*, 1908.)

as they go, and up which they return to resume their feeding. A sudden jar of an infested tree will cause great numbers to drop or "spin down" several feet in this way. When feeding has been completed, the larvae enter the ground and pupate a few inches below the surface in a silken cocoon, from which the moths escape late in the fall.

The spring cankerworm (*Paleacrita vernata* Peck).—The adult male of this species averages slightly less in its wingspread than the fall cankerworm and its wings are somewhat lighter in color. This species is found throughout most of the eastern United States, in Canada, Texas and California and is particularly injurious at times in the Mississippi Valley. This pest escapes from its pupa in the ground, as the adult, very early in the spring, and the females crawl up the trees on which they lay their clusters of eggs, frequently under loose bark or in crevices. These eggs hatch about the time the leaves open and the larvae feed during about the

Fig. 253.—Silkworm (*Bombyx mori* L.): adult moth and its cocoon; about natural size.

same periods as the other species, and enter the ground to pupate at nearly the same time. This insect also has the habit of spinning down on a thread when disturbed.

*Control of cankerworms.*—The wingless condition of the females, which necessitates their crawling up the trunks of the trees in order to reach the places where their eggs are laid, offers an opportunity for control by banding the trunks, in the fall for the fall cankerworm, and at the first warm days after winter has broken (even in February in New England, in some seasons) for the spring species, either with sticky bands which the insects are unable to cross or with loose fluffy cotton in which they become entangled. Care should be taken to keep the bands fresh or in order, so that no gaps through which they can crawl, or bridges of their dead bodies over which they can cross, are formed. If the caterpillars are already feeding when their presence is discovered, spray with lead arsenate, standard formula.

*Family* BOMBYCIDÆ (true silkworms).—The only representative of this family in North America is the silkworm (*Bombyx mori* L.) introduced many years ago because of the silk obtained from its cocoon.

Silk raising, however, has not become established commercially in this country because of the cost of the hand labor required, as compared with its cost in the Orient. The silkworm was domesticated in Asia many centuries ago and is now unknown in the wild state.

The adult moth (Fig. 253) spreads about an inch and three-quarters and is creamy white in color, with two or three faint lines across the fore-

FIG. 254.—Adult eastern tent caterpillar (*Malacosoma americana* Fab.); about natural size. (*From Sanderson: Insects Injurious to Farm, Garden and Orchard; after Lowe.*)

wings. The larvae feed on the leaves of the mulberry and Osage orange trees and when full-grown leave their food and spin their cocoons (Fig. 253). When spinning has been completed, these are gathered and the insects within are killed by heat or fumigation. Now the loose silk of the outside is removed and the cocoons are ready to market. From 50 to 75 million pounds of raw silk are produced annually in the world, making the silk-producing industry one of great importance.

FIG. 255.—Egg belt of the eastern tent caterpillar, encircling a twig; natural size. (*From Britton, Thirteenth Rept. Ent. Conn. Agr. Expt. Sta.,* 1913.)

*Family* **LASIOCAMPIDÆ** (the lasiocampids). This small family includes several species which are common and at times quite important pests. The moths are of only medium size, with rather stout bodies, antennae fringed on one side (pectinate) and with a large shoulder at the base of the hind wing, instead of a frenulum. The larvae feed on the leaves of trees.

The **eastern tent caterpillar** (*Malacosoma americana* Fab.).—This native insect is at times a pest for several years in succession, after which it practically disappears for some time. It is found almost everywhere from Canada to Florida and west to the Rocky Mountains. From there to the Pacific coast several other species occur.

The adult moth (Fig. 254) is rather stout, with a reddish-brown body and wings, the front pair of which have two whitish lines crossing them. The male spreads about an inch and a quarter and the female about half an inch more. They fly at night and do not feed as adults. The wild

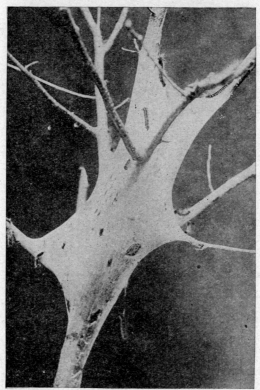

Fig. 256.—Tent of the eastern tent caterpillar; about half natural size.

cherry and apple appear to be the preferred food plants of the caterpillar, but other fruit and shade trees are sometimes fed upon.

The moths appear during the early part of the summer and lay their eggs (Fig. 255), 200 or 300 in number, in belts around small twigs, one belt probably being all that is laid by one insect. These belts more or less completely surround the twig, and after depositing a belt, the insect covers the eggs with a layer of brown, sticky substance, beveled down to the twig at each end, which soon hardens and glistens. Within the eggs the larvae develop and are ready to hatch by winter but remain within the eggshells until spring. They then leave the eggs and may feed first on the material covering the eggs but soon crawl together to some near-by fork of the tree and there spin a web (Fig. 256) in which to live. From this they go out during the day to feed, spinning a thread as they go, perhaps to aid them in finding their way back. As they grow, the tent or web is enlarged by the addition of outer layers and may be nearly a foot long and seven or eight inches across before the larvae are full-grown, the feeding period being about six weeks.

Fig. 257.—Larvae of the eastern tent caterpillar; natural size. (*From Britton, Thirteenth Rept. Ent. Conn. Agr. Expt. Sta.*, 1913.)

Though at first very small, the larvae grow rapidly and when of full size are about two inches long, black with a white stripe along the middle of the back and a row of pale-blue spots on each side, with a velvety-black spot in front of each blue one (Fig. 257). Fine yellowish hairs are also present.

When about through feeding, the caterpillars scatter and finally spin rather large, quite thick white cocoons in any protected places they may find, and within these they pupate, taking about three weeks in this stage before the moth appears.

An unusual feature in this life history is the long period spent in the egg, which may be almost ten months.

*Control.*—Although this insect has numerous enemies both among birds and insects, there are periods during which these are unable to prevent trees from being stripped by the pest. In general, the calyx spray used on apples and pears for the codling moth is sufficient to destroy this caterpillar also. On wild cherry and other trees not usually sprayed, however, it finds a breeding place from which the fruit trees may be restocked, and such trees should also be cared for, to prevent this. Examination of such trees any time between August and March, to find, cut off and burn the eggs, and the destruction of the caterpillars while in their tents on rainy days or at night, either by crushing or by burning with a torch, are desirable auxiliary treatments in addition to spraying.

FIG. 258.                                        FIG. 259.

FIG. 258.—Adult forest tent caterpillar (*Malacosoma disstria* Hbn.); natural size.
FIG. 259.—Egg belt of forest tent caterpillar; natural size.

The torch method should not be used on young fruit trees, however, as holding the torch at a fork a moment too long is liable to injure this place, and in later years the injury will show, as the fork becomes an important one, in the form of a splitting at that point under the weight of the branches and fruit beyond.

**The forest tent caterpillar** (*Malacosoma disstria* Hbn.) is also a native of North America. It greatly resembles the last species, both in appearance and in some of its habits; though occasionally found feeding on some of the same food plants, it appears to prefer the oak, maple, poplar and other forest and shade trees.

The adult (Fig. 258) is of about the same size and general appearance as the eastern tent caterpillar, but the general color is lighter brown and the lines or bands across the forewings are darker, instead of lighter, than the ground color. The egg belts (Fig. 259) are similar but quite squarely cut off at their ends instead of being rounded down to the twig. The caterpillar (Fig. 260) has a row of rather oval white spots instead of a white stripe along its back, and its sides are noticeably light blue, with two broken, longitudinal yellow lines. The caterpillars make no tents and scatter during the second and third instars. Otherwise the life history, time spent in the different stages, and the periods of the year during which these occur are the same in both species.

*Control.*—Where the caterpillars can be reached by sprays, control is comparatively simple, as with the eastern tent caterpillar. In forests,

Fig. 260.—Full-grown larvae of forest tent caterpiller (*Malacosoma disstria* Hbn.). (*From Slingerland and Crosby; Manual of Fruit Insects, by permission of The Macmillan Company, publishers.*)

however, where large trees are stripped of their foliage, this method is rarely practicable. Destruction of the egg belts is of value, but these can seldom be reached in any numbers, being usually high up on the small twigs. Jarring the trees, where these are small enough for this, will cause many of the caterpillars to drop to the ground, and by the use of sticky or cotton bands they may be prevented from crawling back again. The caterpillars frequently cluster in large numbers on the trunks of the trees, and at such times spraying these clusters with any strong contact insecticide is an effective treatment.   For the most part, however, little can be done and in "sugarbushes" extensive defoliation with a consequent reduction of the vitality of the tree and of the sap flow will follow, only relieved after a year or two by an increase in the enemies of this insect to such an abundance as to reduce it to unimportance.

Some of the western species of tent caterpillars make tents, but others do not.   Occasionally one species or another may become so abundant as to strip everything in one place; in such cases the larvae crawl off in enormous numbers seeking for more food.   In one instance

FIG. 261.—Adult male of the white-marked tussock moth (*Hemerocampa leucostigma* S. & A.), about natural size. (*From Britton, Fifth Rept. Ent. Conn. Agr. Expt. Sta.,* 1905.)

their line of march was across a railroad, where they were crushed by the car wheels until the rails became so slippery that trains were unable to run except by sweeping the caterpillars off or by blowing them off the track ahead of the engine by jets of steam!

*Family* **LYMANTRIIDÆ** (the tussock moths).—This family, though small in numbers in this country, includes some serious pests.   The moths are of medium size, and the females in some cases are either wingless or nearly so.   The legs are rather thickly clothed with hairs.   The group as a whole is one of night-flying insects but a few fly freely in the daytime.

The larvae are often highly, even brilliantly, colored and are thickly covered with hairs.   These may be quite uniformly distributed, but in some cases there are also bunches or "tussocks" of them projecting some distance from the skin, and long, slender "pencils," composed of a few hairs which may be a quarter as long as the body of the caterpillar. Most of them feed on the foliage of trees but some have a wide range of food plants.

**The white-marked tussock moth** (*Hemerocampa leucostigma* S. & A.). This common species is found along the entire Atlantic coast from Nova Scotia to Florida and westward to Colorado and British Columbia. It is mainly a pest of shade trees, and most injurious in and near cities and towns, but at times it attacks fruit trees and causes much injury.

The adult male moth (Fig. 261) spreads about an inch, and its wings are gray with wavy dark bands and light marks.   Its antennae are heavily fringed.   The female (Fig. 262) is wingless, with a gray body.

The winter is spent in the egg stage, the larvae hatching in the spring, feeding until full-grown, on foliage, then crawling away to pupate, sometimes on the twigs but usually either on the bark of the trunk or lower limbs or on other objects near by.   The cocoons are composed of silk mixed with hairs from the body of the caterpillar and are gray in color.

The female on emerging from the pupa stage crawls to the surface of the cocoon and later lays there from 300 to 500 eggs (Fig. 262) which she then covers with a white froth which soon hardens and forms a crust covering and hiding the eggs.  This white crust on the gray background of the cocoon and the generally dark bark of the tree makes the egg masses very conspicuous objects.

The eggs soon hatch and the caterpillars thus produced feed on the leaves until full-grown (Fig. 263), then pupate as in the preceding generation and the moths, appearing later, also lay their eggs on their cocoons

Fig. 262.

Fig. 263.

Fig. 262.—Adult female of the white-marked tussock moth with an egg mass covered by a white crust, resting on her cocoon; about natural size.  (*Modified from N. Y. Agr. Expt. Sta. Bull.* 312.)

Fig. 263.—Caterpillar of white-marked tussock moth.  Note the four "tussocks" of hairs; slightly reduced.  (*Modified from N. Y. Agr. Expt. Sta. Bull.* 312.)

and cover them with white froth.  It is probable that, throughout the northern part of the territory inhabited by this insect, these eggs will be laid so late in the season that they will not hatch until the following spring and the white crusts covering them will therefore be prominent objects during the winter.  We accordingly find two generations of this insect in the middle states, one in the north, and probably three in the south, corresponding, to some extent at least, to the length of time during which food is available.

The moths are seldom seen, though the males fly somewhat during the day.  The egg clusters, however, are objects that attract attention and the caterpillars are highly colored and so peculiar in appearance as to be very noticeable.  A full-grown caterpillar is nearly an inch and a half long, with a bright-red head and also two red humps above, near the hinder end.  Between the head and the middle of the body is a row of four large cream-colored tufts or "tussocks" of hairs standing up some distance above the surface of the body.  The side is grayish with a yellow band above and below.  Projecting upward, forward and outward from just behind the head are two slender clusters of black hairs or "pencils" about half an inch long, and a single similar but gray pencil of hairs projects upward and backward from near the hinder end of the body. These characters make the caterpillar of this insect a very striking and noticeable animal.

*Control.*—Gathering and destroying the egg clusters or applying creosote to them freely enough to penetrate the crust and reach all the eggs beneath are methods that can be made use of whenever the clusters are observed. Spraying for the caterpillars, using lead arsenate, standard formula, is also effective. Trees not infested, whose branches do not touch those of other and infested trees, can be protected by the use of sticky or cotton batting bands around their trunks during the periods when the caterpillars are crawling.

**The gypsy moth** (*Porthetria dispar* L.).—This European insect was introducedin to this country near Boston, Mass., by accident, about 1869 and has

Fig. 264.—Adults of the gypsy moth (*Porthetria dispar* L.): female on left; male on right; natural size.    (*From Britton, Fifth Rept. Ent. Conn. Agr. Expt. Sta.*, 1905.)

gradually spread until it now covers the greater part of the New England states and is also present in parts of New York, Pennsylvania and Canada.

The adult male moth (Fig. 264) is brown with some yellowish markings and spreads about an inch and a half. It flies freely during the day. The female (Fig. 264) has nearly white wings, with dark markings; a stout, heavy body covered behind with buff hairs; its wings spread about two inches, and though having well-developed wings this sex does not fly.

Winter is passed in the egg stage, the caterpillars hatching in the spring and feeding on many kinds of leaves, though the apple, oak, willow, alder and birch appear to be favorites; shrubs and herbaceous plants do not escape. Ash is not fed upon, nor is pine during the first two instars.

Feeding until early in July, the caterpillars become full-grown (Fig. 265) and may then be nearly three inches long and as large as a lead pencil. They are brown, partly hairy, the hairs being somewhat clustered, and on the back bear five pairs of blue spots, followed behind by six pairs of red ones. At the end of the feeding period the caterpillar crawls to any satisfactory place, usually the underside of some limb or on the trunk, and there spins a few threads to hold its body in place rather than for concealment or protection, and in this exceedingly scanty cocoon it pupates (Fig. 265); after a period of a week to seventeen or eighteen days, the moth emerges.

The eggs are now laid in oval clusters thoroughly covered by buff hairs from the abdomen of the moth, and each cluster may contain from four to five hundred. There seems to be little choice where the clusters are placed, many being on the trunks and limbs of the trees, but others are found in cavities in the trunks, on the stones of stone walls, even in the middle of the wall, or, in fact, anywhere the female may crawl to. They hatch the following spring.

Distribution appears to be accomplished by the crawling of the caterpillars; by carrying to other places objects on which egg clusters have been deposited; by

Fig. 265.—Pupae and larvae of the gypsy moth; natural size. (*From Britton, Fifth Rept. Ent. Conn. Agr. Expt. Sta.*, 1905.)

caterpillars spinning down on threads from the trees on to passing vehicles; and by the wind.

The injury caused by this insect is often very serious. The caterpillars have voracious appetites and eat large amounts and their abundance has often resulted in the stripping of large areas, which repeated several years in succession usually causes the death of the trees. With evergreens, a single defoliation is usually sufficient to kill the trees. In many parts of eastern Massachusetts the thinning of woodland areas, in consequence of the work of these insects, is very evident.

Parasites and other enemies of the gypsy moth have been introduced in large numbers by the Federal govenment, and where these have become abundant they have done good work, though, of course, nothing like extermination of the pest has been accomplished. A wilt disease, present in favorable seasons, kills many of the larvae at such times. In general, though, outbreaks of this insect in any locality are not repressed by their natural enemies for several years, and in the meantime the damage is great. This condition therefore calls for the use of control methods.

*Control.*—The egg clusters constitute one place where control measures can be applied. It is much easier to kill 400 or 500 insects concentrated in a space an inch square or less, than the same number in the larval stage, scattered over a tree. Soaking the egg clusters, at any time after they are laid until they hatch the following spring, with creosote to which a little lampblack has been added (to show by its color which clusters have been treated and which have not) is a good treatment. Care must be taken, however, in using this material, to take enough to reach all the eggs in the cluster. Usually a swab on the end of a stick, soaked in the creosote, is used for this work. The difficulty with this method is that of finding all the egg clusters in their varied places of concealment.

While the caterpillars are very small, spraying infested trees and other plants with lead arsenate, about 2½ pounds in 50 gallons of water, is a good treatment, but as the larvae become larger they seem to develop a greater resistance to poisons and spraying becomes less effective.

Tall shade trees and forests have been very effectively sprayed, by using large power sprayers, large hose and nozzles throwing a solid stream well up to the tree tops. The addition of fish-oil to lead arsenate as a "sticker" has proved advantageous.

As the larvae feed largely at night and seek concealment during the day, put loose bands of burlap around the trunks of infested trees, where they may hide in the daytime. Success with this method of control is dependent upon daily visits to the bands and the destruction of the caterpillars found under them.

Sticky bands around the trunks of noninfested trees will keep the caterpillars off them as long as the bands remain fresh and in good order.

As the caterpillars do not feed on the pine until after they have passed their second instar, pure stands of pine may be protected by removing all undergrowth other than pine and banding the trees as above, to prevent older larvae from crawling to them from places outside where they have obtained their earlier food. It is possible also so to manage the composition of mixed forests as to reduce the number of favored food trees and provide some degree of permanent control.

In 1923 a barrier zone about thirty miles wide was established, extending from Canada to Long Island Sound with the Hudson River as its western boundary for most of this distance. Here continual warfare has since been waged to destroy all gypsy moths, thus preventing the normal westward spread of the insect. Thus far this procedure has seemed to be quite effective.

**The brown-tail moth** (*Nygmia phæorrhæa* Don., Fig. 266, 1, 2).—This is another European pest which was accidentally introduced into this country near Boston, reaching there about 1892. Since that time it has spread as far as Nova Scotia and New Brunswick and also practically covers all of New England.

The moths are white except for the abdomen which has a few brown hairs, and the tip is covered by a tuft, large in the female, of golden-brown hairs— the character which has given this insect its common name. The moths spread about an inch and both sexes are strong fliers, appearing early in July. They are somewhat attracted to lights but in most cases the females found thus attracted appear to have already laid their eggs. The moths lay 200 or 300 eggs in a cluster, usually on the leaves, and cover them with brown hairs from the tip of the abdomen (Fig. 266, 3). They hatch in two to three weeks and the little caterpillars feed on the foliage in company during the early fall, leaving the veins and thus skeletonizing the leaves. Early in September they go

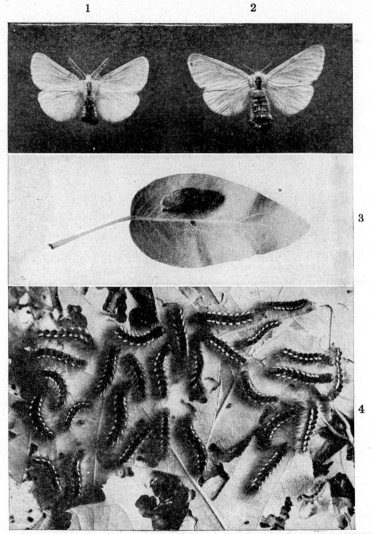

Fig. 266.—Brown-tail moth (*Nygmia phæorrhæa* Don.): 1, adult male; 2, adult female; 3, egg cluster covered by brown hairs from body of female, on leaf; 4, caterpillars feeding: all about natural size. (*From U. S. Dept. Agr. Ent. Bull.* 87.)

together to the tip of some twig and there spin a very tough, dense silvery tent, incorporating some of the leaves in it, to use as their resting place for the winter. The size and form of this tent will vary with the number of caterpillars contributing to its formation, but it is usually three or four inches long and an inch ᴏr two in diameter at its widest place.   After the leaves fall, these tents at the tips of the twigs are very conspicuous objects during the winter.   At the time of the formation of the tent the caterpillars are about one-third of an inch long.

In the spring as soon as the leaf buds begin to open, the caterpillars leave their tents and scatter, feeding until June when they become fully grown and are about an inch and a half long, brown, slightly mixed with orange, fairly well covered with fine reddish-brown hairs, and with two bright red tubercles, one behind the other, on the middle line of the body above, near the hinder end.   These red tubercles are very distinctive and give a positive recognition of this caterpillar.

The hairs just mentioned are delicate, brittle, barbed in some cases, and secrete a poisonous fluid very irritating to the skin.   As the caterpillars molt these hairs are, liable to be broken off and carried through the air to persons or onto their clothing, and a painful rash somewhat resembling that caused by poison ivy is produced, known as the brown-tail rash.

Pupation usually occurs among the leaves and after about twenty days is fol-

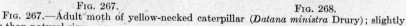

Fig. 267.                                      Fig. 268.

Fig. 267.—Adult moth of yellow-necked caterpillar (*Datana ministra* Drury); slightly less than natural size.

Fig. 268.—Yellow-necked caterpillars on a branch, showing characteristic attitudes assumed when disturbed; natural size.   (*From Britton, Eighteenth Rept. Ent. Conn. Agr. Expt. Sta.*, 1918.)

lowed by the emergence of the adult moths.   The cocoon, though more developed than with the gypsy moth, is not very thick or dense, and the pupa can generally be seen through its walls.

*Control.*—Cutting off and burning the winter tents at any time between September and April is an effective method of control where the size of the tree is such that the tents can easily be reached.   Spraying with lead arsenate, standard formula, either in the fall if no fruit is involved or when the larvae first resume feeding in the spring, is also a good treatment.

Many of the parasites imported by the Federal government to destroy the gypsy moth attack this species also and appear to have done good work.

During the last twenty years this insect has varied greatly in abundance, at times being scarce and at others quite abundant in some localities. This may be due in part to occasional unfavorable climatic conditions and in part to the varying abundance of its enemies.

*Family* **NOTODONTIDÆ** (the prominents).—The prominents, as the insects of this family are often called, are of medium size as adults and usually not at all brilliantly colored. Few of them are serious pests, and then generally only for a year or two at a time. The caterpillars of the different species differ greatly in appearance, some having dorsal humps or projections, others a much elongated end of the body, or other modification of the typical form of caterpillar.

One group in this family consists of moths known as the Datanas. The larvae of these insects feed on orchard, shade and forest trees, keeping together in

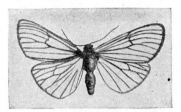 

Fig. 269.    Fig. 270.

Fig. 269.—California oak worm moth (*Phryganidia californica* Pack.); about natural size. (*After Essig, Inj. and Benef. Ins. of Cal.*)

Fig. 270.—Caterpillar of the California oak worm; natural size. (*Modified from Essig, Inj. and Benef. Ins. of Cal.*)

groups, and when resting or disturbed they bend the ends of the body nearly at right angles to the middle part in a very characteristic attitude. They feed during July and August and when full-grown are about two inches long. One species is common on the apple (Figs. 267, 268); others occur on the oak, walnut, hickory and other plants. The presence of 100 or 200 caterpillars feeding together on a single branch, and of considerable size as they get older, often disturbs the owners of infested trees who unnecessarily fear serious injury to their trees.

The fact that the caterpillars feed in groups renders control easy, however, either by removing the groups by hand or by spraying the region attacked, with a stomach poison, which is very effective for these insects.

*Family* **DIOPTIDÆ.**—This family appears to have but one North American representative, found only on the Pacific slope. It is known as the California oak worm (*Phryganidia californica* Pack.) (Fig. 269), the caterpillar of which feeds upon the leaves of the live oak and deciduous oaks. The adult moth is light brown with darker veins and a wingspread of about an inch and a quarter. The eggs are laid on the leaves of the oaks and various other plants in October and November and hatch during the five months following. Those on the deciduous oaks fall with the leaves, and larvae from them rarely find anything to feed upon and therefore die. The eggs laid on the live oak, eucalyptus and chestnut, however, produce caterpillars (Fig. 270) which can generally obtain food; they become full-grown in May and June and pupate in any protected place, spinning no cocoon. The moths from these pupae emerge after about two or three weeks and lay their eggs for a second generation, the larvae of which feed during the last of

July, August and September.   Pupation follows, after which the moths appear
and lay their eggs as already indicated.   When these insects are abundant, the
trees upon which they feed are liable to be entirely stripped of their foliage and
this sometimes happens over large areas.

*Control.*—Spraying the trees when the caterpillars are abundant, as they
begin to feed, with lead arsenate, 2 to 2½ pounds in 50 gallons of water, is effective where the size of the trees permits this treatment.   Power sprayers and
nozzles giving a fine mist are the most effective for this purpose.

*Family* **PHALÆNIDÆ** or **NOCTUIDÆ** (the owlet moths).—This is
the largest family of moths in this country and its members are everywhere abundant.   Within the group there are great differences in the

FIG. 271.—Catocala moth; natural size.

appearance of the moths and in the habits of their larvae.   Lochhead
has divided the family into nine sections, based mainly on differences of
larval habits.

Some members of this family are known as the Catocalas or underwings.
Some of these are quite large, spreading three inches or more, the forewings with
quiet colors and marked so that they resemble the bark of trees (Fig. 271).   One
has forewings similar to the bark of the white birch; another resembles the bark
of the beech; and many kinds of trees are thus imitated in color and markings.
The hind wings are often brightly, brilliantly colored.   It appears to be the habit
of the moths, which fly at night, to rest during the day on the tree trunks whose
bark their forewings resemble, folding these over their gaudy hind wings, in this
way obtaining, through concealment, protection from their enemies.   How far
in the course of thousands of generations the weeding out by their enemies of
those least closely resembling the bark, leaving behind to continue the race the
closest imitators of the bark, has resulted in giving to the present members of the
group a closer resemblance than their ancestors is a question for speculation.
The larvae of the Catocalas feed on foliage but are rarely if ever injurious enough
to be of importance.

The largest phalænid found in this country is known as the black witch (*Erebus
odorata* L.).   It does not live in the United States, being an inhabitant of the
tropics, but its size and powerful wings, which often spread six inches, enable it
to fly long distances and it is often captured in the late summer and fall in the

northern United States. It has dark wings of various shades of brown, and a small "eye" spot in each forewing.

**The cotton leafworm** (*Alabama argillacea* Hbn.).—The cotton leaf worm is not a native of this country but of more tropical countries, from which it frequently comes and attacks cotton in the southern states. The moths (Fig. 272) are of a nearly uniform reddish-brown or tawny color and spread a little over an inch. They lay their eggs singly on the cotton leaves and these eggs hatch in from three to more than twenty days, according to the temperature. The caterpillars are at first yellowish green with pale yellow heads. Later they vary much in color and markings, some changing little, whereas others acquire a black stripe along the middle of the back, with a fine central yellow line, and each segment has four black dots above. The full-grown larva webs a leaf or two together and pupates in this place, remaining there a varying length of time before the adult emerges.

Fig. 272.—Adult moth of the cotton leafworm (*Alabama argillacea* Hbn.); about one and one-half times natural size.

Fall flights northward of cotton leafworm moths occur frequently and may extend into the northern states and Canada, where these insects are sometimes abundant in September and October. Apparently they do not winter in the United States.

*Control.*—Dry calcium arsenate dusted over the plants when these insects first appear, using from two to four pounds per acre, according to the size of the plants, appears to be a satisfactory treatment. It is usually applied while the dew is on the plants. Ordinarily this insect is not important where the crop is poisoned for boll weevil control. The moth itself by means of the spines on its tongue can break soft-skinned fruits to suck the fluids within and frequently is thus quite injurious.

The dagger moths are leaf feeders on various shrubs and trees in their larval stages. The forewings of the moths are various shades of gray in most cases, and the larvae are usually quite well covered by rather uniformly distributed gray hairs.

Several species are known as green fruit worms, the caterpillars being greenish, without hairs, and feeding on the leaves and small fruit of apple and other trees during the later spring months. They are not often seriously abundant.

Some of the noctuids are stalk borers, tunneling in the stems of cultivated and other plants, among the plants affected in this way being corn, tomatoes, potatoes, asters and dahlias. The larva feeds during the summer months and as a rule pupates in the lower part of its tunnel. Accordingly, all wilted plants should be examined, and if a borer is present the plant should be destroyed with the borer, either as larva or as pupa, within it.

**The corn earworm** (*Heliothis armigera* Hbn.).—This widely distributed pest is known by several common names, such as the cotton boll worm, tomato fruit worm and false budworm of tobacco, in addition to the one first given. In the south it attacks cotton bolls and tobacco seed pods, as well as tomatoes and corn which are its usual food in the north. It is present practically everywhere in the world between the parallels of 50° north and south latitude; its original home is problematical.

The adult insect (Fig. 273a) spreads about an inch and three-quarters and is extremely variable in color, so that several varieties have been recognized. It ranges from a pale reddish brown to olive, with a greenish

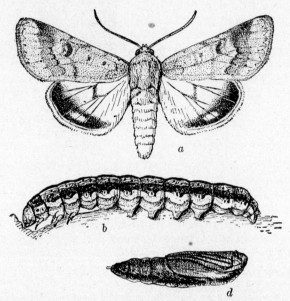

Fig. 273.—Corn earworm (*Heliothis armigera* Hbn.): *a*, adult moth; *b*, larva; *d*, pupa; all enlarged. (*From U. S. Dept. Agr. Farmers' Bul.* 890.)

tinge toward the outer margin of the forewings, with darker bands and spots, and the hind wings are lighter, with dark veins and a blackish shade crossing from one outer angle to the other, leaving more or less of a lighter color between this and the outer margin.

The insect appears to pass the winter as a pupa in the ground, the adult emerging in the spring. The eggs, varying in number from less than 500 to nearly 3,000, are now laid on different parts of the food plants and on weeds or even on the ground. They hatch in a week or less, according to the temperature, and the larvae (Fig. 273b) begin feeding, at first on the surface of the plant but soon bore into it at some tender place.

With cotton, injury is caused by eating out the squares and the more tender bolls. In the case of corn the first attack is by boring into the bud and eating down into the developing leaves. Later, the tassels are often injured before they open, and after the silk appears eggs are laid on this and the caterpillars which hatch from them bore into the ears of corn to varying distances, often entirely destroying the ears, particularly in the case of sweet corn. Tomatoes are injured mainly by the larvae boring into the green or partially ripened fruit, and in some cases by boring into the tips of the plants or eating the blossoms. With tobacco the larvae attack the bud leaves at the tip of the plant and later bore into the pods. Peaches, peas, beans, etc., are also sometimes injured and the average annual loss by the ravages of this pest in the United States has been estimated as over eighteen million dollars.

There are several generations of this insect each year, four or five being produced in the far south and this number reducing northward until in the northern states and Canada there is but one. The larvae vary greatly in color and markings and are most easily recognized by the nature of their work. When full-grown, they are about an inch and a half long.

*Control.*—Late fall plowing to break up the earthen cells in the ground where the insects winter as pupae, provided the plowing is rather deep, is a helpful procedure. As the larvae feed for a short time on the leaves of such plants as the tomato before boring into the fleshy parts, the application of derris dusts at or just before this time is advisable. With the increasing numbers in the later generations of the insect, fertilization, culture and any methods possible for hastening the maturity of the crop are desirable. Green corn is the preferred food plant of this insect and rows of corn planted in and near cotton fields, if in tassel and silk about the first of August, will attract most of the moths, leaving the cotton much more free than otherwise. On corn for table use, treating the fresh silks at the ear tip with a refined light or medium petroleum oil, or clipping off the tips of husks and silks bearing eggs and young larvae before the latter have time to reach the ear, is said to be somewhat effective on a small scale.

In the Phalænidæ are a number of species where some of the abdominal feet of the caterpillars are not functional or are absent, as a result of which these larvae travel like those of the geometers or "inchworms" already described. Several of these species are occasionally injurious to cultivated plants. In most cases at least, such larvae can be controlled by the application of lead arsenate.

The armyworms also are members of the Phalænidæ, this name being given to the insects because of their habit of marching from place to place all together, like armies. They are periodically injurious insects, appearing in great abundance at times, but rarely troublesome for more than one season at a time in the same place.

**The armyworm** (*Leucania unipuncta* Haw.).—This pest is probably a native of North America. It occurs over the entire eastern United States as far west as Kansas and Nebraska and has been reported from the southwestern states and California.

The adult moth (Fig. 274) spreads about an inch and a half and is quite uniformly brownish gray with a tiny white spot near the middle of each front wing and a rather dusky outer margin on the hind wings. The moths fly at night and are often attracted to lights.

In what stage this insect passes the winter does not appear to have been conclusively proved, but it is probably as the partly grown caterpillar hiding in rank, dense weedy growth. In late spring, at least, the nearly full-grown larvae have been found feeding on grasses primarily and then on small grain. The larvae mature quite rapidly, pupate in the ground and produce the moths in June, at least in the north. Eggs are now laid on grass and similar plants and hatch in eight or ten days and the larva feeds for three or four weeks until about an inch and a half long. It is now a nearly naked caterpillar (Fig. 275), somewhat variable in color but generally rather greenish, with a broad dark stripe along its back with a fine, broken white line along its middle, and a dark stripe along each side.

Fig. 274.—The armyworm (*Leucania unipuncta* Haw.); adult moth; enlarged one-third.

Before this size has been attained, all the food where these insects are may have been consumed if the larvae are abundant; in this case they march off in armies to find new feeding grounds, and it is these marching armies which usually attract attention in July or August. When feeding has been completed, they pupate in the ground and the moths emerge in September or October and probably lay eggs which soon hatch, the caterpillars thus produced feeding to some extent before winter. The spring-feeding generation appears to be little noticed, the destruction seen being by the summer generation.

When the caterpillars are abundant, numerous flies resembling, but larger than, houseflies and called tachina flies are usually noticed flying about the army. These are, nearly always at least, parasites laying their eggs on the caterpillars. The maggots that hatch from these eggs bore into the caterpillars and feed upon and finally kill them. There are also several other insect enemies of the armyworm.

*Control.*—If armyworms are discovered before they begin their march, spraying all the plants where they are with a stomach poison is an effective treatment; or if the infested area is small, straw can be spread over it and burned. Once on the march, protection of any crops toward which the caterpillars are marching, either by destroying the insects

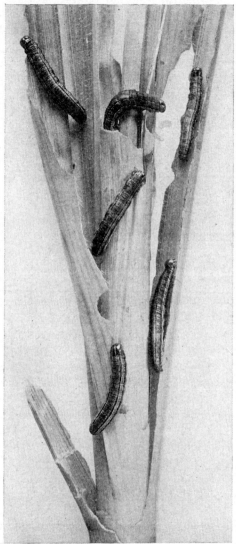

Fig. 275.—Armyworm caterpillars feeding on corn; natural size. (*From Britton, Fourteenth Rept. Ent. Conn. Agr. Expt. Sta.,* 1914.)

or by preventing their reaching the crops, is the aim of any treatment. Poisoned baits (see cutworms, page 275) may be used for this purpose, or where the ground over which the insects are marching is fairly smooth and firm the use of a heavy roller is possible. A ditch dug across their line of march or around an infested area is often used, and a log dragged along in the ditch as the caterpillars become thick in it will kill multitudes. Food in a strip ahead of their line of march, sprayed with a stomach poison, will result in the poisoning of those which feed there. In some cases the caterpillars while marching can be reached and killed by a strong contact insecticide.

**The fall armyworm** (*Laphygma frugiperda* S. & A.).—This insect in many ways resembles the true armyworm. It has numerous common names such as the grassworm, overflow worm and alfalfa worm and it is called the fall armyworm only in the middle and northern states, as it does not appear there before fall.

This insect is probably a native cf this country. Although most destructive in the south, it may spread during the season far to the

Fig. 276.                                    Fig. 277.

Fig. 276.—Moth of fall armyworm (*Laphygma frugiperda* S. & A.); about natural size. (*Modified from U. S. Dept. Agr. Farmers' Bul.* 752.)

Fig. 277.—Full-grown caterpillar of fall armyworm; somewhat enlarged. (*Modified from U. S. Dept. Agr. Farmers' Bul.* 752.)

north, reaching the New England states, southern Wisconsin and southeastern Montana, and extending westward to the Rocky Mountains.

The moth (Fig. 276) spreads about an inch and a quarter. Its front wings are mottled gray, usually with a light spot near the tip, and the hind wings pearly white, edged with a rather narrow dark line. It does not seem to be able to live over winter north of the southern parts of the Gulf states. The caterpillar (Fig. 277) feeds upon native grasses primarily, but when these are not sufficiently abundant it may attack grains, sorghum, alfalfa, clover, cotton and other crops.

In what stage this insect spends the winter does not seem to have been positively determined, but it is probably the pupa. The eggs, from fifty to several hundred in number, are laid preferably on grass blades and in the south hatch in a few days. The caterpillars feed two or three weeks before reaching full size and are then very similar to those of the armyworm. They then pupate for ten to fourteen days in the ground, after which the adult moths emerge. Many of these moths now fly northward, often several hundred miles, before laying their eggs, and in this new location another generation is produced, the adults of this generation also flying northward to lay their eggs. In this way the northern part of the country becomes infested in the fall but frost puts an end to the development of these insects near their northern limits before more than one generation can be produced. Going southward, more are possible, and in the Gulf states there may be six in the course of a season.

Where corn and cotton are grown, the destruction caused by this insect is often very great, the caterpillars as they get large having voracious appetites. They usually feed more at night than during the daytime and, like the armyworm, march to other places to find food when the supply where they are becomes exhausted.

In general the methods used for controlling the armyworm apply to this insect also.

A number of other species of noctuids have the habit of marching in armies when their food becomes scarce. Their life histories and habits are for the most part quite similar to those of the two species already described, and control methods for them are generally the same.

**Cutworms.**—In this section of the family Phalænidæ the insects are found practically everywhere in the United States. They are called cutworms (Figs. 278 and 279) because of the habit of the larvae of feeding on the stems of succulent plants at about the level of the ground and thereby either partly or entirely cutting them off at this point. Several hundred species have this habit and many kinds of garden and field crops suffer in this manner during the spring and early summer months. A

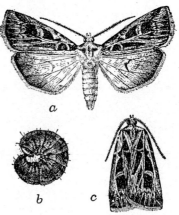

Fig. 278.—Dingy cutworm (*Feltia subgothica* Haw.): *a*, moth, wings spread; *b*, larva (cutworm); *c*, moth, wings folded; all somewhat enlarged. (*From U. S. Dept. Agr. Farmers' Bul.* 856.)

few have the habit of climbing up the plants at night and feeding there, some distance above the ground.

The moths are usually of medium size, spreading from an inch to about two inches, and are generally quiet colored, gray, brown or blackish, more or less mottled, streaked or banded on the forewings, and the hinder pair are nearly white and unmarked except for darker margins in some cases. Some species are more strongly marked, however, and have brighter colors.

Most of these insects winter either as pupae or partly grown caterpillars. In the spring the latter pass the day in the ground, coming up at night to feed. They are generally dull colored with rather faint spots and lines and without a hairy covering and when full-grown will average an inch to an inch and a half in length. When feeding has been completed, they pupate a few inches deep in the ground. Some species have one generation each year; others two.

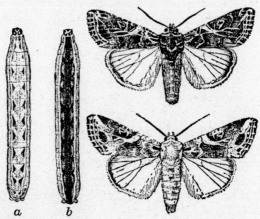

Fig. 279.—Yellow-striped armyworm (*Prodenia ornithogalli* Guen.): *a*, light form of cutworm; *b*, dark form; dark form of moth above; pale form below; all somewhat enlarged. (*From U. S. Dept. Agr. Farmers' Bul.* 890.)

*Control.*—Late fall plowing to bring up and expose the insects to the fluctuating temperatures of the cold season and its rains is a useful treatment, but other measures are also necessary. When cutworm work is seen, the use of a poison bait is desirable. For this purpose one good formula is

|  | Large Quantity | For Small Gardens |
|---|---|---|
| Bran | 50 lb. | 1 pk. |
| Paris green | 2 lb. | ½ lb. |
| Cheap molasses | 2 qt. | 1 pt. |
| Water | 3 to 7 gal. | 4 to 6 qt. |

The second formula is for use where only a small quantity is desired.

Mix the bran and poison together thoroughly, dry; mix the water and molasses and combine with the other mixture and stir thoroughly, adding enough more water finally to produce a rather stiff dough. This can be used in gardens, placing about a teaspoonful close to the base of each plant liable to attack, but should be put on toward night so that it will not dry up in the sun and lose its attractiveness to the cutworms. Fowls should be shut up while this treatment is being used, to prevent their feeding on the bait and being poisoned.

Where large fields are to be treated, a modification of this formula is desirable, reducing the amount of water to a point where the mixture is dry enough to spread broadcast, yet wet enough so that each flake of bran has been moistened by the molasses sufficiently to make it attractive and also to bear a little of the poison. The amount of water to add to obtain this condition must be determined by testing the mixture at intervals to see that the bran is dry enough to spread, and also that it has been able to take up the other materials. In any case the mixture should stand for several hours before use, to allow the bran time to take up the other constituents. The larger quantity given in the formula is sufficient to spread broadcast over several acres. Sometimes two or three oranges or lemons are chopped finely and added to the mixture in the belief that this added flavor makes the bait more attractive.

The size of the family Phalænidæ and the abundance of its members in all parts of the country, as well as the various methods of feeding present in the group, make it one of the most destructively important families of Lepidoptera in the United States.

*Family* **ARCTIIDÆ** (the tiger moths).—The arctiids are mainly medium-sized moths, often brilliantly colored. Most of the group are not serious pests,

FIG. 280.                          FIG. 281.
FIG. 280.—Isabella tiger moth (*Isia isabella* S. & A.); slightly reduced.
FIG. 281.—Hickory tussock moth (*Halisidota caryæ* Harr.); natural size.   (*From Britton, Seventh Rept. Ent. Conn. Agr. Expt. Sta.*, 1907.)

but individuals, particularly in their larval stages, are often seen. Many of these caterpillars are quite densely and uniformly covered with long hairs and are sometimes called woolly bears. One of them often seen crawling about in the fall is covered with reddish-brown hairs at each end and black ones in the middle and is sometimes given the particular name of banded woolly bear. The adult (Fig. 280), not often seen, is an orange-buff moth, its hind wings tinged with pinkish, and spreads a little over two inches. It is called the Isabella tiger moth (*Isia isabella* S. & A.). Another caterpillar, the salt-marsh caterpillar (*Estigmene acræa* Drury), has a blackish head and body, well covered with long, tufted brownish hairs. The adult is about the size of the Isabella tiger moth, the male having white forewings spotted here and there with black and the female having all its wings white and spotted. The abdomen of both sexes is orange. The hickory tussock moth (*Halisidota caryæ* Harr, Fig. 281) is quite common in the northeastern United States and Canada, west to Minnesota and south to North Carolina and Ohio. The larvae, which occur in the summer and fall, feed on many kinds of trees and are sometimes rather injurious. At first they feed in company but during the latter part of their larval life they scatter. The full-grown larva (Fig. 282) is an inch and a quarter or more in length, covered with grayish-white and black hairs. Along the middle of the back is a row of tufts of black hairs and there may also be longer, slender black tufts or "pencils." The insect winters as the pupa under rubbish on the ground, and the moths emerge in late spring and early summer and are yellowish in color, the forewings sprinkled with brown dots and two brownish streaks. These wings are rather narrow for their length and somewhat pointed. The hind wings are nearly transparent and almost white. The moths spread about two inches. Control is by spraying with a stomach poison as soon as the work of the caterpillars is noticed.

**The fall webworm** (*Hyphantria cunea* Drury).—This insect is a pest on shade, fruit and ornamental trees. It is found everywhere in the eastern United States and as far west as Montana and Texas. In the south and northward about to New York there are two generations each year

FIG. 282.  FIG. 283.

FIG. 282.—Full-grown caterpillar of the hickory tussock moth; natural size. (*From Britton, Seventh Rept. Ent. Conn. Agr. Expt. Sta.*, 1907.)

FIG. 283.—Fall webworm (*Hyphantria cunea* Drury); about natural size.

and a correspondingly greater amount of injury than where one is the rule.

The adult moth (Fig. 283) spreads about an inch and in the north has pure white wings. Farther south black spots are present on them, a difference that has led to the belief, still held by some persons, that there are really two species concerned. The winter is spent as the pupa in the ground, the moths emerging in the late spring and laying their eggs in clusters, often 200 or 300 in number, on the underside of the leaves. These hatch in about ten days and the larvae pass together to the outer foliage of some branch, where they form a thin white web over the surface, feeding on the leaves enclosed within the web (Fig. 284). As the caterpillars grow and consume this foliage, the web is extended to cover more leaves; by the time full size has been attained by the caterpillars, the web may be as large as a bushel basket. The full-grown larva (Fig. 285) is over an inch long, quite hairy but not sufficiently so to conceal the body which is generally "pale yellowish or greenish, with a broad, dusky stripe along the back and a yellow stripe along the sides; they are covered with whitish hairs which spring from

FIG. 284.—Branch covered by web of the fall webworm. (*From N. H. Agr. Expt. Sta. Bul.* 139.)

black and orange-yellow warts" (Packard). The head is black. The larvae pupate in the ground.

Where there are two generations, the moths appear in June or even earlier and the second-generation moths develop early enough in the fall for the larvae from their eggs to become full-grown before the leaves drop. Where there is but one generation, the webs appear the last of July and in August and reach full size in September.

FIG. 285.—Full-grown larva of the fall webworm. Natural size.

*Control.*—There are several ways by which to check the ravages of this insect. When the webs first appear, they may be stripped off by hand and the then small larvae crushed. Branches attacked may be cut off if the tree is of sufficient size not to be marred in this way. Spraying around the tent with a stomach poison, standard formula, will poison the leaves next to be brought within the web by its further enlargement and thus provide the caterpillars with poisoned food.

*Family* **CERATOCAMPIDÆ** (the royal moths).—In this family are included several very large moths and a few smaller ones. The regal moth (*Citheronia regalis* Fab.) may have a wingspread of six or seven inches (Fig. 286). Its forewings are rather dusky but the veins are lined with orange-red and there are numerous yellow spots. The hind wings are lighter, with some yellowish areas, and veins lined as in the other pair. The stout body is brownish orange with

Fig. 286.—Regal moth (*Citheronia regalis* Fab.); about half natural size. (*From Felt, N. Y. State Mus. Mem.* 8.)

narrow, yellowish cross lines. The caterpillar (Fig. 287), which feeds upon various trees, is four or five inches long when full-grown and has a green body bearing numerous black spines. Just back of the head, there are a number of very long reddish spines bending backward and tipped with black. The head is red. The terrifying appearance of this caterpillar has probably been the reason for calling it the hickory horned devil. The insect is found from Massachusetts to Louisiana, Texas and Missouri but is not very abundant and therefore does little

Fig. 287.—Full-grown larva of the regal moth; slightly less than half natural size. (*From Packard, Mem. Nat. Acad. Sci.* IX, *Part* II.)

injury. It feeds on the black walnut, butternut, hickory and a number of other trees and has once or twice caused some damage to cotton. It winters as a pupa in the ground.

Another large moth belonging here is the imperial moth (*Eacles imperialis* Drury, Fig. 288) which has about the same distribution as the regal moth. The adult often spreads six inches and is yellow, with lilac or purplish-brown areas or bands and spots. The caterpillar (Fig. 289) is green (or brown sometimes), from three to four inches long when full-grown, rather well covered with long, white hairs, and has two pairs of rather stout, upward projecting tubercles or horns behind the head. It feeds on quite a list of trees, including some of the evergreens, and pupates in the ground during the winter. Like the last species it is rarely if ever abundant enough to be of economic importance.

Fig. 288.—Imperial moth (*Eacles imperialis* Drury). Slightly more than half natural size. (*From Felt, N. Y. State Mus. Mem.* 8.)

Several insects in this family are quite common at times and locally may be numerous enough to cause some injury to oaks, maples and other trees they feed upon, but their presence is noticed for only a year or two at a time.

Fig. 289.—Full-grown larva of imperial moth; somewhat reduced. (*Reduced from Packard, Mem. Nat. Acad. Sci.* IX, *Part* II.)

*Family* **SATURNIIDÆ** (the giant silkworms).—In this family belong most of the common, very large moths found in North America. Though their size and that of their caterpillars attract attention, these insects are of little economic importance as the number of eggs laid by an individual is not very large and they are generally well scattered so that few larvae are often found on any one tree. If the silk of their cocoons could be utilized, they would become industrially important, but the thread is frequently broken so that reeling it is difficult and expensive.

FIG. 290.—Cecropia moth (*Samia cecropia* L.); slightly over half natural size.

One of the more common species in this family is the cecropia moth (*Samia cecropia* L.), a very large brownish-gray insect (Fig. 290) with a whitish crescent-shaped spot, partly shaded with brown, near the center of each wing. Outside

FIG. 291.—Polyphemus moth (*Telea polyphemus* Cram.); about three-quarters natural size.

this spot a whitish line crosses the wing and the outer margin is more or less broken by black spots on a whitish ground. The abdomen is brown with white crossbands. The caterpillar (see Fig. 22), which when full-grown is from three to four inches long, is green with tubercles along its back, two pairs near the head being coral red and the others yellow except the first and last pair, which are blue.  The insect feeds on many kinds of plants, including some fruit and shade trees.  The moths appear in late spring, the larvae feed during the summer and in the fall spin rather dense cocoons on the twigs of the trees, in which they pupate and pass the winter.

Fig. 292.—Male promethea moth (*Callosamia promethea* Drury); about two-thirds natural size.

A rather similar moth, though usually a little smaller, is the polyphemus moth (*Telea polyphemus* Cram.), with brown wings crossed near the outer margin by a blackish band (Fig. 291).  The front wing has a transparent eyespot with a yellow margin, around which is a black line.  The hind wing has a somewhat similar spot, but the black around it covers quite an area, particularly toward the base of the wing.  The caterpillar is green with a yellow oblique line on the side of most of the segments of the abdomen and it feeds on many fruit and forest trees.  The cocoon is spun among leaves on the ground.

Somewhat smaller, spreading about four inches, is the promethea moth (*Callosamia promethea* Drury).  The male moth (Fig. 292) is dark brown except toward the outer margin of the

Fig. 293.—Female promethea moth; about two-thirds natural size.

wing, where the color lightens somewhat outside a whitish cross line, and the outer margin is light grayish with fine brown lines.  Near the apex of the front wing is a black eyespot, margined on the inner side with blue.  The female (Fig. 293) is brown with a triangular white spot near the center of each wing, a short distance outside of which the brown ends abruptly in a very irregular edge against white, which shades off into brown again.  The outer margin is as in the male and the eyespot is also present on the forewing.

The caterpillar is pale green with very small black tubercles in pairs above, except two pairs not far behind the head, which are coral-red and larger than the others, and a yellow one above, near the hinder end. The larvae feed on many kinds of trees and shrubs, appearing to prefer the sassafras, wild cherry and ash. When through feeding, each selects a leaf, the petiole of which it spins around, fastening it in this way to the twig on which it grew, so that it cannot drop off in the fall. It then forms its cocoon with the leaf as a partial wrapping, drawing the edges around the cocoon (Fig. 294). Here, in this hanging cocoon, swaying in the winds, the insect passes the winter.

One of the largest insects in this family is known as the luna moth (*Tropœa luna* L.). Its body is densely covered with white hairs, giving it a woolly appearance; its wings are pale green, with more or less complete purplish margins, particularly strong along the costa of the forewing (Fig. 295). In the front wing is a rather oval eyespot connected by a purplish band with the costa. The hind wing also has an eyespot, more circular in outline, shaded with darker on the side nearest the body, and the wing itself extends backward into a long narrow tail. The green caterpillars, between two and three inches long when full-grown, feed upon a number of kinds of trees and pupate among leaves on the ground in the fall. The insect is found from Canada southward throughout the United States east of the Rocky Mountains.

One of the smaller, very common moths of this group is the io moth (*Automeris io* Fab.), which spreads between three and four inches (Fig. 296). The two sexes differ in color, the ground color in the male being yellow; in the female that of the forewings is purplish red. The yellow of the male forewing has irregular spots and a wavy line of brownish; in the female

Fig. 294.—Cocoon of the promethea moth; n a t u r a l  s i z e. (*From Britton, Thirteenth Rept. Ent. Conn. Agr. Expt. Sta.*, 1913.)

the ground color is broken by irregular shadings and a lighter wavy line. The striking feature of the hind wing in both sexes is a large, circular, bluish eyespot with a white dot forward of its center. The bluish shades into black outside and is surrounded by the yellow ground color. Between the eyespot and the outer margins are a black line and a dull-rose band, and the base and hinder margin are dull rose.

The caterpillar is about two inches long when full-grown, with a rather wide reddish-brown stripe edged with white below, on each side of the body. It has many spines that branch, the branches being tipped with black. Touching the caterpillars produces a nettling of the skin, owing to a poison conveyed through the tips of the spines. The larvae feed on fruit, forest and shade trees and usually make their cocoons among leaves on the ground.

There are quite a number of kinds of giant silkworms, the family being represented in all parts of the country. One generation a year, the moths appearing earlier or later in the spring according to the length of the season, the larvae

FIG. 295.—Luna moth (*Tropœa luna* L.); slightly over half natural size. (*From Felt, N. Y. State Mus. Mem.* 8.)

feeding during the summer, and pupation in the fall, with the winter spent in this stage, appears to be the general rule, though with some exceptions, for most, if not all, of the species.

FIG. 296.—Female io moth (*Automeris io* Fab.); about two-thirds natural size. (*From Felt, N. Y. State Mus. Mem.* 8.)

*Family* **SPHINGIDÆ** (the hawk moths).—This large and widespread group of insects has long and rather narrow forewings and its members have a strong flight. Most of them are of quite large size (Fig. 297) and fly chiefly at dusk, visiting flowers for the nectar, upon which they feed. They do not alight on the flower but hover over it, running the tongue, which is often much longer than the body, into the nectary. The body is usually rather stout, spindle-shaped, and it and the wings are often

Fig. 297.—Hawk moth (*Sphinx chersis* Hbn.); natural size.

beautifully colored with combinations of black, gray, olive, tan and rose or pink. The antennae are large, usually somewhat thickened near the middle, and the end is in some cases curved a little, like a hook.

The larvae feed upon the leaves of various trees and other plants. They are naked and generally green, though frequently of other colors;

Fig. 298.—Day-flying hawk moth (*Hemaris diffinis* Bdv.), about natural size.

in the former case they often have oblique white streaks on the sides of the body and a long horn projecting upward and backward from the upper side near the hinder end. Some, when full-grown, may be two or three inches long. Pupation is usually in earthen cells underground, though some form partial cocoons of leaves and silk on the surface. In some species the tongue at the time of pupation is not enclosed by that part of the pupal skin which covers the body, but by a separate portion which joins the remainder at the front of the head and touches the body about halfway back; this makes it resemble the handle of a pitcher or jug in its relation to the pupa as a whole (Fig. 300).

A few species have their wings only partly covered by scales. These are among the smaller species and they fly during the day (Fig. 298).

Of the various species of hawk or hummingbird moths, as they are sometimes called, only two or three are usually of any great economic importance.

**The tobacco and tomato hornworms.**—There are two closely related hawk moths whose larvae feed on tobacco and tomato leaves. One

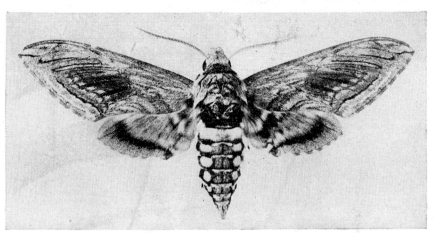

Fig. 299.—Tomato hornworm moth (*Protoparce quinquemaculata* Haw.); natural size. (*From Britton, Sixth Rept. Ent. Conn. Agr. Expt. Sta.*, 1906.)

of these is known as the tomato hornworm (*Protoparce quinquemaculata* Haw.) and the other as the tobacco hornworm (*Protoparce sexta* Johan.).

The adult is a moth (Fig. 299) spreading from four to five inches. In the tomato hornworm the color of the forewings is ashy gray and the abdomen has a row of yellow spots, usually five in number on each side, and in the tobacco hornworm the forewings are brownish gray and there are usually six yellow spots on each side of the abdomen.

The life history in both species is quite similar. Winter is passed as a pupa (Fig. 300) in the ground and in these insects the tongue has a separate case in the pupa. The moths appear in the spring and lay their eggs singly on the leaves of their food plants and the caterpillars feed for three or four weeks, becoming three or four inches long, green or sometimes brown in color. In the tomato hornworm each abdominal segment is marked on the side by an oblique greenish-white stripe joining a similar horizontal one at its lower end, forming a series of whitish V's. On the

Fig. 300.—Pupa of the tobacco hornworm (left) and of the tomato hornworm (right); natural size. Note difference in length of the tongue case. (*From Britton, Sixth Rept. Ent. Conn. Agr. Expt. Sta.*, 1906.)

hinder end of the body above is a projecting green horn with black sides.

The larva of the tobacco hornworm (Fig. 301) has only the oblique bands and the horn is usually reddish. In the northern part of the range of these species there is one generation a year. Farther south, two seems to be the rule, and in the Gulf states three or four are claimed to occur.

Fig. 301.—Full-grown larva of tobacco hornworm; natural size.   (*From Britton, Sixth Rept. Ent. Conn. Agr. Expt. Sta.*, 1906.)

*Control.*—Hand-picking is a frequent method of control where the larvae are not abundant. Spraying, when the caterpillars are first seen, with lead arsenate, standard formula, has proved effective. Applied as a dust it has also given good results, but this material either as a spray or as a powder should not be used on tomatoes after the fruit is half grown.

### RHOPALOCERA (butterflies)

The remaining families of Lepidoptera to consider are those of the suborder Rhopalocera, or butterflies. Most of the insects in this section are rarely of much economic importance, their larvae feeding chiefly on plants not utilized in any way as food. Occasionally some species may cause local injury, but only a few need special consideration from this standpoint.

*Family* **HESPERIIDÆ** (the skippers).—These are rather small butterflies which have a curious "skipping" style of flight. They are most frequently black, or yellow and black, in color, often with silvery spots or streaks (Fig. 302). The larvae in this family have heads much larger than the part of the body next behind, making them easy to recognize. One of the larger members of this group, found in the south, feeds as a caterpillar on the bean and is known as the bean leaf roller.

*Family* **LYCÆNIDÆ.**—In this group belong the little blue butterflies spreading, in most cases at least, less than an inch; similar-sized dark-brown butterflies; and others which are of a red or coppery color (Fig. 303), with black spots. Many of these insects are very common but are of no importance economically. One species here departs from the general rule as to the food of Lepidoptera, its larva being carnivorous and feeding on plant lice. Unfortunately it is not common enough to be very beneficial.

Some of the species in this family have more than one generation each year and the adults of the two generations are so different that until one kind was bred from eggs laid by the other they were supposed to be different species. Difference in color, markings or both may therefore be correlated with the season

FIG. 302.            FIG. 303.

FIG. 302.—Skipper butterfly (*Proteides clarus* Cram.); natural size.
FIG. 303.—Little copper butterfly (*Lycæna hypophlæas* Bdv.); about natural size.

of the year, and insects having two different forms according to the season present cases of what is called seasonal dimorphism.

*Family* **DANAIDÆ.**—This small family is of interest in the United States mainly because it includes one of our largest and most widely

FIG. 304.—The monarch (*Danaus plexippus* L.); natural size.

distributed butterflies, the monarch (*Danaus plexippus* L.). This is common in nearly all parts of the country and has a striking way of sailing about in the air. The ground color of the wings is tawny brown marked with black lines along the veins, and broad black borders containing white spots (Fig. 304). The caterpillars feed upon milkweed and are greenish yellow with black crossbands and a pair of soft fleshy projections on the back a little behind the head, and another pair not far from the hinder end of the body. The pupa (chrysalis) is usually attached to the plant and is about an inch long, stout, bright green with golden dots.

Though the monarch breeds in the northern states during the summer, it appears to come from the south each spring, and in the fall multitudes often gather and fly southward together. Apparently they produce a generation in the south in the early spring, the members of which work northward with one or two generations on the way.

Fig. 305.—The viceroy (*Basilarchia archippus* Cram.); natural size.

This insect is practically free from attack by birds, probably because it is able to produce a disagreeable odor.

*Family* **NYMPHALIDÆ.**—This large afmily includes many familiar forms, most of them large or of at least fair size. Their forelegs have been reduced so much that they are no longer used but are carried folded up against the thorax.

Several of the common species in this group are found in Europe as well as in this country and a few occur nearly everywhere in the world where food and temperature permit their existence. The larvae of some species feed on the currant, gooseberry and hop in the list of cultivated plants but are not often important pests.

In one section of the family the insects are usually black with blue or green and occasionally red spots, and one or two species have a white band across the wings. One of this group, however, differs greatly in color from all the rest of its relatives, being reddish brown with black-lined veins, black wing borders enclosing white spots, and so closely resembling the monarch that it has been called the viceroy (Fig. 305). It differs from the monarch, to the eye, however, by the presence of a narrow black band across the hind wings and by its somewhat smaller size.

This radical departure in color and pattern of this insect from that of all its near relatives is believed to be because this group is one freely attacked by birds for food, while the monarch, perhaps because of a disagreeable odor, escapes. Any imitation that would deceive the birds would accordingly protect insects possessing it and enable them to avoid destruction. How such a change could be rapidly developed, however, to such a degree as to enable its possessors to benefit by it, has not been satisfactorily explained, and if it were not so developed the individuals in which the change began could hardly differ enough from their former condition to escape. Here remains one of the unsolved problems of insect life.

*Family* **SATYRIDÆ** (the satyrs).—The insects belonging in this family are of medium size and nearly all have gray or brown wings with spots more or less

Fig. 306.—A satyr butterfly (*Minois alope* Fab.); natural size.

resembling eyespots (Fig. 306). They are common near the edges of woods and sometimes drift out into the fields. One species is found only on the tops of the White Mountains in New Hampshire and on the higher Rocky Mountains. How these colonies became so widely separated is a question, though explanations for it have been suggested.

*Family* **PIERIDÆ.**—In this family belong the medium-sized or small yellow butterflies of various shades and the white ones, common in all parts of the country. About fifty kinds occur in the United States and some of them are occasionally, and others almost always, injuriously abundant in one place or another.

**The imported cabbage worm** (*Pieris rapæ* L.).—This insect, a native of Europe, appears to have reached Quebec about 1859. It spread rapidly and ten years later had reached Massachusetts. Other specimens arriving at New York and Charleston, N.C., also established centers from which the insect spread in all directions, and it is now found nearly everywhere in the United States.

The adult (Fig. 307a) spreads a little less than two inches.  Its wings are white, the tip of the front wing grayish.  In the male there is a black spot near the center of the front wing and one on the front margin of the hind wing, while in the female the front wing has a second black spot behind the other.

The insect passes the winter as a pale-brown chrysalis (Fig. 307d) about three-quarters of an inch long, attached in some protected place. The adults emerge in the spring and lay their eggs singly (Fig. 307b)

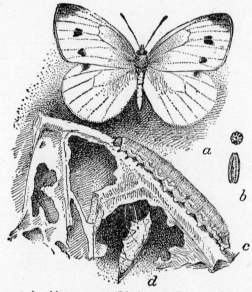

Fig. 307.—Imported cabbage worm (*Pieris rapæ* L.): *a*, adult, slightly enlarged; *b*, egg, from side and from above, considerably enlarged; *c*, caterpillar, somewhat enlarged; *d*, chrysalis, somewhat enlarged.  (*From U. S. Dept. Agr. Farmers' Bul.* 856.)

on the leaves of cabbage, cauliflower, mustard, nasturtium and other plants of the family Cruciferæ, and about a week later the caterpillar hatches and begins to feed.  At first it is pale green, but when full-grown, after about two or three weeks, is a soft, velvety green, and about an inch long (Fig. 307c).  At first it feeds on the under surface of the leaf but, after growing, eats holes through and may leave only the veins.  It often bores into the forming heads also, in search of more tender food.  It feeds for from two to three weeks, then pupates for a rather shorter period, at the end of which time the adult emerges and lays eggs for a second generation.  There are usually two or three generations in the northern states and as many as five or six in the South.

Where these insects are abundant, they cause considerable injury, not only to the leaves but by boring into the heads reducing their value.

*Control.*—Spraying or dusting with ground derris or cube as soon as the caterpillars make their appearance is a successful treatment. The ground roots should contain four or five per cent rotenone. A spray should contain three pounds of derris or cube in fifty gallons of water with a sticker such as soybean flour added. For dusting, the derris or cube root may be mixed with an inert carrier such as talc or sulfur (not lime), one part of the ground root to seven parts of the carrier. About twenty-five pounds of the dust should be used per acre. The use of arsenicals is not advisable because of the poisonous residues that may remain until harvest, especially in the case of cauliflower, broccoli and other plants the sprayed parts of which are eaten.

FIG. 308.—Male clouded sulfur butterfly (*Colias philodice* Godt.); natural size.

A native cabbage butterfly, closely resembling the last, was formerly common in the north but appears to have suffered from competition with its imported rival. A southern native species has also become somewhat reduced in abundance, but less so than the northern one.

FIG. 309.—Alfalfa caterpillar butterfly (*Colias eurytheme* Bdv.); adult about 1½ times natural size. (*From U. S. Dept. Agr. Bul.* 124.)

The common sulfur-yellow butterflies (Fig. 308) with more or less of black markings on their wings are, for the most part, feeders on clover in their larval stages. One of them, the alfalfa caterpillar (*Colias eurytheme* Bdv.), is frequently a pest on alfalfa. It occurs everywhere in the United States west of the Allegheny Mountains and has been taken occasionally along the Atlantic coast but is chiefly of importance in the southwest.

The adult (Fig. 309) spreads about two inches and its wings are orange yellow with black outer borders; a black spot in front of the center of the forewing and two reddish-orange spots, which touch each other, near the center of each hind wing. In the female the black wing border has yellow spots in it. Sometimes the orange color in the female is replaced by whitish. The caterpillar is brown at first but later becomes dark green with a white stripe on each side (Fig. 310). Alfalfa, clovers, vetches and other legumes are fed upon. The number of generations seems to vary in different parts of the country from two in the north to six, or possibly more, in the far south. The colder or, in the southwest, the dry months may be passed as larva, pupa or adult. Treatment is by cultural methods such as pasturage, or early and close cutting of the crop, followed if necessary by rolling or brush dragging.

FIG. 310.— Alfalfa caterpillar; slightly enlarged. (*Modified from U. S. Dept. Agr. Bul.* 124.)

*Family* **PAPILIONIDÆ** (the swallowtails).—The butterflies of this group are nearly all large, and with a backward-projecting lobe or tail on the hind wing. One species or another may be seen in almost every part of the country but they rarely do much injury, feeding for the most part on plants of little importance. The black swallowtail (*Papilio ajax* L.) is probably the most important species, as it occurs all over the United States and feeds on celery, carrots, parsnips and other plants.

The butterfly (Fig. 311c) spreads between three and four inches. Its wings are black with two rows of yellow spots crossing each wing, with blue shadings between the two rows on the hind pair. There is also a black spot surrounded by orange on the outer part of the inner margin of the hind pair. In the male the inner row of yellow spots becomes a band on the hind wing.

In the south the butterflies winter over, but in the north this period is spent as the pupa. Eggs are laid singly on the leaves of the food plants (Fig. 311d) and hatch in about ten days. The caterpillars feed for from ten days to several weeks, then form their chrysalids (pupæ) on some part of the plant (Fig. 311f) and in from ten days to two weeks more the adult butterflies emerge. There are two generations in the north and more in the south.

The caterpillar when full-grown (Fig. 311a and b) is about two inches long, green with a black crossband on each segment, which may enclose six yellow spots or may fail to close these in on the front side of the band. Just back of the head is an opening out of which a soft, widely forked horn can be protruded when the insect is disturbed. Such structures are called osmeteria and give off a disagreeable pungent odor and are probably to drive away enemies that may attack the insects.

This insect is rarely if ever important enough to call for any control other than destroying the larvae by hand, though in most cases spraying or dusting with derris would be entirely effective if such a treatment were necessary.

A similar species present on the Pacific coast has the same habits.

Fig. 311.—Black swallowtail (*Papilio ajax* L.): *a*, full-grown caterpillar; *b*, head of same showing osmeterium extended; *c*, male butterfly; *d*, outline of egg; *e*, young larva; *f*, chrysalis. All about natural size except *d*, which is much enlarged. (*From U. S. Dept. Agr. Farmers' Bull.* 856.)

The spreading of an insect introduced into a country is always of interest, even if no financial factor is involved, and several of the species considered in this chapter supply good examples of this. Its method of introduction, its establishment, the rapidity with which it spreads and the final limits of its distribution are all topics for investigation.

In the case of the gypsy moth its introduction was apparently intentional, though it was far from the plan of the scientist who brought it to this country that it should escape. It is stated that this scientist had in mind testing the silk-producing possibilities of various Lepidoptera and imported a number of species for that purpose. Unfortunately, in some way, some of the gypsy moth specimens escaped and, as he could not find them, he issued a notice calling attention to the fact and warning the public of the possible menace they might become.

The brown-tail moth appears to have been brought to this country as a winter tent containing young caterpillars, on an importation of roses from Europe. This occurred before the inspection of nursery stock imported into this country was required by law. How the imported cabbage worm arrived is not known, but it was probably the chrysalis on some material brought as freight.

It is evident that, in any case, either an adult female able to deposit fertile eggs or else several individuals at least, in some early stage, must be imported at about the same time, if the species is to obtain a start. Then with an individual ready to lay its eggs, suitable food plants for its young must be found. There can be no doubt, in theory at least, that there have been many cases in the past where failure to succeed in this has resulted in the failure to establish themselves of many species which would have been serious pests.

Once started, however, even in a small way, an increase in numbers and in distribution becomes possible. If some of the insects, however, were parasitized and the parasites escaped, as well as those not so affected, the spread might be checked because of the small number of the pests that would not be found by the parasites.

The spreading of a species from the point where it starts has been aptly compared to that of a ripple caused by throwing a stone into water, which passes out in every direction on its surface. Such a spread will extend as far as the insect can find food on which it can live and a temperature and humidity under which it can survive. It follows that, for many insects adapted to northern climatic conditions, a point will be reached in its southward spread where the temperature and humidity are such as to prevent its going farther. A lofty and continuous mountain range may, by producing such conditions, also prove a barrier to further extension in that direction, even though beyond the range a favorable climate may again be found. Absence of any food upon which an insect can live will also put an end to distribution in that direction, and a pest adapted to the moist climate of the eastern states may find itself unable to establish itself in arid regions. The rapidity with which it spreads appears to be determined by its fecundity, power of flight in many cases and food supply at least generally, an insect having a high rate of increase, abundant food and being strong in flight sometimes spreading several hundred miles in a year. The much larger area to the north and northeast of Boston than to the south and west, now occupied by the browntail moth, appears to be due, in part at least, to strong southwesterly winds while the moths are flying.

Study of these and other factors involved shows that northern insects as they spread southward are found, chiefly at least, on higher land. One living at near the sea level in the northern states will generally be found in the mountains in the south, and if it extends into Mexico it will there occur only on the higher Cordilleras, gaining by its elevation the lower temperature it has lost by its change of latitude.

Thus we find that, with sufficient information at hand, the distribution of many insects can be mapped, and that there is a division of the country into regions, the insects of one region rarely spreading far beyond its limits, and then only forming outposts of the species.

It is true that some species are less affected than others by these conditions. The monarch butterfly, the housefly and many others appear to be able to live under wide differences of temperature, humidity and the other factors concerned. As a whole, though, an insect will spread within certain limits and only within these, and this applies to other animals and to plants as well.

# CHAPTER XXX

## ORDER MECOPTERA

### (Panorpatæ)

The Mecoptera is a small order of insects, both in numbers and in the size of its members. The adults usually have wings that are membranous, long and generally narrow, with numerous veins. In a few

FIG. 312.—Adult mecopteron (*Panorpa nuptialis* Gerst.); natural size, showing beak projecting downward from the head, on the end of which are the mouth parts.

cases, however, they are reduced or even rudimentary. The head is elongated on its underside, forming a sort of beak or rostrum, at the end of which are the chewing mouth parts (Fig. 312). In the males of one genus the terminal segments of the abdomen are drawn out and curl upward, suggesting the position of the end of the body in the scorpion, and from this the common name scorpion flies has been applied to the order, though some of its members do not have this character. The larvae considerably resemble small caterpillars.

The distinctive characters of the order are

*Insects which when adult nearly always have four membranous wings, long and narrow and with numerous veins; head prolonged downward forming a beak, bearing chewing mouth parts at its end. Larvae more or less caterpillar-like. Metamorphosis is complete.*

Mecoptera occur in nearly all parts of the world but nowhere appear to be very abundant. They seem to prefer to live in places having rank growth and in low, damp woods and are apparently carnivorous both as larvae and as adults. A few species are found on snow during the winter months and are wingless, or nearly so, but most of the group have wings longer than their bodies and fly quite well. The eggs are usually laid in masses in the ground and the larvae live in burrows in the ground, coming out to feed. They have legs supporting the abdomen and these are more numerous than in caterpillars. As far as is known, they pupate in earthen cells in the ground.

The adults certainly feed upon other insects; larvae in confinement can be fed upon meat, but their natural food is probably any animal material they can obtain. Under such circumstances, these insects must be regarded as being, at best, of little economic importance. Fossil forms belonging to the Mecoptera have been discovered in different parts of the world. Less than 500 species are known.

In a general way this order appears to have the Diptera, Trichoptera and Lepidoptera as its nearest relatives.

# CHAPTER XXXI

## ORDER DIPTERA

The Diptera or flies are small insects, the largest species known being slightly more than two inches long, but the majority are much smaller, and many are almost microscopic. The flies as a group are distinguished from other insects by the presence of only one—the front—pair of wings, attached to the mesothorax. Sometimes these are absent, the insect being entirely wingless, but there are only a few such cases. The hind wings have been transformed into a pair of curious structures known as halteres. They are small and each resembles a sort of knob joined to the body by a stalk, usually slender and variable in length. They are believed to have special functions but what these are is far from settled.

The wings are usually transparent, though sometimes smoky or otherwise colored; in some instances scales are present either along the veins or elsewhere, and in one family they entirely cover both the body and wings. The veins are usually quite numerous but often show a tendency to unite toward the outer margin of the wing, forming closed cells in this way as well as by the more usual method with cross veins. In some families, the veins are very few and sometimes several appear only as faint traces. The hinder margin of the wing not far from its attachment to the body frequently has a notch called the axillary incision or sinus, and the membrane from here to the base may form one lobe or by other incisions consist of two or even three lobes. The one nearest the base in some instances appears to become enlarged and lie over the base of the halter, often partly or entirely concealing this structure from above.

The head of the fly is connected with the thorax by a small neck which permits considerable rotation. Much of its surface is occupied by the very large compound eyes which frequently meet above, particularly in the males. Between the two eyes, or behind their point of meeting, are usually three ocelli on the top of the head.

The antennae vary greatly. They may consist of as many as thirty segments or as few as three, in the latter case a bristle, frequently feathered, being often present, joined to the outer segment.

In one section, a crescent-shaped cleft occurs above the attachment of the antennae to the head, curving downward on each side. This slit is called the lunule, and at the time when the fly escapes from its pupa case a large bladder-shaped structure is pushed out through this from the inside of the head and, pressing against the end of the case, forces it off, enabling the fly to escape. Later, this structure which is called the ptilinum is drawn back into the head.

The mouth parts of flies are for sucking, and in some cases for piercing, also. True "biting flies" do not exist, the "bite" being really caused by the plunging of the sharp-ended, piercing mouth parts into the object attacked. There seems to be little doubt that the mouth parts of flies have been derived from ancestors with chewing structures, but the

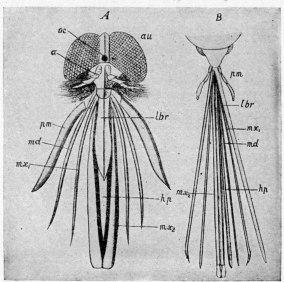

Fig. 313.—Mouth parts of: *A*, a tabanid; *B*, a mosquito: *a*, antenna; *au*, compound eye; *hp*, hypopharynx; *lbr*, labrum; *md*, mandible; *mx₁*, maxilla; *mx₂*, labium; *oc*, ocellus; *pm*, maxillary palpus. (*Modified from Lang's Lehrbuch.*)

changes have been so great that to identify the different pieces with the corresponding ones of chewing insects is very difficult. Different views on this have been advanced by students of the subject.

Without going into details, it may be stated that in the more typical fly mouth parts there are six bristle-shaped structures enclosed by a sheath, and one pair of segmented palpi (Fig. 313). The sheath is generally regarded as representing the labium or hinder lip, while the bristles represent the front lip or labrum, the tongue or hypopharynx, the two mandibles and the two maxillae. At the outer end of the sheath is a pair of lobes, often large, which are considered as the labial palpi, leaving the segmented pair to represent the maxillary palpi. In some cases, the surfaces of the lobes regarded as labial palpi are roughened and adapted to the rasping of surfaces. Bringing together certain of the bristle-like mouth parts forms two tubes or, in some cases, grooves more or less completely closed, through which fluids can be drawn into the body, and saliva be led into the wound made by the tips of the bristles. Solid food is utilized only by first dissolving it in saliva.

The thorax, though composed of three segments as usual, has these very closely and firmly united. In the abdomen, the number of visible segments varies from nine to five, or even four in some instances. The legs, usually at least, are well developed, with a pair of claws ṛ ̣ the tip and a pulvillus at the base of each claw. Between the claws there is often a membranous pad, similar to a pulvillus, or it may be a bristle. In either case, this centrally placed structure is called an empodium.

On the surface of the body, bristles are often present which have definite positions and are of aid in identifying the species.

Fly larvae are usually called maggots. Some have well-developed heads while in others no structure of this nature can be recognized. True legs appear to be absent, though projections of the body which can be utilized in moving about are common and often bear circlets of hooks. These vary in their position in different species. The larvae breathe through spiracles, but the location of these differs greatly. In some they are found along the sides of the body as usual; in others there is a pair near each end of the body; in still others there is only one pair at the hinder end, and these may occur at the tip of a very extensible tube which, when fully stretched out, may be several inches long. Nourishment is sometimes obtained by osmosis directly through the body wall of the larva but it is generally taken into the mouth. The mouth parts in the least modified forms are of the chewing type but in most members of the order they are greatly modified. In some cases, a pair of claws or hooks appear to be the only structures, while in others a chitinous "rake," consisting of a crossbar bearing a row of teeth and connected with a single rod running backward, serves to rasp and break open the vegetable cell walls and expose their fluid or semifluid contents of which the larva avails itself.

Some flies construct regular cocoons but the pupa is usually either naked or located in a puparium (Fig. 35c), which is the last larval skin. In this case, the larva, when ready to pupate, shrinks away from its skin and pupates within it, using this skin or puparium as a protection instead of making a cocoon. Escape from the puparium may be through a T-shaped split on the back near the front end; a transverse split between the eighth and ninth abdominal segments in a few cases; or through a circular opening in the front end.

The chief distinctive characters of the Diptera are

*Insects which when adult have, with a few wingless exceptions, only two wings, these attached to the mesothorax; the hind wings greatly modified, each consisting of a small knob attached to the metathorax by a stalk, these structures being called halteres; mouth parts for sucking, and sometimes for piercing also. The larvae are called maggots and are without true legs. Metamorphosis is complete.*

This is one of the large orders of insects, over 60,000 species being known, and members of the group are found in all parts of the world. They differ greatly in their habits, food and general modes of life. Some are serious pests, either of crops or of man, while others are among the most beneficial insects known, acting as parasites. A number of species function as carriers of disease-producing organisms and are of importance in that way.

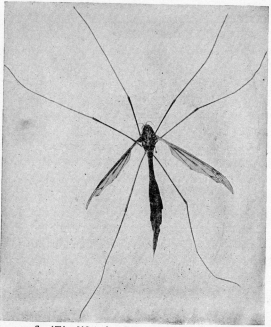

Fig. 314.—Large crane fly (*Tipulidæ*), head bent downward and almost wholly concealed; halter of right side showing plainly; natural size.

About fifty families of Diptera are recognized, many of them very large; others contain few species.

*Family* **TIPULIDÆ** (the crane flies).—This is a large and widely distributed family composed of Diptera having long and rather slender bodies and very long legs, often resembling enormous mosquitoes in appearance though many are very small (Fig. 314). The antennae are generally thread-like and there is a broad V-shaped groove or suture on the top of the thorax.

The larvae of crane flies in most cases live in the ground and feed on the roots of grasses and grain and at times cause much injury in this way. Some exceptions live in decaying wood, on leaves, in water or elsewhere. There seem to be two generations each year, adults appearing in the spring and fall, and winter is passed as the partly grown maggot. Injury is most often noticed on low or poorly drained land or where a field has been left in grass for a number of years. Control of these insects, when they are sufficiently injurious to make it pay, is by draining, rotation of crops and plowing early in the fall, when the insects are in the pupa stage just below the surface of the ground, to crush them there.

*Family* **CULICIDÆ** (the mosquitoes).—These are small insects, familiar to everyone as they attack man and other animals. In most species the females feed upon blood. A few species appear to consume plant juices. The mouth parts of the males are much reduced and the members of this sex seem unable to make punctures through which to obtain food. There are many kinds of mosquitoes but the larvae of all live in water and generally not in large ponds but in more or less stagnant water. The most abundant species develop in temporary pools.

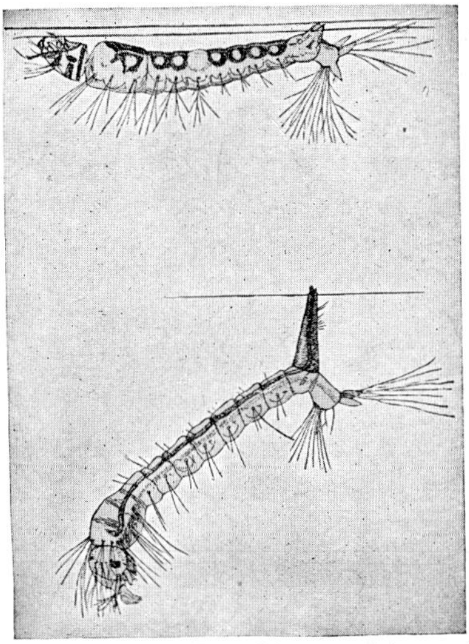

The adults have scales fringing their wings and also along the veins. The antennae of the males are plumose (feather-like) and very noticeable. The winter is passed as the egg, larva or adult, according to the species concerned.

The eggs may be laid singly, in small clusters or in masses often called

Fig. 315.—Breathing position of larva of Culex (below), and feeding and breathing position of Anopheles (above); much enlarged. (*Modified from U. S. Dept. Agr. Div. Ent. Bul. 25, n. s.*)

rafts on the surface of standing water or even on the ground, hatching in the latter case after rains or the melting of the snow in spring. The number of eggs laid by one insect varies in different species but probably averages several hundred.

The larvae or "wigglers" live in water and move with a motion which has given them their common name. The head and thorax are large and distinct, while the abdomen is slender, and projecting from next to the last segment of this section of the body is a respiratory tube which is usually rather long and near the end of which the breathing organs open by a sort of spiracle. When air is desired, the larva floats to the surface and projects the tip of the respiratory tube just above the water level, to renew its supply (Fig. 315).

The larvae have mouth parts of the chewing type, and some are plant feeders. Most of them, however, are predaceous, feeding on tiny water animals and even on other mosquito larvae, a pair of small brushes at the mouth being used to cause currents in the water and bring food within their reach. They molt four times and, after a varying length of time (a week or ten days in many cases) in different species and at different seasons of the year, transform into pupae. These are quite different in appearance from the larvae, the head and thorax forming a large rounded mass, joined by a slender abdomen. Differing from most insect pupae, the pupal mosquito is active, moving through the water by a curious tumbling end over end. On the top of the thorax in this stage are two breathing tubes (Fig. 316), and when air is desired the tips of these are pushed above the surface of the water. The animal

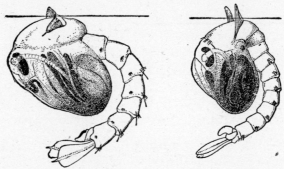

Fig. 316.—Pupa of Anopheles (left) and of Culex (right) showing position when breathing. Difference of form, position in the water and in the breathing tubes are shown; greatly enlarged. (*Modified from U. S. Dept. Agr. Div. Ent. Bul. 25, n. s.*)

swims by making use of a pair of leaf-like appendages at the end of the abdomen.

After a brief pupal stage, usually lasting only a few days, the animal comes to the surface of the water and a split of the pupal skin along the middle of the back of the thorax appears, through which the adult mosquito escapes, balancing itself on this skin until it is ready for flight.

Of the many kinds of mosquitoes known, a small number are of particular importance aside from their habit of attacking man, being disease carriers.

**The northern house mosquito** (*Culex pipiens* L.).—This is a very common species almost everywhere in the northern United States east of the Mississippi River and north of North Carolina. It is probably a native of the Old World where it is also abundant. Though as far as known it is not a carrier of any human disease, yet it is a most irritating pest, and its control is important on that account.

Winter is passed as the adult (Fig. 317) in protected places and, in spring, egg clusters containing from 100 to about 300 eggs are laid on the surface of the water. These eggs hatch in one to four or five days and the larval stage usually continues for a week or two (Fig. 318). During this period, the larvae spend much of their time at the surface, the respiratory tube projecting slightly above the water line and the body hanging downward. Pupation for a few days follows, after which the

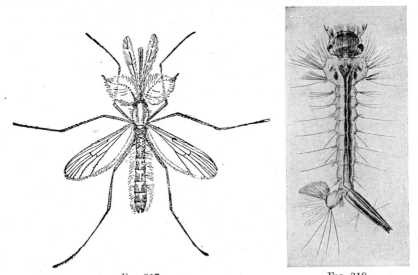

FIG. 317.                    FIG. 318.

FIG. 317.—Male northern house mosquito (*Culex pipiens* L.); greatly enlarged. Note the large feathery antennæ of this sex.    (*From U. S. Dept. Agr. Div. Ent. Bul.* 25, *n. s.*)

FIG. 318.—Larva of northern house mosquito; greatly enlarged. (*After Howard, Dyar and Knab.*)

adult appears. There are a number of generations each season. The adult has unspotted wings and, when at rest, its body is parallel to the object on which it has alighted (Fig. 319).

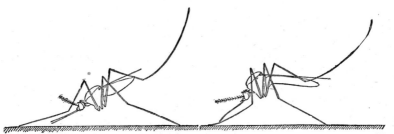

FIG. 319.—Alighting positions of Anopheles (left) and Culex (right) mosquitoes. (*From U. S. Dept. Agr. Div. Ent. Bul.* 25, *n. s.*)

A number of other species not concerned in carrying disease are also liable to be pests. Near salt marshes of the eastern and southern United States, the salt-marsh mosquito (*Aedes sollicitans* Walk.) is very troublesome, and this species may fly quite a long distance inland. In the west, other species are abundant.

**The malarial mosquitoes** (*Anopheles quadrimaculatus* Say and others). The species of Anopheles are carriers of malaria. The adults (Fig. 320) are larger than those of the house mosquito and their wings are usually marked with light and dark spots. In alighting on an object, the body is tipped at quite an angle to the object on which it rests (Fig. 319) and these two differences will at once serve to distinguish the malarial mosquitoes from other species. Another distinction is in the length of the palpi

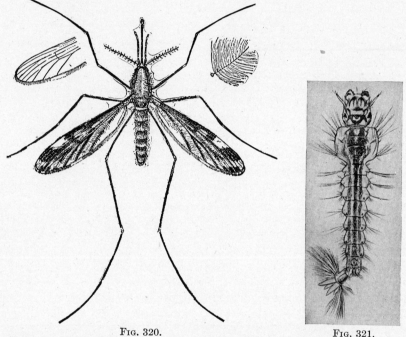

FIG. 320.                                        FIG. 321.

FIG. 320.—Female Anopheles mosquito (*Anopheles punctipennis* Say); much enlarged. Antennae of male at right. (*From U. S. Dept. Agr. Div. Ent. Bul. 25, n. s.*)

FIG. 321.—Larva of Anopheles mosquito; greatly enlarged. (*After Howard, Dyar and Knab.*)

of the female which in the house mosquito are short, whereas in the malarial mosquito they are as long as the beak and therefore quite noticeable.

Species of Anopheles are found from Canada to Mexico, east of the Rocky Mountains, *Anopheles quadrimaculatus* Say, the chief malaria carrier, being particularly abundant in the southern states.

Winter is passed as the adult, and the eggs are laid singly on the surface of water and hatch two or three days later. The larvae (Fig. 321) resemble those of the house mosquito but have a shorter respiratory tube and lie horizontally just below the surface instead of hanging head downward (Fig. 315).   The larval period is about two weeks, followed by a pupal stage lasting two or three days.   Accordingly, a new generation of these mosquitoes may appear about every three weeks.

Most species of Anopheles attack man chiefly during the twilight and early morning hours.   The various species of Culex seek their food at night, though often beginning their work late in the afternoon.

The species of Anopheles must all be regarded as at least potential carriers of malaria until this can be proved erroneous, but they vary greatly in their activity in this regard, some being evidently of little importance, as they do not feed habitually on man.   Several of the species can carry not only the tertian but also the quartan and estivo-autumnal types of malaria.   In other parts of the world other species also act as carriers of these forms of the disease.

The animals causing malaria belong to the Protozoa and those causing the disease in man are chiefly of three closely related kinds.   With any of these the animal when introduced into the blood of man is a rather long and slender spindle with pointed ends.   It now assumes an amoeboid form and attacks a red blood corpuscle, working into it, feeding on its hemoglobin contents and producing black granules.   It feeds on the hemoglobin in the corpuscle until this has all been consumed and grows until it nearly fills the corpuscle.   It now divides into many parts, each similar to the one which first entered the corpuscle, and these proceed to attack other corpuscles in a similar way.   This breaking up of the animal into parts coincides with the "chill" of the disease and the interval of time between successive chills determines which type of malaria is present, a period of two days indicating the tertian type; three days the quartan type; a varying period indicates the estivo-autumnal type.   As the parasites increase in abundance and consume more of the corpuscles, the patient becomes anemic and weaker.

Some of the products of division in the corpuscle, however, do not proceed to attack other corpuscles and increase in numbers but are of two different kinds which are the sexual stages.   When these are taken into the stomach of an Anopheles which attacks a person having malaria, the two kinds fuse and the resulting animal penetrates the cells of the stomach wall of the mosquito and there remains, forming a cyst.   Division of the animal here results finally in the production of cells like those which enter human blood, and these now escape into the body cavity of the mosquito and gradually gather in its salivary glands, whence they are expelled into the wounds caused by the feeding of the mosquito thereafter.   The time that must elapse after a mosquito has received the malarial parasites before it can transmit these to man varies but is usually at least ten or twelve days and may in some cases be more than this.

In 1930, a mosquito (*Anopheles gambiæ* Giles) reached Brazil from Africa and has proved to be a carrier of a serious type of malaria often fatal to man. Vigorous efforts by the Rockefeller Foundation and the Brazilian government apparently greatly reduced the area occupied by this insect and it is now thought (1942) to have been exterminated there. If it should reach the United States and be able to live here the malaria situation in this country would become much more serious than it now is.

**The yellow-fever mosquito** (*Aedes ægypti* L.) is the only known carrier of yellow fever in North America. It occurs in the tropical and subtropical regions and during warm weather may extend into the temperate regions but can survive there only while the temperature remains fairly high.

The adult (Fig. 322) is a small mosquito with silvery lines along the back of the thorax and with white bands on its legs. It flies in the daytime and occurs mainly in towns and cities, being found only rarely in the country. Its eggs are laid singly or in small clusters on, or close to, water in houses or near by, it having apparently become a "wholly domesticated" species. The eggs hatch in ten hours to about three days, and the larvae hang downward from the surface. After a week or ten days in this stage, they pupate for two or three days before the emergence of the adult. Feeding by the adult appears to be mainly during the warmer hours of sunny days though extending somewhat into the evening. Apparently about 12 days is required after feeding on a yellow-fever patient before the mosquito is able to transmit the organism causing the disease, but from that time on it can do this for well over a month.

Fig. 322.—Adult yellow-fever mosquito *Aedes ægypti* L.); considerably enlarged. Note black and white banding of the legs. (*After U. S. Dept. Agr. Farmers' Bul.* 547.)

For a time it was hoped that since *Aedes ægypti* lives near houses it might be possible to eradicate yellow-fever from the Western Hemisphere. But the discovery that a form of the disease called jungle fever exists in the wilds of Brazil in many wild animals and is carried from one to another by at least two other species of mosquitoes makes eradication doubtful as there is always a chance of the *Aedes* mosquito obtaining the disease from a jungle animal and transmitting it to man.

Dengue and filariasis, two other important diseases of man in tropical and subtropical regions, are also known to be carried by mosquitoes.

*Control of mosquitoes.*—There are many ways by which mosquitoes can be more or less effectively controlled. The thorough screening of houses to keep them out is a desirable practice and is also of value as a protection against houseflies. Nettings over beds for the same purpose are often used where entire houses are unscreened. Out of doors, veils covering the head and gloves for the hands are often necessary in places where these insects are extremely abundant. Protective materials rubbed on exposed parts of the body are also often used and various substances have proved of value for this purpose. Among these are spirits of camphor, oil of pennyroyal and oil of citronella, which seem to be the favorite substances used in this way. Smudges will keep away mosquitoes where the smoke is, and burning insect powder in a room stupefies the insects so that they fall to the floor and can be swept up. Other materials for use in a similar way are also available.

Destruction of the larvae, pupae and eggs is the most direct way in which to control mosquitoes in large numbers, and many methods for accomplishing this have been tried. As mosquitoes develop only in water, the removal of the places where they can breed, such as the drainage of marsh land, filling up small pools, hollows in trees containing standing water and all such situations, will accomplish a great deal. The drainage of the salt marshes of the New Jersey coast and elsewhere has resulted in a marked relief from the attacks of mosquitoes in those localities. Where the water cannot be drained off, covering it with a film of kerosene or a mixture of kerosene and crude oil will suffice to destroy the eggs on the surface, larvae and pupae at, or coming to, the surface for air, and any adults that may alight on the water to lay their eggs. Oil used should be sprayed on the water, working preferably along the windward side and using about one fluid ounce to every fifteen square feet of surface. The oil will spread if simply poured on to the water, but rather more of it will be required by that method. It is important to be sure that little detached pools along the shore receive their film of oil also. This treatment should be repeated every ten to fifteen days unless heavy rains carry off the oil soon after a treatment, in which case the oil should be renewed sooner. Sawdust soaked in kerosene has been found to give up the oil slowly and thereby preserve the film on the surface longer, when this material is scattered along the edge of the water. Rainwater barrels and cisterns for storing water for use can be screened, and ponds where the use of oil is undesirable may be stocked with small fish (sunfish or top minnows) which feed voraciously on these insects.

A more recent method for killing malarial mosquitoes in ponds, marshes and similar places is to sprinkle them with ninety nine parts of road dust or hydrated lime and one part of Paris green, well mixed, using one pound of the Paris green per acre. The airplane is now much used for this where extensive marsh land needs treatment and the proportions in the dust used vary from one part in fifty to equal parts, according to local conditions.

The catch basins of sewer openings are usually favorite breeding places for mosquitoes and must be given attention, along with cesspools and any tin cans or other receptacles that can be found containing rain water.

*Family* **ITONIDIDÆ** or **CECIDOMYIIDAE** (the gall midges).— These tiny flies are very numerous. Most of them produce galls on plants, living in these galls, but some suck plant juices without producing galls, and a few live in decaying wood or fungi or even feed on aphids. The adults have long antennae with, in the majority of the species, a whorl of hairs on each segment. All parts of the plant are attacked by one species or another. The galls produced are typical for the species in each case.

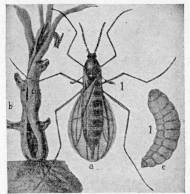

FIG. 323.—Hessian fly (*Phytophaga destructor* Say): *a*, adult fly; *b*, wheat plant affected; *c*, maggot. Hair lines show true length of *a* and *c*. (*From Berlese.*)

The gall appears to be the result of the irritation caused by the larva feeding, and to some extent its size is dependent upon the number of larvae present. Winter is frequently spent as the larva inside the gall and, in many cases, there is but one generation each year, though, on the other hand, some species have several generations.

The larvae are small, often brightly colored maggots. The method of pupation varies in different species, some forming true cocoons; others have a puparium and others are without any covering.

**The hessian fly** (*Phytophaga destructor* Say).—This insect is one of the nongall-making Itonididæ, is a native of Europe and was first noticed in this country about 1779 on Long Island, N. Y. Since that time, it has spread over most of the wheat-growing regions of the United States and Canada, as well as other parts of the world, and is now one of the most important insect pests in the country, often destroying wheat valued at millions of dollars. It feeds on wheat, rye, barley and several other species of grasses but never attacks oats.

Its life history differs somewhat in different places, apparently being modified by the different methods of wheat growing. Where wheat is planted in the fall, the eggs are laid on the leaves of the plants soon after they come up, the time varying with the latitude from late August and September in Michigan to the last of November in Georgia. The eggs are placed in irregular rows of about half a dozen, generally on the upper surface of the leaf, and each fly lays 100 to 150 in all. They hatch after a few days, and the tiny pinkish or reddish maggots work their way down between the leaf and the stem to a point just above the joint (Fig. 323). Here they remain, sucking the sap until the approach of cold weather and turning more nearly white in color. Their presence at this time is at first indicated by the dark color of the leaves, missing stems which would otherwise begin to show and, later, the yellowing and death of the plants. After feeding about a month, the larva pupates within its larval skin, which therefore becomes a puparium and so greatly resembles a flaxseed that in this condition the insect is generally spoken of as being in the "flaxseed" stage. In this condition, it spends the winter and the adult flies (Fig. 323) emerge in the spring—early in the south, later in the north. These now lay their eggs on the wheat and, as by this time the plants may be a number of inches high, the eggs can be laid at different heights on the plant, and the larvae will pass down to the joints immediately below the leaves on which the different eggs are laid. Feeding at these joints continues during the spring and the flaxseed stage is reached at or before harvesting time. Some of the flaxseeds will be in the straw cut and harvested, but many more will remain in the stubble. The flies emerge from the flaxseeds during the early fall as already indicated, ready to attack the fall-planted wheat as soon as it comes up.

In regions where the wheat is planted in the spring, the insect winters in the flaxseed stage in stubble and volunteer wheat, and the adults appear in May. The second generation quickly follows the first, particularly in wet seasons, and there seems to be no period of delay such as occurs during midsummer in the fall-wheat regions.

*Control.*—The hessian fly has numerous parasites which are undoubtedly of much value, as where great loss occurs these insects are few in number. It is often the case, though, that the fly is so abundant that parasites cannot be relied upon and other measures, largely preventive in their nature, must be taken.

It is evident that, if fall planting can be delayed until the adults that appear at that time are gone, the crop will be protected from attack. To carry out this plan, however, latitude, elevation and humidity perhaps, as well, must be taken into consideration. These factors are now well enough understood so that at least most of the wheat-growing states through their state experiment stations can furnish dates, to those who desire them, of the safe time to sow for any given locality. The great difficulty with this plan is that, under unusual conditions which sometimes develop, more than two generations (up to five) may be produced. In such cases the sowing dates are less reliable.

Many of the flaxseeds are left in the stubble at harvesting. This stubble should be plowed under as soon as possible, for the flies are unable to dig themselves out when thus buried. Unfortunately, however, the general custom of planting grass and clover in such fields, to come up as the grain progresses toward harvesting, too often makes this control impracticable.

Volunteer wheat, as it is called, coming from grain scattered through and around the wheat fields by accident, starts early and provides plants for the hessian fly to lay its eggs on before the main planting is available. This will produce an abundance of the insects to attack the crop the following spring. All such plants should be destroyed before the maggots in them have reached the flaxseed stage.

The rotation of crops is also of advantage, driving the flies elsewhere to lay their eggs and making them more liable to destruction while en route.

*Family* **TABANIDÆ** (the horseflies, deer flies or gadflies).—These pests of cattle, horses and occasionally of man also (Figs. 324, 325) are in

Fig. 324.                    Fig. 325.

Fig. 324.—Large horse fly (*Tabanus stygius* Say); slightly reduced.

Fig. 325.—Small horse fly or deer fly (*Chrysops vittatus* Wied.); over twice natural size.

many cases quite large insects, with bodies an inch long, though most of them average a third to half an inch in length. The head of the adult is large and fits on to the thorax somewhat like a cap. Only the females feed on blood, the males lacking some of the necessary mouth parts with which to pierce the skin. They therefore feed on such plant juices as they may be able to obtain, honeydew and other similar materials.

The eggs are laid in masses on plants over water or marshes, and the larvae live in water or damp places or in the earth, when it is soft, and are carnivorous, feeding on snails, small insect larvae, etc.

The family is a large one, both in this country and elsewhere. The larger species (one has a black body and smoky wings) are often noticed around domestic animals because of their size. Many of the smaller kinds have wings banded with dark. Some of these are called green-heads because of the bright-green color of their eyes (Fig. 325). Their attacks irritate and disturb the animals and, in the case of milch cattle, this may reduce the amount of milk produced.

As these insects attack domestic animals only for their blood, any repellent measures that prevent this are sufficient. Fly nets covering the greater part of the animals are sometimes used for this purpose; smearing the ears and legs with substances having an odor objectionable to the flies is also practiced. One of several materials often applied is fish oil, either alone or mixed with tar. The following mixture has proved effective against those tabanids which preferably attack the ears and the region around the eyes of the animals: pine tar, one gallon; fish oil or crude carbolic acid, one quart; powdered sulfur, two pounds. These materials are thoroughly mixed and rubbed on the parts most liable to be attacked. As so many tabanids pass their early stages in stagnant water,

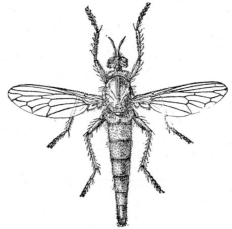

Fig. 326.—Robber fly (*Scleropogon picticornis* Loew); about twice natural size.   (*From U. S. Dept. Agr. Bul.* 124.)

the treatment of such breeding places with kerosene will destroy the larvae as they hatch and enter the pools.

*Family* **SIMULIIDÆ** (the black flies and buffalo gnats).—The small flies that compose this family feed upon the blood of man and other animals, attacking them at all exposed places. As in the Tabanidæ, only the females are concerned and these are active only during the daytime. The eggs are laid in such places that the larvae can enter water and, in most cases, swiftly running streams where they feed on small animals. They usually anchor themselves to some object in the water and have a pair of fan-shaped structures at the mouth which are used to produce currents toward the mouth. Serious outbreaks of the southern buffalo gnat frequently occur in the lower Mississippi Valley and in some years large numbers of domestic animals are killed by the attacks of these insects. There are usually, though not for all species, several generations a year. The best control methods known are the use of repellent materials on the animals, such as fish oil three parts, kerosene one part. Care should be taken, however, that the animals are not injured by too liberal applications of oily mixtures. Animals kept in dark stables are not attacked there. Smudges are also frequently used.

*Family* **ASILIDÆ** (the robber flies).—These insects as adults prey upon other insects, attacking any species they are able to overcome (Fig.

326), but using little discrimination as to the importance to man of their captures. They can hardly be regarded as more than accidentally beneficial to man. Some species (Fig. 327) so closely resemble bumblebees that a careful examination of the number of wings present is necessary to determine what the insect is. The larvae are found chiefly under bark, in decaying wood or in the ground where decaying vegetable matter occurs, and they feed upon insect larvae present in such places.

Fig. 327.—Bee-like robber fly (*Bombomima grossa* Fab.); slightly reduced.

This family is one of the largest in the order and its members average large, ranging from a length of about a fifth of an inch to nearly two inches.

*Family* **SYRPHIDÆ** (the syrphus flies).—This is one of the largest families of Diptera. The adults range from quite small to rather large insects which visit flowers, feeding on the pollen and nectar, and are most noticeably abundant in bright, sunny weather. They are often rather brightly colored.

The larvae of these insects vary greatly in their appearance, five types of them having been recognized. Some are rather flattened, elongate, often green with white spots, and are found with clusters of plant lice on which they feed. Others have nearly cylindrical bodies and bore into the bulbs of various plants. Others live and feed in filth and have short extensible tubes for respiration. Another class which also inhabits filth has extensible respiratory tubes which, when extended to their limit, may be several times the length of the body. Still another group are short, broadly rounded, flattened beneath and high above, somewhat hemispherical in form. These are usually found under logs and in ants' nests and may easily be mistaken for rather peculiar snails.

Though the adults consume pollen, their visits to flowers are valuable to man for the cross-pollination and the resulting "setting" of seed. The insect-eating larvae often destroy enormous numbers of insect pests, and the filth-inhabiting forms are at least cleaning up decaying matter, which is generally considered desirable. On the other hand, some are injurious by boring into the bulbs of cultivated plants, and several species cause myiasis (the presence of fly maggots in the body) in man and some of the domestic animals, these insects in one way or another entering the body and passing through their larval development there.

The narcissus bulb fly (*Merodon equestris* F.).—The larva of this fly feeds inside narcissus and other cultivated bulbs. It is a native of Europe but has been in this country some years; it is well established in the northwest and is frequently reported from different parts of the United States. Apparently the insect winters as a larva or pupa, either in the bulb or in the ground, and the adult lays its eggs near the crown of the bulb. The maggots from these eggs bore into the bulbs and feed upon their contents, becoming nearly three-fourths of an inch long and quite often entirely destroying the bulbs. There seems to be only one generation a year. One means of control is by putting the least infested bulbs into hot water kept at 110 to 112°F. for 2½ hours and by the destruction of the

Fig. 328.—Adult female throat botfly (*Gasterophilus nasalis* L.); nearly twice natural size. (*From U. S. Dept. Agr. Bul. 597.*)

badly infested ones. Infested bulbs are generally lighter in weight and softer than noninfested ones and often show signs of decay.

Another treatment is by the use of calcium cyanide dust, sixteen ounces per hundred cubic feet of space, at a temperature of over 60°F., and an exposure of four hours or more.

A smaller fly—the lesser bulb fly (*Eumerus tuberculatus* Rond.)—has similar habits. It attacks about the same list of bulbs and also the onion. It is reported from many parts of this country where bulbs are grown, attacking them in the same way as the narcissus bulb fly, but apparently there are two generations each year. Control is the same as for the other species.

*Family* **ŒSTRIDÆ** (the botflies).—The botflies in their early stages are parasites in mammals. The adults are of medium to large size, with rather stout, thickset bodies and frequently with reduced mouth parts, not feeding in this stage (Fig. 328). Though the group is not a large one, its members are included among the more important pests of domestic as well as of other animals. The parasitic part of the life of these insects is in some species spent in the stomach (Fig. 329) or intestines, in others in the pharynx or nasal cavities and frontal sinus, in others under the skin.

**The ox warbles or cattle grubs** (*Hypoderma lineatum* Vill. and *Hypoderma bovis* De G.).—These two insects, both natives of Europe, are present in this country, the former widely distributed, the latter most abundant in Canada and a few of the northern states. The adult fly (Fig. 330) is about half an inch long. The eggs of both species are laid on the hairs of cattle on almost any part of the body during the late spring or summer months. The larvae bore through the skin into the connective tissue and then wander through the body in the connective tissue until

FIG. 329.—Nearly full-grown larvae (bots) of a horse botfly attached to the inside wall of the stomach. (*From U. S. Dept. Agr. Bul.* 597.)

late fall or winter when they locate along the back, a few inches from the backbone. Here each makes a hole through the skin through which to escape but remains inside, feeding on the pus and bloody matter produced by its presence there, and the swelling caused by the insect is called a warble. Finally the maggot, now nearly an inch long (Fig. 331) and grayish white in color, works its way out through the hole and drops to the ground, which it enters for an inch or two, and forms a pupa within a brown puparium from which the adult fly appears from three to six weeks later, the larval period within the cattle being eight to ten months.

The presence of the maggots of the ox warbles in the cattle is shown by a loss of flesh, reduction of the milk in the case of milch cattle and the presence, during late fall and winter, of the sores on the back.

*Control.*—Formerly the usual method was to locate the holes in the skin along the back made by the maggots and squeeze out the maggots. The best method known now, however, is the use of any rotenone-containing preparation such as derris or cube in the form of an ointment, wash or dust. The ointment is rubbed into the lumps containing the maggots, the wash or dust brushed in liberally all over the back at monthly intervals as soon as the lumps appear. The wash should consist of one pound of powdered derris root in a gallon of strongly soapy water.

Various other botflies attack animals. Among them are the horse botflies (*Gasterophilus* of several species), the larvae of which live in the

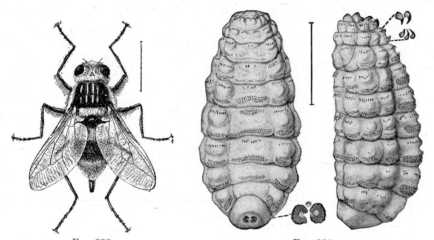

FIG. 330.                    FIG. 331.
FIG. 330.—Cattle grub (*Hypoderma lineatum* Vill.). Real length shown by hair line. (*From U. S. Dept. Agr. Div. Ent. Circ.* 25.)
FIG. 331.—Full-grown warble (larva), dorsal view (left) and side view (right). Real length shown by hair line. (*From U. S. Dept. Agr. Div. Ent. Circ.* 25.)

stomach of the horse during the fall, winter and spring, and the sheep botfly (*Œstris ovis* L.) which in its larval stage lives in the nasal cavities and frontal sinuses of sheep during the same period.

*Family* **TRYPETIDÆ** (the fruitflies).—This family includes some very important pests, these being small flies which attack many of our important fruits, completely ruining them. Other members of the family mine the leaves of plants, occur in blossoms or form galls in the stems or roots of plants. Those which live in fruit are of economic importance. Most of the flies belonging here have dark bands, or dark markings enclosing transparent spots on their wings. Two species attack cherries; one feeds in currants and gooseberries; one in the apple, thorn, blueberry and huckleberry; other species injure citrus fruits.

**The apple maggot or railroad worm** (*Rhagoletis pomonella* Walsh).—This pest is apparently a native of this country and its original food seems to have been the berries of the thorn and possibly the blueberry. It has been found in various parts of Canada and the eastern United States as far west as North Dakota and Colorado and as far south as North Carolina and Arkansas, but it is most serious in the northern and eastern portion of this territory. A smaller western race is found in the Pacific coast states feeding on the snowberry.

The adult (Fig. 332) is about a fifth of an inch long and has a wingspread of about half an inch. Its body is black with light marks on the upper side of the abdomen, and the wings have heavy dark bands. The flies first appear in the orchards early in July in New England (somewhat earlier farther south) and attack the early varieties of apples. Later-appearing flies may sometimes be found into September, and these select fall and winter fruit for egg laying. Some varieties of apples are much more subject to the attacks of this insect than are others. Sweet and subacid summer and fall varieties are the greatest

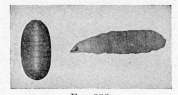

Fig. 332,                              Fig. 333.

Fig. 332.—Adult fly of the apple maggot (*Rhagoletis pomonella* Walsh); slightly over four times natural size. (*Reduced from Nova Scotia Dept. Agr. Bul.* 9.)

Fig. 333.—Puparium (left) and full-grown maggot (right) of the apple maggot; about three times natural size. (*Modified from Nova Scotia Dept. Agr. Bul.* 9.)

sufferers, though winter varieties do not escape, and the amount of injury caused where this insect is abundant is often very great.

Egg laying begins about twenty days after the fly emerges and probably continues for two or three weeks, the total number of eggs laid being several hundred. These are inserted singly under the skin of the apple and preferably where the surface is not exposed to sunlight. They hatch in four or five days and the little whitish maggots tunnel through the pulp of the fruit in all directions. At first, the rapid growth of the fruit may fill up these tunnels, but after a time the walls around the tunnels instead of filling in, turn brown and the fruit softens, decay may follow and the entire apple is spoiled for sale. The maggot (Fig. 333) has no real jaws with which to tunnel but has a pair of small hooks at the mouth opening with which the pulp is rasped and torn, freeing the juice upon which the insect feeds.

The length of the larval stage depends upon the temperature and upon the ripeness of the fruit. In warm weather and with rather soft pulp, about two to four weeks is usually the time necessary; but with colder weather and in late-maturing varieties, growth toward maturity is delayed and some maggots may possibly even winter in this stage in extreme cases. When the larva has completed its feeding, however, it leaves the fruit (usually as this becomes ripe) and enters the ground, where it burrows below the surface often some distance, and pupates in a puparium (Fig. 333), remaining here until the following summer when the flies emerge. Where infested fruit is gathered and stored before the maggots leave it, the puparia may be found on the bottom of the barrels or bins where the fruit is kept. A few of the earlier pupating maggots appear to transform to flies the same season, giving a second generation, but so few do this that it is of little or no economic importance. On the other hand, a few seem to require two years for the completion of their life history.

The adult flies feed freely and also seem to require water during their life, specimens supplied with food but no water dying within a few days. They do not appear to fly freely, for long distances at least, and orchards in which they are abundant and others where they are few may occur not very far from each other.

*Control.*—Infested fruit falls to the ground early, and the maggots in it rarely leave it for the ground to pupate until about a week later. Gathering and destroying this fallen fruit promptly should, therefore, be of much assistance in controlling the insect but the amount of labor involved in carrying out this plan makes it impracticable in many cases.

It has been found that the minimum effective treatment is a careful spraying about a week after the flies begin to appear, using lead arsenate at 1½ pounds in 50 gallons of water, and repeating this 2 to 3 weeks later. The addition of molasses has sometimes been advised, but it is doubtful if the gain will repay

Fig. 334.—Adult Mediterranean fruit fly (*Ceratitis capitata* Wied.); greatly enlarged. (*Modified from Cal. Fruit Growers Exchange, Bul.* 6)

the extra cost. If in doubt when to apply the first spray the nearest state experiment station will be able to advise the date for that year.

**The Mediterranean fruitfly** (*Ceratitis capitata* Wied.).—This small fly, about a fifth of an inch long, is probably the worst pest of many fruits and vegetables known and is now present in every continent except North America. It is included here because it was found in central Florida in March, 1929, though it now seems to have been exterminated, and is an example of what may sometimes be accomplished in control work. It has been bred from over seventy different kinds of fruits and vegetables but is particularly destructive to the orange, grapefruit, guava, Surinam cherry and a number of other fruits. The adult fly (Fig. 334) makes a hole in the skin of the fruit and in this lays an egg which hatches in three or four days; the maggot feeds on the pulp, riddling the fruit and causing it to decay. After feeding from four to ten days, the larvae are full-grown and leave the fruit, going into the ground to pupate. Nine to ten days later the adult flies emerge and after about a week begin to lay their eggs. In Florida, when the daily mean temperature averages 80°F. the life cycle may be completed in eighteen to twenty days, but when it averages about 68°F. the development is delayed and a life cycle will require forty to seventy days. These temperatures represent the average summer and winter temperatures of central Florida and it is evident that there can be quite a large number of generations in a year.

When this pest was discovered, the U. S. Plant Quarantine and Control Administration and the Florida State Plant Board united in an investigation to learn the limits of the infested area and to determine the action to be taken. The area finally placed under quarantine was over 15,000 square miles and it was decided to attempt the eradication of the fly. Quarantine, prohibiting shipment of all fruits and vegetables liable to be hosts of the fly, except after sterilization; destruction of all fruit infested or liable to infestation (over 500,000 boxes of fruit were destroyed); inspection and cleanup of all properties within the infested area and tests to determine what plants the fly would breed in were all taken up. At first, doubtful fruits (*e.g.*, peas) were destroyed, but as soon as it was found that a plant was not a host it was dropped from the list. Host trees in areas where fruit had been destroyed were sprayed with lead arsenate (later, copper carbonate), brown sugar and molasses as a bait for the adult flies to feed upon, and kerosene traps were also used, the males being attracted by kerosene. The last specimens of the fly were found in July, 1930, and the quarantine was removed in November, 1930. Since then no specimens of this insect have been reported.

FIG. 335.—Housefly (*Musca domestica* L.); rather more than twice natural size. (*Reduced from Hewitt, The House Fly.*)

The complete eradication of a small insect like this from such a large area is one of the finest pieces of control of this kind known. Whether the eradication work alone accomplished this or some unfavorable climatic factor aided in the destruction of the last of these flies, it is impossible to say. In any case the extermination of this pest has been almost wholly the result of the eradication work done, which was remarkable for its efficiency.

The Mexican fruitfly (*Anastrepha ludens* Loew), an abundant fruitfly in Mexico, attacking citrus and other fruits, is occasionally found in Texas and, if it should become established in any citrus-growing section of the United States, would undoubtedly be a serious pest. The United States Federal quarantine service has made many captures of this insect in fruit brought across the border. Its life history appears to be similar to that of the Mediterranean fruitfly.

*Family* **MUSCIDÆ** (the muscid flies).—This large family contains many species that are important to man though none appear to be crop feeders. The adults range from small to medium size and are very abundant in most cases.

**The housefly** (*Musca domestica* L.).—This insect, always a household pest, has during the last twenty-five years assumed a greater importance to most people because of the discovery that it is a carrier of a number of serious human disease-producing agents.

The adult flies (Fig. 335) hardly need any description. They are rather small, with reddish-brown eyes, transparent wings and blackish bodies. Their mouth parts are for sucking and a "biting" fly found in a house at any time is of some other species.

Winter is, at least usually, spent as the pupa or perhaps in some cases as the larva. As the weather becomes warm in the spring, the flies emerge and, in temperate regions, begin breeding early in June, though it is probable that in warmer climates this may continue throughout the year. Most of the flies breed in manure piles, particularly those exposed to light, but almost any decaying animal or vegetable matter may be selected for the purpose. The eggs (Fig. 336) are laid in clusters, about 125 at a time and about 500 to 600 in all, though over 2,000 eggs have been known to be laid by a single fly. The eggs hatch in eight to twelve hours during warm weather but may take two or three days if the temperature is

Fig. 336.              Fig. 337.

Fig. 336.—Eggs of the housefly; much enlarged.

Fig. 337.—Full-grown maggots of the housefly; much enlarged.

low. The larvae (Fig. 337) feed on the manure, or other material in which they are located, for a varying number of days but probably averaging about five days. Pupation for about the same length of time follows, but many of the maggots may leave the place where they feed and travel a short distance away to pupate. Thus pupae may be found in the ground around a manure pile within a foot or two. Pupation is within a puparium, the fly pushing off the front end when ready to emerge, by means of its ptilinum. After the emergence of the adult fly, a period of three to twenty-three days elapses before egg laying begins and the average time from one of these periods to the next during warm weather is about twenty-four days. From seven to ten generations are liable to be produced, therefore, in a long season in the north or under ordinary conditions in the south, and it has been calculated that the descendants of a single fly which deposits its eggs the middle of April would number 5,598,720,000,000 by the middle of September, if all the eggs hatched and lived to be adults which reproduced in their turn. Fortunately, this is not actually the case, eggs failing to hatch and many larvae never reaching maturity.

Houseflies as disease carriers are of extreme importance. Crawling over and feeding upon filth of any kind, their legs and bodies are liable to gather the germs of various diseases, which may also be taken into the flies with their food. Later, visits to houses and human food, over which the flies crawl, lead to leaving some of the germs there, and the well-known habit they have of disgorging some of the food already eaten and of expelling feces, both of which may contain the germs swallowed, is pretty certain to infect the human food over which they crawl.

Doubtless many of the microorganisms thus placed on food are entirely harmless to man but among these are also liable to be those which cause diseases. Milk exposed to the visits of flies may become infected in a similar way.

Among the disease germs often transmitted thus are the typhoid fevers, anthrax, tuberculosis, cholera and yaws, and others are suspected of being carried in this way also. The habit flies have of visiting spittoons, of alighting on sores on persons and, in fact of crawling over everything where disease germs are liable to occur makes them particularly dangerous to man. It should be noted, however, that there seems to be no development of any of these diseases while on or in the flies themselves, the insects acting as passive carriers, only, of the germs. The relation of the insect to the disease, therefore, is a totally different one from that of mosquitoes and the diseases in which they are concerned, where the disease-producing organism actually passes through a part of its life cycle in the insect.

*Control.*—Here there are two problems to keep in mind: (1) the elimination of breeding places and (2) the prevention of food contamination. Because houseflies can travel several miles it is obvious that in most cases any considerable improvement in a serious fly infestation can be made only by organized and unanimous community efforts.

Under the right conditions of light and moisture content all kinds of manure, as well as garbage, decaying meat and piles of fermenting grass and straw furnish the housefly with breeding places. Some of these materials can be eliminated by burning or burying. Others can be treated with chemicals such as borax, sodium fluoride or calcium chloride (chloride of lime), to poison the fly larvae. Manure that is to be used for fertilizer cannot be treated with these larvicides because of the effect of the chemicals upon growing plants, but it has been recommended that such manure be treated with a mixture of calcium cyanamide and acid phosphate, one-half pound of each to a bushel of manure. The chemicals are mixed and dusted on the manure which is then wet down with water just enough to carry in the chemicals thoroughly. This treatment actually increases the fertilizer value.

More practicable than treatment with chemicals are the storage and disposal of the manure in such a manner as to discourage the breeding of flies. When feasible it should be loaded on a spreader and put on the fields daily. Loss of fertilizer value by leaching while the manure stands in a pile will thus be avoided. The spread manure rapidly becomes too dry for flies to breed. Various improved methods of stacking or otherwise storing manure to reduce fly reproduction are described in bulletins available at many of the state agricultural experiment stations.

Although trapping of flies either mechanically or by poison baits has little if any value when unaccompanied by sanitary conditions including the proper disposal of manure and waste products, it will often help to reduce heavy fly populations, especially if carried out on a large scale. If the traps, however, are placed near houses or food they may attract more flies than would come there under normal circumstances.  Houses, dairies and places where foods are manufactured or displayed should be carefully screened.  Garbage pails should be fitted with tight covers, and emptied and cleaned frequently.  Flies are attracted to and killed by feeding on a mixture of a teaspoonful of formalin to a pint of diluted milk.

Fly sprays are usually pyrethrum extract diluted with kerosene and used as contact sprays.  They are particularly useful at the end of a day to eliminate the flies that have entered a building since morning.  On a large scale it is most efficient to use an automatic electric sprayer which will shut itself off after the proper amount of spray has been used.  The fallen flies should be swept up and burned because it is well known that there is considerable recovery of flies from the action of pyrethrum.

**The tsetse flies** (*Glossina* of several species).—These muscid flies are the conveyers to man of the dreaded disease known as sleeping sickness.  The insects occur only in parts of Africa where they are found along wooded streams and where large game animals are present.  The mouth parts of these flies include piercing structures and the insects normally attack the wild game, but man is also liable to their visits.  The disease is caused by a protozoan animal (*Trypanosoma gambiense*) obtained by the flies while feeding on infected animals, and the trypanosomes may be directly conveyed into another animal during the next day or two, after which the fly becomes innocuous for about four weeks.  By this time, those of the parasites which entered the stomach of the fly have gone through a development in the body of the insect and have gathered in the salivary glands.  The fly is now dangerous again for about three months.  In man, the disease appears as an irregular fever and an enlargement of the glands, followed after a time by nervousness and sleep, the patient becoming comatose and finally dying.  The earlier stage of the disease may last for several years but the last usually continues only from four to eight months.

Another species of trypanosome carried by Glossina flies causes the disease of domestic animals, particularly horses and dogs, known as nagana.  This is almost always fatal to these animals.

*Family* **CALLIPHORIDÆ** (the blowflies).—Some of the flies in this family lay their eggs on meat, either fresh or decaying, which is then spoken of as "blown."  The flies that do this are usually the ones commonly called bluebottle and greenbottle flies.  Maggots of a few of these which infest wounds have been found to secrete there a nitrogenous substance which aids in healing.

**The screwworms** (*Cochliomyia macellaria* Fab. and *C. americana* Cushing & Patten).—These pests of livestock are most important in the southern and southwestern states. Until very recently it was supposed that only one species was concerned in these injuries, but two are now recognized, the adults so nearly alike as to require microscopic study to distinguish them.

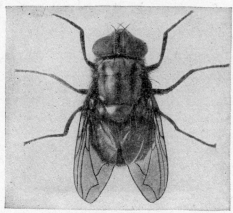

Fig. 338.—Screwworm fly (*Cochliomyia macellaria* Fab.); greatly enlarged. (*From U. S. Dept. Agr. Farmers' Bul. 857.*)

The adult fly of both species (Fig. 338) is dark bluish green in color and has three black stripes along its back. It is considerably larger than the housefly. *Cochliomyia americana* seems to be the more injurious of the two species. It lays its eggs in clusters on the edges of wounds or blood spots on the body of any warm-blooded animal, sometimes even on man. The other species usually lays its eggs in such places a little later, but both kinds of maggots are sometimes

Fig. 339.—Full-grown screwworm maggot; greatly enlarged. (*From U. S. Dept. Agr. Farmers' Bul. 857.*)

found in the same wound. Scratches from horns or barbed wire, or exposed injuries from any cause are the most usual places of attack at which the eggs are laid. In a few hours the eggs hatch into maggots which bore into the tissues, destroying them and enlarging the injury, and, if vital organs are reached, the death of the animal follows. After four to seven days the full-grown maggot (Fig. 339) drops to the ground and enters it to pupate, escaping as the adult fly from seven to twelve days later. Thus there may be a number of generations in a season. Dead animals may also be attacked.

*Control.*—Prevention may be (1) by not branding, dehorning or marking the animals during the fly season (generally from May 1 to Nov. 15); (2) by removing all places, such as projecting nails, the ends of boards and splinters, etc., from buildings, fences or other places where the stock is kept; (3) by keeping the animals free from ticks that attack the ears and there cause conditions favorable for screwworms; (4) by burning all dead animals; and (5) by treating all injuries promptly, applying pine-tar oil or finely ground crystalline diphenylamine to the wounds.

Treatment is best given by cleaning out all wounds with absorbent cotton to remove the blood and serum and then injecting benzol or chloroform into the wounds, for which purpose an oilcan may conveniently be used. A second treatment a few minutes after the first is desirable to ensure reaching all the maggots. Then cover the wound and an area around it with commercial pine-tar oil. Do not use home-run pine tar as this irritates the wound.

Fig. 340.—Adult sarcophagid fly (*Sarcophaga* Sp.); much enlarged. (*From U. S. Dept. Agr. Farmers' Bul.* 857.)

*Family* **SARCOPHAGIDÆ** (the flesh flies, Fig. 340).—This is a large family of flies, some of which lay their eggs on dead animals. Others

breed in manure, decaying matter and similar materials. Because of these habits there is always the possibility of their becoming carriers of disease-producing germs, though as they seldom visit human food in houses, the chance that this may result in disease is much less likely than in the case of the houseflies. Many lay their eggs or larvae on other insects and the flies develop in these hosts.

*Family* **TACHINIDÆ** (the tachina flies).— This family has by some students of the subject been regarded as the most useful family of insects from an economic standpoint, its larvae being parasitic on other insects and being very abundant. This estimate of their importance is perhaps too high but the group is certainly very valuable in the control of injurious

Fig. 341.—Adult tachina fly (*Tachina mella* Walk.); over three times natural size. (*From Britton, Tenth Rept. Ent. Conn. Agr. Expt. Sta.,* 1910.)

forms. The adults (Fig. 341) somewhat resemble the Muscidæ, but the abdomen is apt to be stouter and in many cases bears numerous stiff bristles which are very noticeable. The eggs (or larvae, in some cases) are laid on caterpillars and other insects or, in some cases, on the leaves which these will feed upon; on hatching, the maggots bore their way into the host and feed upon its tissues, finally killing it. The adults are common around flowers and also in places where plants are growing rankly, and there are many species.

Fig. 342.—Adult male and female flies of the cabbage maggot (*Hylemya brassicæ* Bouché); about three times natural size. (*After N. Y. Agr. Expt. Sta. Bul.* 419.)

*Family* **ANTHOMYIIDÆ** (the anthomyiids).—This family contains many injurious species, the larvae of some mining in the roots and of others in the stems and leaves of important crop plants. Others breed in decaying vegetable and animal materials and excrement, and from their habits it is suspected that they may be disease carriers like the housefly. Some writers now place this family in the Muscidæ.

**The cabbage maggot** (*Hylemya brassicæ* Bouché).—The cabbage maggot is a native of Europe but has been present in this country for many years. The adult (Fig. 342) is a small clear-winged fly about two-tenths of an inch long, not often noticed or at least distinguished from other small flies present in the fields. Winter is passed as the pupa in its puparium underground, and also possibly to some extent as the adult, in protected places. At all events, the adult flies are present in the spring as soon as the cabbage and other cruciferous plants are available. The eggs are now laid on or close to the plants. They hatch in a few days, and the maggots (Fig. 343) attack the stem just below the level of the ground where they feed for about three weeks, lacerating the cell walls and feeding on the softer tissues, using for the first process a pair of stout black hooks attached at the mouth which seemingly are extremely modified mouth parts. When full-grown, the larvae leave the plants, enter the ground and form puparia from their larval skins within which they pupate for a period of from twelve to eighteen days in most cases, after which the adults emerge and eggs are laid for a second generation.

Fig. 343.—Young cabbage plant showing maggots on its stem; natural size. (*Modified from Britton, Fourteenth Rept. Ent. Conn. Agr. Expt. Sta.,* 1914.)

The number of generations in a season has been worked upon by several investigators with somewhat differing results. It seems probable, however, that in the latitude of New York the insect as a rule has three generations, though in favorable seasons four are possible, and in unfavorable ones only two may occur. Presumably, the number farther north will usually be two, and farther south four may prove the usual number. Weather conditions apparently have an influence on this—hot, dry weather hardening the roots of the food plants so that feeding is slower than would otherwise be the case, and this same kind of weather also seems to lengthen the pupa stage. It is interesting to note that the insect, though present in the Gulf states, does not seem to be a serious pest south of the latitude of southern Pennsylvania. It is generally distributed over the northern United States and parts of Canada and is a pest at Sitka, Alaska!

Whatever the number of generations a season, the insect seems able to reach the pupa stage before winter and possibly become adult in some cases.

The cabbage maggot is most serious as a pest on cabbages and cauliflowers. It also attacks turnips, radishes, mustard and other cruciferous plants, however, and late generations may live more on these plants as the cabbage and cauliflower roots get older, tougher and less attractive to the insects.

*Control.*—Cabbage and other plants liable to attack while in seedbeds can be protected by being covered with screens of cheesecloth. Solutions of corrosive sublimate (bichloride of mercury) are still used extensively for protecting seedlings of cabbage, cauliflower and Brussels sprouts, but they are likely to injure such tender plants and will also corrode metal containers. Calomel, although practically insoluble, does not have these disadvantages. It is used at the rate of one ounce to ten gallons of water. In order to keep the calomel in suspension it should be worked thoroughly into a small amount of thick gum arabic paste before adding it to the water. This suspension is poured along the rows to moisten the soil next to the plants. The treatment is made when the seedlings are young and repeated 2 or 3 times at weekly intervals.

Another treatment is to coat the cabbage seed with fine (300 mesh) calomel before planting. The seed is moistened with water to which a little gum arabic has been added, then stirred up with the calomel, which will adhere to and coat it. If sown by a seeder the drill must be set to allow for the extra size of the coated seeds. Usually $1\frac{1}{2}$ to 2 pounds of calomel will be retained by one pound of seed. This treatment gives the greatest protection with later, rather than the earlier plantings, but does not appear to be of value with turnip or radish seeds to protect them from their maggots.

**The onion maggot** (*Hylemya antiqua* Meig.) is often a serious pest, mining in the bulbs and quickly causing their decay. Like the cabbage maggot, it is a European insect but has been known in the United States for many years and is now widely distributed. Details of its life history are not so well known as could be desired, but it is probable that the insects pass the winter as larvae or pupae in the ground, or in cull onion piles, and perhaps as adults also. The flies (Fig. 344) lay their eggs on the onions soon after they come up in the spring. The eggs hatch in a few days, forming whitish maggots which attack the bulbs and feed during a period varying according to weather conditions for from two to four or five weeks, after which they pupate in the ground or, occasionally, in the outer layers of the onion itself. During the summer, this stage continues about two weeks, after which the adult flies appear and in about ten days begin to lay eggs for a second generation.

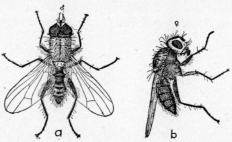

Fig. 344.—Adults of the onion maggot (*Hylemya antiqua* Meig.): about four times natural size; *a*, male; *b*, female. (*Modified from Ill. State Natural History Survey*.)

In some parts of their range there are probably only two generations a year, but elsewhere there seem to be three. The injury caused by this insect when abundant is sometimes large, entire fields consisting of many acres having nearly every onion affected. It varies greatly in importance in different years, however, there being in some seasons practically no maggots.

*Control.*—The most practical method is seed treatment with fine calomel as described for the cabbage maggot. In Illinois "a very effective control" has been obtained by a spray consisting of 1½ gallons of an oil-emulsion stock thoroughly mixed with 48½ gallons of the fungus-disease spray, Bordeaux mixture, using the 4–6–50 formula (4 pounds of copper sulfate, 6 pounds of lime and 50 gallons of water). This is sprayed on the onions, beginning when the plants are an inch high and repeating four more times at intervals of a week. This "will give practically 100 per cent control."

Other members of this family are frequently injurious, and, among these, the seed-corn maggot, often attacking peas and beans also, the beet and spinach leaf miner and the radish maggot may be mentioned. Methods of control for these insects are at present far from being as satisfactory as could be desired. The lesser housefly and several other small house-inhabiting flies which belong here are also of some importance as probably being disease carriers.

## PUPIPARA

There are several families of extremely modified aberrant forms which are generally classed together as a suborder of the Diptera called the Pupipara. Some of these insects are winged, while others are wingless when adult. The majority of them suck the blood of birds or mammals, though one species thus far rare in America is found on the body of the honeybee. Swallows appear to be favorite hosts for

Fig. 345.                    Fig. 346.
Fig. 345.—Adult engorged female sheep tick (*Melophagus ovinus* L.); greatly enlarged. (*From Marion Imes, Bur. An. Ind., U. S. Dept. Agr. Farmers' Bul.* 798.)
Fig. 346.—Young sheep tick just after emerging from its puparium; greatly enlarged. (*From Marion Imes, Bur. An. Ind., U. S. Dept. Agr. Farmers' Bul.* 798.)

some of these insects and bats for others. The most familiar insect belonging here lives on the sheep and is commonly called the sheep tick. A number of others of the group are also wrongly called ticks, probably because of their color, which is similar to that of some common ticks, their leathery external skin and the places where they are found. True ticks have eight legs, however, and never have wings, while six legs only are present in the Pupipara as with the other insects.

**The sheep tick** (*Melophagus ovinus* L.).—This pest of sheep is a wingless brown insect about a quarter of an inch long. It occurs in most of the countries where sheep are raised and is present practically wherever sheep are found in the United States, though most abundant in the west in the large flocks. The adult lives in the fleece of the host except when feeding, at which time it moves to the surface of the skin of the animal, punctures it and sucks the blood and lymph causing irritation which, when many of the insects are present, makes the sheep restless, preventing their feeding considerably and resulting in their failure to grow and fatten as they should.

The adult (Fig. 345) does not deposit eggs, these being retained within the body of the parent until they have hatched into larvae and during this period being nourished by the secretions from glands in the body of the parent.  When the development of the larva has been nearly completed, it leaves the parent and is then covered by a soft white membrane which, after some hours, turns brown and hard and becomes a puparium within which the animal pupates for a period of from nineteen to twenty-four days, after which the adult emerges.  After about ten to fourteen days more, the first larvae, ready to pupate, appear.  A full-grown larva is produced by a female every seven or eight days, twelve to fifteen being about the usual number in all per individual.

*Control.*—The most widespread method for controlling these insects is by dipping the sheep in some material that will kill the ticks.  The most important dips used for this purpose are either coal-tar creosote or nicotine.  Selection of the best dip for the purpose must be determined by the availability of soft water, ease of obtaining the materials and other local factors.  In general, two dippings are necessary and, if done during the early fall, should be twenty-four days apart.  Where shearing is done in the spring, the dipping should be in July and August unless the lambs become thickly infested soon after shearing, in which case dipping should be as soon as the shear cuts heal.  Many details connected with dipping make it necessary to become thoroughly acquainted with the process before treatment is actually attempted, if the best results are desired. Dipping should not be done in cold weather.

# CHAPTER XXXII

## ORDER SIPHONAPTERA

### (Aphaniptera)

The Siphonaptera or fleas are curious small insects, ranging from about a twentieth to a sixth of an inch long. They are evidently related to the flies in many ways but are much modified. Most of the members of the group have their bodies laterally compressed so that they are narrow (Fig. 347). The head is not sharply separated from the body and the antennae are short and stout. The mouth parts are for piercing and sucking and modified in a different way from those of other insects which feed in this manner. Although the identity of the various parts has not been conclusively proved, it seems probable that a long median pricking structure is the labrum or else the hypopharynx; a pair of similar structures are the mandibles; a pair of rather short, stout structures at the sides, each with a palpus, are the maxillae. The labium is represented by a rather stout basal portion bearing two long segmented pieces, perhaps the palpi, so shaped as together to form a loose sheath for the piercing parts. Compound eyes appear to be absent.

Fig. 347.—Adult dog flea (*Ctenocephalides canis* Curt.); greatly enlarged.

Backward-projecting spines occur on the body, largely at least, preventing backward movements between the hairs on the body of the host animal. Rows of stout spines may be present on the head just above the mouth or on the pronotum or in both places. These are called taenidia and are useful in identifying the species. The legs are long and powerful. Wings are absent but flat scales present on the meso- and metathorax are generally regarded as their rudiments. The larvae are worm-like, with chewing mouth parts, and pupate within a cocoon.

These insects are distinguished as

*Insects which as adults have their bodies strongly compressed sideways; are without wings and compound eyes but have legs; mouth parts for piercing and sucking; larvae worm-like. Metamorphosis is complete.*

331

Adult fleas feed entirely upon the blood of mammals and birds; although each species has what may be termed its preferred host, there seems to be some latitude in this, and other animals may also be attacked.

The eggs are laid loosely among the hairs of the host and drop to the ground where they hatch.  The larvae, which are slender, whitish and rather worm-like, with chewing mouth parts, feed on decaying vegetable and animal matter for a period varying from a few days to several months.  When feeding is completed, the larva spins a silken cocoon in which it pupates.  Here it may remain only a few days or for a time which may be more than a year, according to circumstances, before emerging as the adult.  The adults in hot weather and with no food will live only a few days; when food is available they may live a month or even nearly a year.  Winter in the north is usually spent in one or another of the early stages, but in the south the adults may be present on their hosts at any time.

Hot, dry weather is not favorable to the rapid breeding of these insects but in damp, rainy weather they increase rapidly, particularly in sandy localities as the moisture there is more uniform where the early stages live, though too much moisture is injurious to them.

Fleas are mainly household pests, coming in on cats and dogs, the cat flea being the most common generally, though in the west and south the human flea is also abundant.  The eggs dropped by the fleas fall to the floors and the larvae feed on any material found under rugs and mattings, in floor cracks and similar places and, on reaching maturity, attack the first animal they can reach.

Various animals besides those already mentioned serve as hosts. Among them are hogs, poultry and other birds.  Horses, cattle and sheep are not often attacked.

Fleas have become of importance to man aside from their attacks on his person with the discovery that they may carry the germs of the bubonic plague.  This much dreaded disease with its high mortality caused by *Bacillus pestis* occurs in rats' blood, and by feeding on this the flea brings the germs into his own body.  When a flea attacks a person, it often ejects partly digested blood and also feces near the "bite."  If, while the wound is still open, this place is rubbed or scratched the germs are liable thus to be introduced into the blood of the person. Their absence from the mouth parts and the saliva of the flea, as far as observations have yet gone, indicates therefore that inoculation with the germs from fleas is accidental; but as most persons generally scratch a flea bite, it is at least frequent enough to produce many cases of the disease.  In several Pacific coast and Rocky Mountain states the disease has also been found in ground squirrels and in one species at least of squirrel flea so that these fleas are also a menace to man.

*Control of fleas.*—The basis for flea control is rat eradication, disposal of excess cat and dog hosts, and the destruction of the fleas on pet animals and of their early stages in the sleeping quarters of those animals. Frequent dusting of pets with derris powders or washing with derris soaps is effective against the fleas and harmless to the host animals.

Treating rooms into which adult fleas have been brought thoroughly with pyrethrum or rotenone sprays or dusts will control a light infestation. Animals that are attacked by fleas should not be allowed under houses as is so often the case in the south when no cellars are present and the house is placed on low posts. In such cases, these places are excellent locations for fleas to breed and, when adult, to enter the houses.

To destroy the early stages successfully, the food of the larvae should be kept in mind and all such material be removed. Thorough cleaning, removing all dust, much of which is flea food; soaking cracks, where it might gather, with kerosene; airing and beating rugs, carpets, straw mattings and, in fact, all floor coverings are all important control measures.

There are other ways in which fleas may be controlled. One is to sprinkle five pounds of flake naphthalene over the floor of an infested room and close tightly for 24 hours; then open and sweep it into any other room needing treatment and manage in the same way. Several rooms can be treated with the same material. Fumigation with sulfur, using 4 pounds to each 1,000 cubic feet of space if the young are present and 2 to 3 pounds if only the adult fleas are involved, the fumigation to continue 12 hours, is also a successful control. Cellars infested should be thoroughly cleaned and whitewash used freely.

Flea "bites" if troublesome may be relieved by the use of carbolated Vaseline, camphor or a 3 per cent solution of carbolic acid in water.

One of the fleas commonly called the sticktight flea (*Echidnophaga gallinacea* Westw.) is a rather important pest of fowls in the south and southwest, causing trouble as far north as Kansas. These fleas gather chiefly on the heads of the birds where they are noticeable around the eyes and on the wattles and comb but they may occur elsewhere on the animal. Chickens are often killed by these fleas but older fowls are more resistant. This flea differs from most other species by remaining most of its life on the fowl, whence its common name.

Where the infestation is severe, the use of carbolated Vaseline, or a mixture of lard two parts and kerosene one part, carefully applied only to the places where the fleas are on the fowl; the destruction of rats which also harbor this pest; and a thorough cleaning of the poultry houses are desirable. The floors, dropping boards and nests where the fleas breed should be thoroughly cleaned and sprayed with creosote oil. The soil outside should be treated with lime.

One species of flea differs somewhat in its habits from most of these insects. It is known as the chigoe or jigger flea (*Tunga penetrans* L.) and occurs in the tropical and subtropical portions of America and also in Africa and India. It should not be confused with a tiny mite (class Arachnida) which has somewhat similar habits and is found as far north as Massachusetts and Lake Erie, which is abundant on tall grass and bushes and which on man burrows into the skin causing considerable irritation (see page 375).

The chigoe is found on domestic animals, birds and man. The female (Fig. 348a) is at first about a twenty-fifth of an inch long, but its abdomen may later become as large as a small pea. The adults move about, but when the female has been fertilized it burrows into the skin of the host and its body begins to enlarge (Fig. 348b and c) by the development of eggs, causing a painful wound like an ulcer. The eggs are expelled into this ulcer or may fall to the ground but,

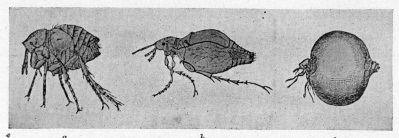

a                                b                                c

FIG. 348.—Chigoe (*Tunga penetrans* L.); *a*, an unfertilized female; *b*, one fertilized, which has penetrated the skin and is beginning to enlarge; *c*, one enormously enlarged by the development of eggs. All enlarged. (*From Berlese.*)

in either case, hatch in a few days, and those in the wound then work out and drop to the ground.

The regions usually attacked in persons are the bare feet, though no part of the body is entirely free from danger. Pus is produced in the wounds, and when many of the fleas are present the ulcers may run together and cause serious results. Protection from these pests is best obtained by keeping the floors clean, using naphthalene as recommended above; cleaning floors and walls with kerosene; and wearing shoes or other foot coverings to keep the insects from reaching the skin. When they are already burrowing, they may be removed by the use of a needle which has been sterilized by passing it through a flame, followed by a dressing of the wound. A drop of turpentine at each spot attacked will kill the fleas and, if ulceration has not gone too far, the wound will generally ulcerate enough more to expel the animal and then gradually heal.

Fleas occur in nearly all parts of the world, and, though less than a thousand kinds are known, their habits and their relation to disease make them an important group of insects.

# CHAPTER XXXIII

## ORDER HYMENOPTERA

The insects that belong in this large order have no general common name, but many of them are well known as bees, ants and wasps. The larger portion of the group, however, consists of small insects such as sawflies, gallflies, parasites, etc., which are seldom noticed.

Most Hymenoptera have wings when adult. These are four in number, membranous, and the front pair is the larger. They have rather few cross veins as a rule, and in some cases nearly all the veins are missing. The two wings on the same side of the body are united by a row of hooks along the middle part of the costa of the hind wing, which catch in a fold of the membrane on the hinder margin of the wing in front, the two wings in this way acting together and much as though they were one. The structures uniting them are called the frenal hooks, or hamuli, and the frenal fold. Over the base of each forewing, except in the ants, is a small arched scale called a tegula, which roofs over the place where this wing articulates with the body.

The body in insects of this order may be quite large and stout, as in the bumblebees, or long, being two or more inches in length in some tropical wasps, but most of them are much smaller insects and in some the body may be only about a fiftieth of an inch long and the entire animal almost microscopic in size.

In the female Hymenoptera an ovipositor, either used for making holes in which to deposit eggs or modified to become a weapon, is almost always present. When developed for its original purpose as an organ connected with egg laying, it may have projections along its lower edge and be used like a saw to cut slits in leaves or other structures in which to insert the eggs. In other cases it becomes a sort of boring organ used in making holes in leaves, stems, wood or animals, in which the eggs are placed. Sometimes the ovipositor is very prominent and is not retractile; in other species it can be drawn entirely within the body. In a large section of the order, however, regarded as containing the more highly developed members of the group, deposition of the eggs is not within objects but on surfaces, and, a hole being no longer needed, the ovipositor has become modified in most cases, glands connected with it produce a more or less poisonous fluid (possibly it is more or less poisonous in the lower forms also) and the sting is thus produced, a structure no

335

longer needed for its original purpose having been transformed into a weapon for defense. In the ants, however, various degrees of reduction of this structure occur, some ants having no stinging power whatever, while a few are effective in this way. From these facts the reason why drone bees and the males of the other Hymenoptera are harmless is evident.

The mouth parts vary in different portions of the order. In the lower forms they are for chewing and quite simple. In the higher forms the maxillae and labium have been elongated and together form a structure for sucking fluids. In most of the lower forms there are two trochanters to each leg, while in the higher ones there is but one.

Development in this order is by a complete metamorphosis. The larvae differ much in appearance in the various families, some feeding on leaves and greatly resembling caterpillars. Others are borers in wood and are modified to adapt them to life under such conditions. Still others, particularly those which are parasitic within the bodies of other insects, may be so changed as to make it seem almost impossible that they can be insect larvae. Many of those living on food provided for them during this stage of their existence greatly resemble and are sometimes called maggots. At pupation a marked change in appearance takes place, antennae, legs, wing stubs and body characters nearly like those of the adults now showing, and the legs and antennae project, encased by sheaths of the pupa skin, the pupa in this order being a pupa libera as already described for some beetles (see page 166, and Fig. 34b).

The Hymenoptera may be recognized as

*Insects which when adult have, in most cases, four membranous wings with few or even no cross veins, the hinder pair the smaller. Mouth parts for chewing, or for chewing and also for sucking. The females have in nearly all cases either an ovipositor or a sting. Metamorphosis is complete.*

The Hymenoptera are important from an economic standpoint. A rather small number are injurious, destroying crops of various kinds, but the majority are either directly or indirectly beneficial, as parasites of destructive insects or by aiding in the fertilization of flowers, and in the case of the honeybees by the value to man of their products. Over 65,000 species are known.

The Hymenoptera are divided into two suborders: the Symphyta or Chalastogastra and the Apocrita or Clistogastra. In the Symphyta the abdomen has no petiole and joins the thorax without being narrowed; the mouth parts are of the chewing type and the ovipositor is saw-like or for boring. The eggs are placed in slits sawed or in holes bored in plant tissues, in plant stems or in tree trunks, and the larvae all feed on plants. In the Apocrita the first segment of the abdomen is so closely joined to the thorax that it seems to be an actual part of it; the front part of the second segment narrows in front to form a slender stalk, long or short, the petiole, which connects it to the first segment. The effect of this is to make the apparent division of the thorax and abdomen come between the first and second segments of the abdomen. The first segment of the abdomen thus closely connected with the abdomen is called the propodeum or median segment. The mouth parts in this suborder may be quite simple, but in the majority of cases they have been so modified as to permit the use of fluid foods. The ovipositor may be used for boring into wood or into other insects; or has been transformed into a sting; or as in some of the ants, it has become lost. Most of the members of this suborder live either as parasites or in other ways on insects, spiders, etc.; a few are feeders on plant tissues or on the pollen and nectar of plants.

## SUBORDER SYMPHYTA OR CHALASTOGASTRA

**The sawflies and stem borers.**—There are a number of families in this suborder, most of which include leaf-feeding insects whose eggs are usually laid in slits in the leaves sawed by the ovipositors of the adult females. In a few families the ovipositor is constructed for boring and the insects make holes, in either herbaceous or woody stems, in which to deposit the eggs.

The plant feeders of this suborder are spoken of in a general way as sawflies and all are injurious to the plants they live on, though, of course, many of these are of little or no importance to man, but a few injure various crop-producing plants. Those boring in wood are called horntails.

Fig. 349.—Imported currant worm (*Pteronidea ribesii* Scop.), adult and larvae; about natural size. (*From Minn. Agr. Exp. Sta. Bul.* 84.)

**The imported currant worm** (*Pteronidea ribesii* Scop.).—This common injurious sawfly is a native of Europe but has been in this country for many years and is widely distributed. It feeds on the leaves of wild and cultivated currants and to some extent on those of gooseberries also. When this sawfly is abundant the plants are quickly and thoroughly stripped of their foliage soon after it develops, which checks or almost entirely prevents the production of the fruit.

The adult sawfly (Fig. 349) is about a third of an inch long, with a pale or reddish-yellow, rather stout body with blackish spots. It passes the winter in the ground within an oval cocoon, rather papery in texture and brown in color. In spring, about when the currant leaves become partly developed, the adults begin to emerge from their cocoons and the females lay their eggs in rows on the leaves, generally along the veins on the underside. The larvae, at first very small and whitish, feed and grow rapidly and, when full-grown, are nearly three-quarters of an inch long, greenish in color and shaded with yellowish at both ends. During the intermediate larval instars the green color of the body is modified by the presence of many black spots. After feeding from two to three weeks the larvae crawl down to the ground and pupate, the cocoons resembling those already described. Adults from these pupae appear in late June or July and lay eggs for a second generation, and in some cases a few of the insects have a third generation before winter. The second and third generations (when present) do not attract much attention generally, as interest in the currants in most cases ceases for the season with the gathering of the crop.

*Control.*—Spray or dust the currant bushes as soon as the leaves have developed or the "worms" have appeared, with derris, cube or pyrethrum. Repeat if new leaves become infested. Derris dust may be used at a strength of 1 per cent rotenone; or one pound of ground derris containing 4 or 5 per cent rotenone may be suspended in fifty gallons of water and several ounces of a sticker added for use as a spray.

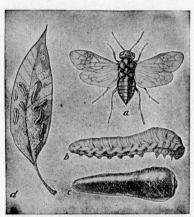

FIG. 350.—Pear slug (*Caliroa cerasi* L.): *a*, adult; *b*, larva with slime removed; *c*, larva from above, covered by its slime; *d*, leaf showing work of the insect and with larvae present. *a*, *b*, and *c* much enlarged; *d* somewhat reduced. (*From Berlese, modified from U.S. Dept. Agr. Div. Ent. Circ.* 26.)

**The pear slug** (*Caliroa cerasi* L.).— This insect feeds on the leaves of the pear, plum and cherry and, though a native of Europe, is now found almost everywhere in this country (Fig. 350).

The adult is a sawfly about a fifth of an inch long, with a black body. It appears after the leaves develop in spring and lays its eggs in slits sawed in the leaves, forming a sort of blister at each place. The larvae soon produce a dark-brown glossy slime which covers them and conceals their true outline, making them somewhat similar to soft snails in appearance. They feed on the leaf tissue, skeletonizing it, and molt four times. After the fourth molt the slime disappears and the larva is orange-yellow and does not feed. It now passes to the ground in which it pupates. A second generation follows, but a few of the pupae remain unchanged in the ground until the following spring. In the south there are three generations, at least in some cases.

*Control.*—Spraying with lead arsenate, standard formula; nicotine sulfate, 40 per cent, one pint in a hundred gallons of water, with three or four pounds of soap; one ounce of white hellebore in three gallons of water; or dusting with freshly slaked lime are effective treatments for this insect, but it is not very often abundant enough to call for the use of control measures.

A similar sawfly often attacks the rose, feeding on the leaves, its dark-colored and slimy, though small, larvae being very noticeable when abundant. When treatment is necessary, the methods given for the pear slug are equally effective with this insect.

A few of the stem and wood borers in this superfamily are of considerable importance, but most of them are seldom noticed. **The European wheat stem sawfly** (*Cephus pygmœus* L.) in the east and **the wheat stem sawfly** (*Cephus cinctus* Nort.) (Fig. 351) in the west often attack growing wheat. The adult of the eastern species punctures the wheat stem in the spring and deposits an egg inside the stalk and the larva, which soon hatches, tunnels in the stem and, as the grain ripens, works its way downward. By harvesting time most of the adults have reached the roots. They then prepare

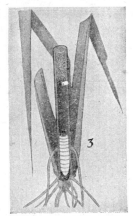

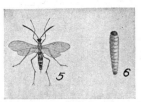

FIG. 351.—Wheat stem sawfly (*Cephus cinctus* Nort.): 3, base of wheat plant showing larva in winter position; 5, adult sawfly; 6, full-grown larva; all natural size. (*Modified from Can. Dept. Agr. Ent. Branch, Bul.* 11.)

for winter, cutting the stalk partly off, generally less than an inch above the surface of the ground. Each now plugs the cavity of the stem below this point for a short distance, leaving about half an inch of space between the plug and the lower end of the cavity, in which it spins a cocoon. The larva winters thus, pupates in March or April, in New York at least, and the adult appears in May.

Where grass seed is not planted with the wheat, plowing the stubble under deeply at any time between harvest and the following May is a fairly efficient control method. Rotation of crops, using corn or alfalfa, is also helpful.

One of the stem borers attacks currant stems. The adult girdles the stem after laying its egg, and the larva feeds below the girdled place, which shows plainly, the part above wilting or breaking over. Cutting off such stems as soon as they are seen, about eight or ten inches below the girdled place, will control this insect.

Most of the borers of this superfamily which tunnel in wood are generally called horntails, the straight, stiff ovipositor somewhat suggesting a horn. Various trees, both deciduous and evergreen, are attacked by different species, and the circular exit holes of the borers after they have become adult permit the entrance of moisture and the spores of fungi, thus providing starting places for decay. Healthy, vigorous trees are seldom attacked, but the death of others is hastened by these insects. One species known as **the pigeon tremex** (*Tremex columba* L.) bores in the maple, apple, pear, elm, beech, oak and sycamore. It varies from three-quarters of an inch to twice as much in length (Fig.

352); its body is cylindrical and nearly as large as a lead pencil. Its color varies from nearly black with yellow spots on the abdomen to

yellow with some black marks. This insect is often noticed on the tree trunks during the summer months. The larva tunnels its course through the wood, going sometimes several inches into the tree but, as the end of its feeding period approaches, turns outward and makes a hole to the outside, leaving only a thin piece of bark to close the opening. It then goes back into the hole a short distance to pupate and the adult on emergence gnaws away the piece of bark and escapes from the tree. An interesting

FIG. 352.—Pigeon tremex (*Tremex columba* L.); somewhat reduced.

and remarkable-looking parasite of this insect will be considered later in this chapter.

## SUBORDER APOCRITA OR CLISTOGASTRA

In this suborder belong enormous numbers of parasites, both on insects and other animals, many gall insects, and the ants, wasps and bees. As already stated, the insects of this suborder have a petiole, propodeum, mouth parts in many cases which can be used for gathering fluid food and an ovipositor, either used as such, modified to become a sting, or lost in some cases. There is a great diversity of structure in the suborder, which has led to the establishment of many families, which are usually grouped into about ten or eleven larger divisions called superfamilies, but all included in the suborder.

FIG. 353.—Example of an ichneumon fly (*Ophion*); natural size.

*Superfamily* **ICHNEUMONOIDEA** (the ichneumon flies).—This is a very large and important group. Its members (see Figs. 353, 354) are all parasites, attacking Lepidoptera, Coleoptera, Diptera and some Homoptera, Orthoptera and Hymenoptera, and also spiders in their early stages, at least in most cases. A few are injurious as they are parasites of beneficial forms. Thus among the Coleoptera parasitized are some of the ladybeetles. In other cases it is the parasites themselves which are parasitized. In this last case the destruction of a beneficial parasite by another makes the latter an injurious insect. There are also some that appear to attack the parasites of the parasites, which places these last as beneficial in their turn. Primary parasites attack nonparasitic forms; secondary or hyperparasites attack primary ones; tertiary parasites attack the secondary ones, etc.

In three of the families in this group the petiole of the abdomen is attached near the top of the hinder end of the propodeum (Fig. 355), giving these insects a very peculiar appearance.

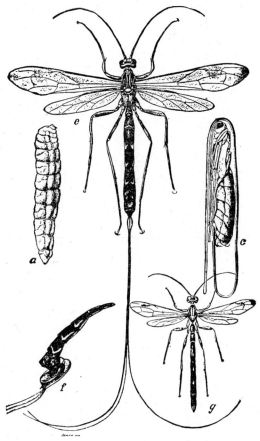

FIG. 354.—Long-tailed Thalessa (*Megarhyssa lunator* Fab.): *a*, larva; *c*, pupa; *e*, adult female; *f*, side view of abdomen of adult female, showing attachment of ovipositor; *g*, adult male; about natural size. (*Modified from Felt, N. Y. State Mus. Mem. 8; after Riley.*)

The importance of the ichneumon flies as parasites is very great, as they are abundant and destroy enormous numbers of injurious forms each year. One group devotes its attention to aphids, puncturing the bodies of these insects and laying an egg in each puncture. The tissues of the aphid are fed upon by the parasite and the body of the host gradually becomes brown, swollen and rather globular, and it dies, holding on to the place where it was feeding at the time of its death.

After pupation within the body of the host, the adult parasite cuts a circular opening in the surface of its host and escapes, and plant lice bodies, swollen brown and with a hole in each are abundant when these insects occur in large numbers. As each parasite obtains all the food necessary for its entire development from the body of a single aphid, these insects are naturally extremely small (see Figs. 128, 129).

Another ichneumon fly which is often noticed has a body an inch and a half or more long and an ovipositor often over three inches; it has been recorded in a few cases as nearly six inches in length. There are two kinds of about this size, one with a black body and a few yellow spots, the other brown with yellow markings, and other smaller species also occur. These insects attack the horntails already described and may often be seen during the summer on trees in which horntail larvae are present. These ichneumon flies are called **the long-tailed Thalessas.**

FIG. 355.—An eva-niid (*Brachygaster minutus* Oliv.); about five times natural size. (*Modified from Kieffer.*)

The female Thalessa (Fig. 354) crawls about over the trunk of a tree which in some way she discovers is infested by horntails, until a satisfactory place is found. Then she settles at that point and begins to force her ovipositor into the bark and wood. The length of the ovipositor is suggestive of the distance it must be pushed in, in some cases, to reach the tunnel of the horntail larva, and it seems almost impossible for such a slender structure to be forced so far through hard wood. When the tunnel of the horntail is reached, the Thalessa lays an egg in it and then draws its ovipositor out of the tree. Sometimes this process results in the death of the Thalessa, the ovipositor becoming so firmly fixed in the wood, either on its way in or during the withdrawal, that it cannot be removed and the Thalessa dies.

The egg left in the tunnel of the horntail soon hatches and the larva travels along the burrow until it finds the borer, to which it attaches itself, and feeds upon its juices. After pupation in the burrow, the adult Thalessa escapes from the trunk either by gnawing its way out or by following a tremex burrow if one is present.

In one of the three families that have the petiole attached near the top of the propodeum (the Evaniidae) (Fig. 355) its members, as far as known, are parasites on cockroaches.

*Superfamily* **CHALCIDOIDEA** (the chalcid flies).—This is an extremely large group, containing thousands of kinds of insects, most of which are very small, a few being only about a fiftieth of an inch long. Some of them live in galls, parasitic either on the gall maker or on inquilines; others are parasitic on various insects, parasitizing the egg, larva or nymph, pupa or adult according to the species; and a few are plant feeders of more or less economic importance. The wings, except in some wingless species, have very few veins, the most prominent one running out from the body about halfway to the tip, then bending forward to the costa, after which it bends back into the wing a short distance and ends. This is the only one in a great many cases, though in a few species weaker veins are often present.

One tiny species, *Trichogramma minutum* Riley, having no common name, is only about one-fiftieth of an inch long and varies in color from pale yellow to dark brown, depending upon the temperature and the race to which the insect belongs. It occurs nearly everywhere in the United States and is also found in other parts of the world. It is an egg parasite and sometimes one host egg provides sufficient food for several Trichogramma larvae. It attacks a great many kinds of injurious Lepidoptera and is therefore very beneficial. It has several generations a year. It has been found so frequently and so abundantly as a

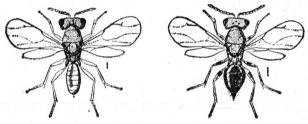

Fig. 356.—*Pteromalus puparum* L., a chalcid parasite of the cabbage worm and other insects: male (left) and female (right). Hair lines show the natural size. (*After Chittenden, U. S. Dept. Agr.*)

parasite of such important pests as the codling moth, the angoumois grain moth and others as to lead to attempts to raise it in large numbers under laboratory conditions. For this purpose the angoumois grain moth is the usual host supplied. Breeding enormous numbers of the parasite has been very successful and material thus produced can now be purchased for distribution in places where its hosts are abundant. The success, however, obtained by liberating these parasites in such places is not certain according to some investigators, and entomologists at the present time are of divided opinion on this point. Some of the hosts which this parasite has been liberated to aid in the destruction of are the codling moth, the oriental fruit moth, the corn ear worm and the sugarcane borer. Reports as to the results obtained differ. Possibly the parasites are more effective against some hosts than others; possibly winter conditions may so affect the parasites in the more northern states as to render their work less effective, as one observer has suggested. Further research on this subject is needed and much attention is being given to it.

Another member of this group, known as *Pteromalus puparum* L. and having no common name, is a parasite on various species of butterflies, particularly the cabbage worms. This insect (Fig. 356) is probably a native of Europe. It was first noticed here about 1870 and is now present wherever its host insects occur and frequently destroys great numbers of them.

The plant feeders in this group produce small galls or at least swellings of the portion of the plant where they live, and one or two, by attacking crop plants, are of importance to man.  A number of species of the genus *Harmolita* attack the stems of different kinds of small grains such as wheat, oats and barley and at times do considerable injury.

**The wheat strawworm** (*Harmolita grandis* Riley).—This insect extends from New York to Colorado and from the Great Lakes to Virginia and Tennessee and is also present on the Pacific coast but has thus far been of little importance east of the Mississippi River.  The adult is a tiny black insect somewhat resembling an ant, with red eyes and legs banded with yellow.  One generation has wings; the other is wingless.

The winter is spent in the pupa stage in the stubble of wheat fields and the adults emerge in April and May in the more northerly states; earlier in the south. These are the wingless forms and are very small.  They lay their eggs in the wheat plants which at this time have grown only a short distance above ground. The larva feeds in the short stem, usually producing a swelling there, and when full-grown it has worked its way to the crown of the plant where it entirely consumes the head, thus preventing the formation of any grain.  By the last of May these larvae have completed their feeding and pass through a brief pupal period, the adults—winged in this generation—emerging in early May in the south, and in June in the north.  These individuals fly freely and spread to other fields. Eggs are now laid in this wheat, preferably well up toward the head where the joints are most tender and juicy.  The larvae from these eggs feed and reduce the yield of wheat by consuming nourishment which would otherwise go to the grain.  Full growth has been obtained before the straw hardens, and pupation occurs during the fall.  Whether the insects will be taken off in the straw or remain behind in the stubble depends on the degree of advancement of the plants, and the height above ground of the cutting.

*Control.*—Crop rotation, raising no wheat on the same land for two years in succession, is a good treatment, as the wingless generation cannot migrate to other fields.  Volunteer wheat in or near such fields should, of course, be destroyed if the rotation is to be more effective.  Burning over or plowing under of the stubble is also desirable, though less effective.  Winter and spring wheat should never be grown near each other.

**The wheat jointworm** (*Harmolita tritici* Fitch, Fig. 357).—This is a species closely related to the last, found throughout the east to the Mississippi River and south to about the same limits as the other species.  Its life history differs from that of the wheat strawworm in there being only one generation a year.  Winter is passed as the larva in wheat straw or in the stems of various grasses, and the adults appear in May or June.  Eggs are deposited as high up the wheat stems as the adult can find an uncovered stem.  The larvae have completed their feeding by harvesttime but do not pupate until the following spring.  Apparently a rotation of crops and care that waste lands, fence borders, etc., do not provide grass stems in which it can breed and winter are about our only methods for the control of this pest.  The injury these two species of *Harmolita* do varies all the way from very little to an almost entire loss of the crop.

Where clover seed production is extensive, considerable injury to the crop is often caused by the clover seed chalcid (*Bruchophagus gibbus* Boh.). Red and crimson clover, and alfalfa to some extent, are attacked by this tiny insect which feeds as a larva within the seed. Another species works in a somewhat similar way in apple seeds.

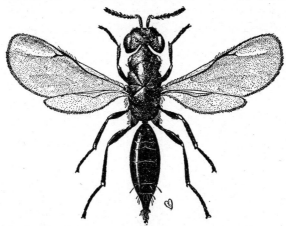

FIG. 357.—Adult female wheat jointworm (*Harmolita tritici* Fitch); greatly enlarged. (*From U. S. Dept. Agr. Farmers' Bull.* 1006.)

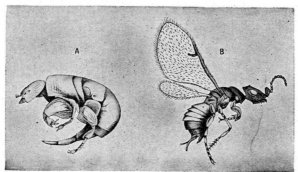

FIG. 358.—Fig fertilizer (*Blastophaga grossorum* Grav.): *A*, male, about fourteen times natural size; *B*, female, about ten times natural size. (*Reduced from Henneguy.*)

A chalcid whose presence is essential in connection with the production of Smyrna figs, which is now becoming an important industry in some parts of this country, is of interest for that reason. This insect, known as *Blastophaga grossorum* Grav. (Fig. 358), and its relation to fig production are well described by Kellogg as follows:

The male Blastophagas are grotesque, wingless, nearly eyeless creatures which never leave the fig in which they are bred, but the females are winged and fly freely about among the trees. A fig is a hollow, thick, and fleshy-walled receptacle in which are situated, thickly crowded over the inner surface, the minute flowers. The only entrance into the receptacle (or fig) is a tiny opening at the blunt free end of the young fig, and even this orifice is closely guarded by scales that nearly close it. The eggs are laid by the females at the base of the little flowers in certain figs. The hatching larvae produce little galls in which they lie, feeding and developing. They pupate within the galls, and the wingless males when they issue do not leave the interior of the fig, but crawl about over the galls, puncturing those in which females lie, and thrusting the tip of the abdomen through the puncture and fertilizing the females. The fertilized winged female gnaws out of the galls, and leaves the fig through the small opening at the blunt free end. She flies among the trees seeking young figs, into which she crawls and where she lays her eggs at the bases of as many flowers as possible. But it is only the wild, inedible, or "caprifigs" that serve her purpose. The flowers of the cultivated Smyrna seem to offer no suitable egg-laying ground and in them no eggs are laid. But as the female walks anxiously about inside the fig, seeking for a suitable place, she dusts all the female flowers with pollen brought on her body from the male flowers of the caprifig from which she came, and thus fertilizes them. This process is called caprification. Without it no Smyrna fig has its flowers fertilized and its seeds "set." It is the development of the seeds with the accompanying swelling of the fleshy receptacle and the storing of sugar in it that makes the Smyrna fig so pleasant to the palate. The trees may grow large and bear quantities of fruit, but if the figs (really the fig-flowers) are not caprified, the size, sweetness, and nutty flavor of the perfect fruit are lacking. To ensure caprification, branches laden with caprifigs containing Blastophagas just about to issue are suspended artificially among the branches of the Smyrna fig. Of course the female Blastophaga entering a Smyrna fig and dying there leaves no progeny, for she lays no eggs. It is therefore necessary to maintain a plantation of caprifigs in or near the Smyrna orchard. These bear three crops or generations of figs: one, the "profichi," ripening in the spring; another, the "mammoni," ripening in the late summer; and the third, or "mammae" generation, which hangs on the tree through the winter. By

means of these successive generations of caprifigs a series of three generations (or sometimes four) of Blastophaga appear each year.

The great importance of the superfamily Chalcidoidea to man does not rest either upon the importance of its destructive members or upon the Blastophaga, but on the enormous number of parasitic forms included in the group. These work in various ways as has already been indicated.

Fig. 359.—Example of a gall insect (*Trigonaspis megaptera* Panz.). About twice natural size. (*Reduced from Henneguy.*)

*Superfamily* **CYNIPOIDEA** (the gall insects).—This group of small insects (Fig. 359) includes species having very diversified habits, but the majority of them pass their early stages within abnormal growths on plants, called galls, which develop in connection with their presence. Some insects other than those of this group also produce galls, particularly many of the dipterous family Itonididæ, but the greater number of the more noticeable galls are produced by cynipids.

The cause of the production of the gall has been much discussed, some investigators claiming that at the time the female insect punctures the plant for egg laying she also injects a little poison into the wound which stimulates the plant cells of that region to grow in an abnormal manner. But the general belief now seems to be that the larva when it hatches gives the stimulus for this abnormal growth, by its presence as a moving body, by its gnawing or by its pouring out of irritating fluids.

The gall includes either one larva or many, according to the species concerned. It stops its growth about the time the larva finishes feeding and dries, forming a protective covering within which the insect pupates and escapes subsequently by gnawing its way out.

Fig. 360.—Various types of galls; about natural size.

In some species such an adult will attack a totally different kind of plant from the one it itself fed upon and the gall produced will be entirely different from the other. Adults from such galls will deposit their eggs in plants of the first kind, however, giving us a series of generations in which two different kinds of plants alternate in supplying food. This may be complicated by one generation consisting only of females, the other evidently being derived by agamic reproduction (parthenogenesis).

Galls may occur on roots, stems, twigs or leaves, and the type of gall produced is always the same on any one kind of plant, for the same species (Fig. 360), so that a student of the subject can tell from the gall alone the species that produced it, in nearly every case. One found on oak leaves is nearly an inch in diameter, globular, with a parchment-like covering and is often called an oak apple. Within its outer covering is a mass of radiating fibers and at the center a small cell in which the insect lives. Protuberances of various forms on the leaves of many kinds of plants are produced by different species of these insects.

Gall insects often are not alone in their habitations. Some members of the same superfamily as the gall makers are frequently found in the galls, living as "guests," profiting by the work of the producers of the galls but not injuring them in any way. These are usually called inquilines and often greatly resemble their hosts. In addition to the inquilines, parasites not only of the host but also of the various kinds of inquilines may also be present, adding greatly to the population of the gall. Some of these may be of the same superfamily as their hosts. Kieffer lists ten species of guests and forty-one species of parasites which he obtained from a root gall on oak, besides the gall maker itself!

Galls are not usually of any great economic importance, for though they may injure the appearance of a plant or tree for two or three sea-

*a*                  *b*

FIG. 361.—*Pelecinus polyturator* Drury: *a*, female; *b*, male; natural size.

sons, and also check its growth somewhat, the abundance of parasites usually stops the work of the gall makers before serious injury has been accomplished.

*Superfamily* **SERPHOIDEA.**—This superfamily, also known as the Proctotrupoidea, contains a large number of insects, nearly all very small, and most of them parasitic on other insects or on spiders. Parasitism of insect eggs seems to be very frequently the habit in the group. Some of the forms attacked by this group are Hemiptera, Diptera, Orthoptera, Lepidoptera, Neuroptera (aphis lions) and Coleoptera, and some are found in ants' nests, parasitic on these insects. None of the members of the superfamily is likely to attract the attention of those not entomologists, with one exception, an insect known as **the long-tailed Pelecinus** (*Pelecinus polyturator* Drury), the female (Fig. 361*a*) of which has a long slender body often between two and three inches long, and glossy black in color. The extremely long abdomen of this insect which in flight is generally carried partly curled up beneath it, and its odd appearance also when at rest, sometimes cause it to be noticed and the remark made that it must be a dangerous animal. This is not the case, however, as the insect is harmless. It is a parasite on June bug larvae, which it evidently seems to hunt for in the ground, and it is particularly abundant in sandy locations. The male (Fig. 361b), which is extremely rare or at least seldom seen, has a short club-shaped abdomen and is about an inch long.

A general survey of the habits of the parasitic groups of the Hymenoptera thus far considered reveals several diversities of life and habits worthy of being presented together. In the first place all stages of the host may be subject to parasitic attack. The egg seems to be selected in some cases and the pupa or the adult in others; larvae, however, appear to be particularly liable to be parasitized. Where the egg state is the one endangered, the parasite may consume its host before the latter can develop to the point where it is ready to hatch, thus preventing any injury whatever if the host be an injurious species. In other cases the host though parasitized is able to complete its embryonic development, hatch and feed for a time as a larva before it concedes victory to the parasite feeding within it and dies. In the case of larvae the parasitism may cause the death of the host before it becomes full-grown, or the latter may pupate but progress no farther. Pupae parasitized are destroyed before becoming adult and adults attacked may or may not be able to live until they reproduce.

These various relations of parasite and host have a bearing on the effectiveness of the parasite. In the majority of cases it is the next generation that is cut off, most of the injury normally caused by the host concerned being done before the parasite stops it, except in the case of those egg parasites which destroy the host before it hatches. Egg parasites of this kind, therefore, are generally regarded as the most beneficial, though the great numbers of the other forms make their work very effective.

Sometimes only one parasite feeds upon its host. In other cases there may be many, as with some of the Ichneumonoidea, where in one instance over 1,200 were bred from a single caterpillar. It would seem that the parent parasite is able to calculate the amount of food furnished by a host and deposit only a sufficient number of eggs to correspond to the food supply. The more probable explanation, however, is that parasites laying many eggs regularly attack only those species of insects large enough to provide for the progeny, while those which lay only one egg in or on a host require all the food provided there for a single parasite. No case is known where a parasite normally laying many eggs in a host will select a smaller one and deposit only one or a few in it.

Variations in the location of the pupa also occur. Some parasites pupate within the body of the host; others on its surface (Fig. 362); still others leave the insect entirely, pupating singly or in groups, away from it. Tomato hornworms and other large caterpillars are often seen in the fall, either dead or dying, and with many small white oval bodies on their backs. These are cases where the numerous parasites, after having completed feeding within the body of the host, have come out and pupated on its back, the white bodies being the cocoons of the parasites.

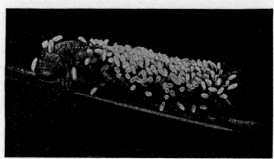

Fig. 362.—Hawk moth larva with cocoons of parasites which have fed upon it, on its back. (*From Felt, N. Y. State Mus. Mem.* 8.)

*Superfamily* **CHRYSIDOIDEA** (the cuckoo wasps).—These are wasps seldom over half an inch in length and generally smaller than this. Their bodies are green, of a metallic or bluish shade which easily distinguishes them from certain of the bees which are also green but brighter. The surface of the body is generally closely covered with fine indentations which give it a roughened appearance (Fig. 363).

These insects are able to sting but no poison gland seems to be present. The abdomen, which has only a few (three to five) visible segments, is flat beneath, and when attacked the insect can roll itself into a ball for protection.

Fig. 363.—Cuckoo wasp (*Chrysidoidea*); somewhat enlarged. (*From Bischoff.*)

The chrysids are parasitic, chiefly on wasps and bees, though a few are claimed to attack sawflies and one is a parasite on the oriental moth. The parent chrysid watches its opportunity to visit the nest of its hosts and lays an egg in a cell with that of the host. On hatching, the larva of the cuckoo wasp may eat the host or it may consume the food stored there, thus starving the proper inmate of the cell. Adult bees and wasps know these enemies of their young and sometimes drive them away from their nests, though frequently without success, the cuckoo wasp watching its chance to return later unobserved. If the nature of the hosts of the chrysids is taken into consideration, it is probable that, as a whole, the group should be considered injurious rather than beneficial.

In the superfamily **SCOLIOIDEA** are a number of families varying in size and habits. Perhaps the Mutillidæ, the velvet ants or stinging ants, are of the most interest.  Many of the species live in the nests of wasps and bees and it has been claimed that others dig holes in the ground and store flies and other small insects there.  The males are winged (Fig. 364), and the females (Fig. 365) are wingless but very active. Both sexes are generally covered more or less with hairs, often long, and usually of two or three contrasting colors, such as black with a red crossband, or white, yellow and black.  The females sting very effectively.

FIG. 364.                    FIG. 365.
FIG. 364.—A male mutillid; about twice natural size.  (*After André.*)
FIG. 365.—A female mutillid; slightly enlarged.  (*After André.*)

Northern species are nearly all quite small but in the south are forms nearly an inch long and stout-bodied.

*Superfamily* **FORMICOIDEA** (the ants).—In this group, seven families of which are recognized in this country, we find colonial forms only.  They occur from the frigid regions to the equator, being present in abundance practically everywhere, and it has been claimed that there are more individuals of ants than of all other terrestrial animals.  They live in colonies which are quite permanent, enduring for many years in some cases.  The life of an individual ant may continue for several years.

Ants are nearly always easily recognized by the presence of a petiole which is enlarged near or behind its middle (Fig. 366e), either being swollen or having a portion projecting upward there, followed behind by a constriction where this segment joins the rest of the abdomen. In some ants the following segment is also more or less similarly shaped. This gives these insects a rather elongate, narrow portion between the thoracic and abdominal masses, enlarged at one or two places, according to the number of segments concerned.

Three classes of ants always compose a colony—males, queens (females) and workers—and there may be subdivisions of each of these in some cases.  The males and females usually have wings during a portion of their lives, these having a simple arrangement of the veins; the workers are wingless, though some have vestiges of these structures. The queens and workers are provided with a well-developed sting in some groups of ants, but in others it is vestigial or entirely absent. The usual colors of ants are yellow, brown, black, red, dull red or brownish yellow.

Colonies of ants occur in many kinds of locations. Some are in the ground and may be of different types of structure; some occur in the cavities of plants, either preformed or else tunneled out by the ants;

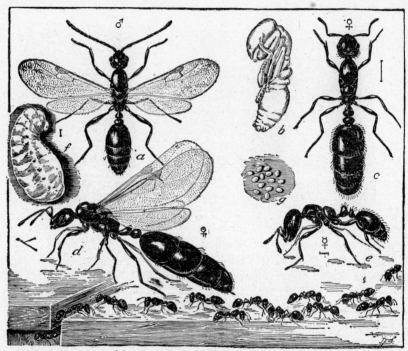

FIG. 366.—Little black ant (*Monomorium minimum* Buckl.): *a*, male; *b*, pupa; *c*, female; *d*, winged female; *e*, worker; *f*, larva; *g*, eggs; workers in line of march below. All enlarged, hair lines showing true length. (*From U. S. Dept. Agr. Farmers' Bul. 740.*)

some form nests on branches, making them of various materials; and some nest in timbers or other unusual places; while a few kinds have no fixed homes.

The food of ants is as varied as are their nest locations. Probably the original food of the group was insects, either dead or helpless, and many species feed on this material. Others take the honeydew supplied by scale insects, leafhoppers and particularly by plant lice. Some raid the nests of other species of ants and feed on their larvae and pupae. Plant seeds, bulbs and the bark on tender roots also form the food of some ants. One tribe raises a fungus in order to feed upon its hyphae. Sweet materials, such as cake, candy, sugar and molasses in houses, often attract ants, which find in these substances satisfactory foods.

Colonies in the ground may vary from those having a single tiny entrance and a few tunnels and galleries below the surface to large anthills several yards in diameter and several feet high, with extensive galleries both above and below the general ground level (Fig. 367). In these nests may be found a queen (frequently several); males, at least at times; and often many thousands of workers. The queen or queens produce the eggs which are carried away and cared for by the workers,

Fig. 367.—Ant hills. (*From a photograph by H. B. Peirson.*)

who also feed the larvae, clean them, transfer them from one part of the nest to another, according to the temperature and other conditions they need, and finally aid them in escaping from their cocoons. They also feed the queen and do all the work of the colony.

The eggs laid may develop into either males or females and workers, and there is some evidence that unfertilized eggs may in certain cases produce workers.

At certain seasons of the year swarming occurs. At such a time enormous numbers of winged males and females, previously produced in the nest, leave it and take flight. Mating occurs in the air and the females soon return to the ground where they remove their now useless wings, either by pulling them off with their legs or jaws or by rubbing them against the ground, stones or grass stems. The queen now prepares a nest by digging a hole in the ground, in rotten wood or elsewhere, forming a small chamber at the inner end and closing the entrance.

In her cloistered seclusion the queen now passes days, weeks, or even months, waiting for the eggs to mature in her ovaries. When these eggs have reached their full volume at the expense of her fat body and degenerating wing muscles, they are laid, after having been fertilized with a few of the many thousand spermatozoa stored up in the spermatheca during the nuptial flight. The queen nurses them in a little packet till they hatch as minute larvae. These she feeds with a salivary secretion derived by metabolism from the same source as the eggs, namely, from her fat body and wing muscles. The larvae grow slowly, pupate prematurely and hatch as unusually small but otherwise normal workers. In some species it takes fully ten months to bring such a brood of minim workers to maturity, and during all this time the queen takes no nourishment, but merely draws on her reserve tissues. As soon as the workers mature, they break through the soil and thereby make an entrance to the nest and establish a communication with the outside world. They enlarge the original chamber and continue the excavation in the form of galleries. They go forth in search of food and share it with their exhausted mother, who now exhibits a further and final change in her behavior. She becomes so exceedingly timid and sensitive to light that she hastens to conceal herself on the slightest disturbance to the nest. She soon becomes utterly indifferent to her progeny, leaving them entirely to the care of the workers, while she limits her activities to laying eggs and imbibing liquid food from the tongues of her attendants. This copious nourishment restores her depleted fat body, but her disappearing wing muscles have left her thoracic cavity hollow and filled with air which causes her to float when placed in water. With this circumscribed activity, she lives on, sometimes to an age of fifteen years, as a mere egg-laying machine (Wheeler).

Of course, there are many fatalities in such a history as this. Birds, dryness in their burrows, excessive moisture or cold, underground insects attacking them, all destroy the great majority of these ants just starting new colonies. Then, too, the amount of nourishment stored in the individual is an important factor, some species having so little that they are wholly unable to start new colonies. An individual of such a species therefore either joins a colony already established, a queenless colony of a related species if she can induce the colony to accept her, or enters a colony of a very different species and, killing its members, raises their young until they emerge when they will accept her as their queen. Rarely two queens may start a colony together.

After the colony is well under way, the queen limits her duties to egg laying and may live many years. In one case a queen lived nearly fifteen years in confinement and may have been older! This is the greatest age known to have been attained by an adult insect. The males die soon after mating.

The relation of ants to aphids is most interesting and has already been referred to (pages 144 and 148). It does not exist with all species of ants but in at least a large number honeydew is an important part of their diet and in some cases it may be their only food. There is every evidence that the benefit is mutual, the ants protecting the aphids, driving away the enemies of these insects or carrying the aphids to protected places. Ants that care for root-feeding aphids keep them in underground chambers or galleries, conduct them to their sources of food supply, collect and store their eggs for the winter and in spring take the young to their food.

The corn root aphid so injurious to corn, as already described, is thus cared for by ants. Scale insects that produce honeydew are also cared for in a sense, for ants are very attentive to them and to quite an extent prevent the attacks of the enemies of the scales by their presence and activities. Thus in an indirect way the protection by ants of aphids, scale insects, whiteflies, leafhoppers and in fact any insects that produce honeydew establishes such ants as injurious.

Some kinds of ants have most remarkable habits worthy of a brief reference here. Some species may make raids on the nests of other kinds and carry off their worker larvae and pupae to their own nests, where many probably serve as food, but a few may be reared and become slaves. Slavery is not essential with all kinds of ants where it is known, colonies having no slaves being able to carry on their lives unaided. With certain species, however, the situation is different. In these the workers have mandibles so constructed that they are unable to gather food, excavate their nests or care for the young. Accordingly, they make forays on the nests of other species, bringing back larvae and pupae which on becoming adult are slaves, do the work of the colony and care for their captors, both as adults and during their early stages.

The honey ants, so called, include species in which the crop is capable of great distension. This power is made use of by collecting honeydew and storing it until the abdominal mass is enormously distended and (in some species) about the size of a large currant, such individuals becoming animated food reservoirs. These members of the colony hang on the ceilings of their galleries, withdrawing from the regular duties of the other workers. The reason for the existence of such a peculiar habit is suggested by the fact that the honey ants are confined to dry plains and desert regions in North America, South Africa and Australia. They are therefore probably true reservoirs of nourishment which may be drawn upon during periods of drought, when the ants must remain for some considerable time in their nests.

Some ants raise fungi upon which to feed, about one hundred kinds which do this being known. These insects in most cases go in large numbers to trees; some climb the trees and cut off the leaves, and other members of the colony pick them up from the ground where they have fallen and carry them to their nests where the fungus is grown on them.

A few species of ants are obnoxious to man, by invading houses, by making their nests in lawns or in trees or by, to some extent, protecting injurious insects.

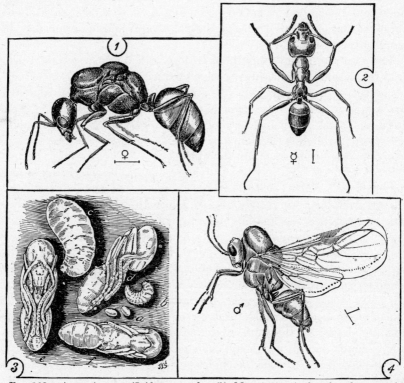

Fig. 368.—Argentine ant (*Iridomyrmex humilis* Mayr.): 1, wingless female; 2, worker; 3, early stages: *a*, eggs; *b*, young larva; *c*, full-grown larva; *d*, side view of pupa; *e*, ventral side of pupa; *f*, dorsal view of pupa; 4, male; all greatly enlarged.   (*From U. S. Dept. Agr. Farmers' Bul.* 740.)

The Argentine ant (*Iridomyrmex humilis* Mayr.) is a native of South America which probably reached this country between 1880 and 1890 at New Orleans and now is present nearly everywhere in the United States south of Virginia, Kentucky and Missouri and is also in California as far north as San Francisco.

The adults (Fig. 368) are brown in color. The queens are about a quarter of an inch long, the males about half that length and the workers about a tenth of an inch long. Their summer nests "may be located anywhere—under sidewalks, under the sills of houses, in brick piles, stone piles, under a piece of board or a piece of tin, in an old tin can—in fact, in any place convenient to the food supply. In the winter months there is a tendency to concentrate into larger colonies, and they seek warm, dry, secure nesting places in which to hibernate" (E. R. Barber).

Egg production is probably quite large—perhaps fifty or more per day under favorable conditions—and an average of forty days in warm weather is required for development from the laying of an egg to the emergence of the adult worker.

This is one of the worst house pests known in the regions where it is abundant. Its small size enables it to enter through the smallest cracks and it goes everywhere in houses after its food. It will eat practically everything in the way of foods, both raw and cooked, and no part of a house is free from its presence. The cold of ice chests does not repel them and beds are not entirely protected by placing the bedposts in dishes of water or kerosene, as after a few hours a film of dust forms on the surface of this, over which with their light bodies they are sometimes able to pass. Though they do not sting, they bite freely and are able to cause some pain in this way. Young children asleep have been found with ants in the nose, ears and mouth, and older persons are frequently inconvenienced by them in a similar way. They visit aphids, soft scales and other insects for honeydew and, to some extent at least, their presence is favorable to these pests and makes their control more difficult.

*Control.*—Heavy rains, causing a flooding of the nests, is a natural means of checking the ravages of these insects, many being killed, particularly in cold weather. Barriers on the legs of tables, beds, etc., consisting of tape, soaked in a saturated solution of corrosive sublimate, $HgCl_2$, dried, and then fastened around such places, will keep the ants away for several months at least. A generous supply of naphthalene in the form of moth balls, placed in a dish in which the leg of a piece of furniture rests, is also effective, provided each leg is thus treated. Kerosene instead of moth balls, as already described, is generally of some value as a protection.

Various ant poisons have been tested, and a sirup of granulated sugar, water, tartaric acid, sodium arsenite, sodium benzoate and honey has been found to be very effective, and it also keeps well. Placed in a tight tin with two sides dented in and with a tin cover, the ants can enter and feed while the sirup remains protected from the weather. A gill or two of sirup and a fairly large piece of sponge floating in it will complete the trap for use. Traps should be placed both in and around the house—of course, out of the reach of children—and by adding a bail or handle can be hung on walls, on the branches of trees and in similar situations. Eight or ten of these are sufficient for an ordinary city house and lot and will be effective at least for six or eight weeks.

**House ants.**—These are of several kinds but the one most usually troublesome is the little red ant or Pharaoh's ant (*Monomorium pharaonis* L.), probably a native of Europe but now abundant in nearly all countries. It is very small, red in color, and makes its nests in walls, floors, sills or other timbers, whence it explores all parts of a house, paying particular attention to those places where food is found. Oftentimes regular lines of these pests may be found marching to their nest from some article of food they have discovered, with another line beside the first, on their way to obtain food. In such cases it is sometimes easy to trace their line of march back to where they enter some timber in which their nest is placed, and then the injection into the holes, where they enter, of carbon disulfide or kerosene may prove sufficient to kill the queen or queens and terminate the life of the colony. In too many cases, though, it is impossible to locate or perhaps to reach the nest. Where this is true, it has been found that small pieces of sponge, soaked in molasses and water and a little arsenic, placed where ants are, will generally attract the pests, which will feed upon the poisoned sirup and be killed. In this way the number of individuals is frequently reduced more rapidly than the colony increases and the ants gradually become less abundant and finally disappear. Dusting sodium fluoride about, where ants appear in houses, will generally drive them away.

When ants are nesting in living trees they usually enter where some limb has been lost and their entrance holes in the wood can be found. Pouring carbon disulfide or gasoline into these and then stopping the holes with putty or mud is, in most cases, sufficient to kill the queen and, in consequence, the colony.

Ants in lawns or elsewhere may make mounds (Fig. 367) or may simply loosen the soil and more or less injure the grass at such places. To destroy such nests a stick, such as a cane or a broom handle, may be driven down to the bottom of the nest, at which point the loosened earth ends and driving becomes hard. These holes should be about a foot apart and enough of them made to cover the entire surface of the nest at this distance. Into each hole a tablespoonful or two of carbon disulfide is now poured and each opening closed at the top, which is sufficiently done by pressing the earth together at each hole with the foot. The carbon disulfide gas penetrating through the underground galleries of the ants will kill them, including the queen, and the colony will disappear.

This treatment should be applied on a warm, dry day, to hasten the change of the liquid to the gas and its rapid dissemination through all parts of the nest.

Calcium cyanide dust may be used in a similar way, putting about a teaspoonful in each hole and getting it well down in the holes by the use of a funnel.

*Superfamily* **VESPOIDEA** (the social wasps).—This common name for the superfamily is misleading, for two of the three families placed here are solitary, not living in colonies. Another and better name is the Diploptera as nearly all of them fold their wings lengthwise when at rest. They vary from quite small to species over two inches long and, in this country, are mostly black and yellow in color.

In this group are species that dig holes in the ground in which to lay their eggs; species that bur-row in plant stems or in wood for the same pur-pose; species that use mud of which to make their nests, sometimes forming cells resembling tiny jugs;

FIG. 369.                                 FIG. 370.
FIG. 369.—Eumenid wasp (*Eumenes fraternus* Say), natural size.
FIG. 370.—Two nests of *Eumenes fraternus* Say; natural size.

and species that make cells of weathered wood which they chew into a sort of paper and mold into the walls of the cells.

Insects of the family Eumenidæ are very abundant in this country. Most of them are rather small (Fig. 369) and black with yellow markings. Some make burrows in the ground; others tunnel in wood and divide the the tunnel into cells by cross partitions of mud; others build cells of mud, some kinds of which, attached to twigs, are like jugs or urns (Fig. 370) in form, with an upper flaring lip which, after the nest has been stocked with food for their young, is sealed with mud. The mud workers of this family are often called the mason wasps. All the wasps of this group are predaceous.

In the family Vespidæ we come to the social wasps, living in colonies, and with three types of members, the males, females and workers, these last being females in which the reproductive organs have undergone little or no development and the insects themselves are smaller than the true females.

The colonial life of these insects continues only during the summer, all but the females dying as winter approaches. In the spring the female (Fig. 371) starts a colony, first building a cluster of six-sided cells which are in some cases attached to the underside of some projecting rock or eaves or in a similar position (*Polistes*). These cells (Fig. 372) are made from weathered wood, chewed up by the insect into a sort of gray paper pulp and then molded into the desired form. In these cells she now places eggs and the young that hatch are fed upon insects partly chewed up, with perhaps the addition of some pollen. The young feed upon this until full-grown, then pupate in their cells. The adults that emerge

FIG. 371.                                    FIG. 372.

FIG. 371.—Social wasp (*Polistes pallipes* Lep.); about natural size.

FIG. 372.—Nest of *Polistes pallipes*, as found before the colony has increased much in numbers; reduced slightly.

are workers which now begin to construct additional cells all in the same layer, feed the young and do other work of the colony. Later in the season males and females are also produced and mate. Late fall stops further growth of the colony and all but the females die.

Other insects of this family (*Vespula*, Fig. 373) use wood, partly decayed, with which to construct their nests, and an outside wrapping is

added. Here one layer of cells will not accommodate the colony and several layers or tiers of cells surrounded by these wrappings are produced, leaving only one or two exit openings. Sometimes these nests are placed in holes in the ground and the wasps locating in such places are often called yellow jackets. Other species construct their nests in trees or bushes (Fig. 374), attaching them to a branch or branches.

FIG. 373.—Social wasp (*Vespula vulgaris* Fab.); about natural size.

There are several outside wrappings of gray papery wood pulp surrounding the tiers of cells within, of which there may be three or four, and the exit opening is usually at or near the bottom of the nest. Insects making nests of this kind in trees or under eaves, gable ends of buildings or similar places are generally called hornets, though there is really no sharp distinction between them and yellow jackets, in the usual use of these names. The life of the colony in the case of these insects does not differ from that of the forms, just described, which make only one layer of cells with no outside wrappings (*Polistes*), but in the yellow jackets and hornets the colony increases much more rapidly and by fall may number several hundred individuals.

To destroy hornets' nests, at night place a thick cloth saturated with chloroform tightly against all the openings into the nest and hold there until all buzzing ceases; then tear the nest down and break it up.

Fig. 374.—Nest of a hornet (*Vespula maculata* Kirby.); about one-eighth natural size.

*Superfamily* **SPHECOIDEA** (the digger wasps).—The insects of this group vary much in size, some being very small; others, particularly tropical species, may be more than two inches long. Some of them are bright colored, yellow, orange, green and black being the more usual colors, and the wings are frequently smoky, with an iridescent luster. A functional sting is present.

Fig. 375.          Fig. 376.

Fig. 375.—Bembecid wasp (*Bembidula quadrifasciata* Say); natural size.
Fig. 376.—Sphecid wasp (*Sceliphron cœmentarium* Drury); natural size.

Some of the insects (Fig. 375) in this superfamily have the petiole connecting the mass of the abdomen with the propodeum very short, but in others (Fig. 376) it is long and slender, the entire first segment behind the propodeum and sometimes a part of the second being very slender and elongate.    These insects are often spoken of as the thread-waisted wasps.

The digger wasps are all solitary in their habits.    The females of many species dig holes in the ground, in some cases several inches deep; others dig out the pith in plant stems; still others make nests of mud, gathered where there is moist earth, placing them under projecting stones, under eaves of buildings or in houses where access is easy through open doors or windows; in some species the nest is excavated in wood; and a few kinds either have not developed the nest-making habit or have lost it and use holes or the deserted nests of other species for themselves. In many instances the nest is subdivided into chambers separated from each other by partitions of mud.

Wherever the nest, and whatever the material that composes it, its purpose is the protection of the young of the insect and of the food that is stored there.    After constructing the nest, by digging, building or otherwise, the parent starts out to provision it.    The food differs with different species.    Some take certain species of grasshoppers; others, flies; Homoptera, Hemiptera, Hymenoptera, Lepidoptera larvae, some Coleoptera, and spiders are also listed as the prey of digger wasps of various other species.

When one of the wasps finds an insect of the desired kind, she attacks and stings it, generally not killing but only partly paralyzing it, and apparently chiefly in the locomotor centers, so that it cannot escape. The prey is then grasped by the wasp and carried to the nest.    In some cases flight is possible to the wasp carrying this load, but in many cases the prey is far too heavy for transfer in this way, at least in the case of those wasps which burrow in the earth, and it is therefore dragged along the ground to the nest.    How the wasp knows the direction to take and how finally to locate the hole it is practically impossible to determine, but in most cases the insect seems to have little difficulty.

Once arrived at the nest the prey is dragged into it and, if it alone provides a sufficient food supply for the young wasp to be developed there, the parent now lays an egg on it and then closes up the opening of the nest.    In the case of nests in the ground this is accomplished by scratching in dirt from around the hole and packing it in firmly.    In three or four cases, species of the wasp genus *Sphex* have been seen by different observers to pick up a tiny pebble with their mandibles and, using it like a hammer, pound down more firmly the earth filled into the hole.    This may perhaps be interpreted as representing the Stone Age in the development of insects!

If the single insect captured will not provide enough food for the young wasp, the parent proceeds to bring in more, until sufficient has been supplied, after which the opening is closed and another nest or cell, according to the kind of wasp concerned, is begun. In a few species the prey, instead of being paralyzed, appears to be killed and it is claimed that the wasp brings fresh supplies of food from day to day for its young.

Detailed studies on the lives and habits of these wasps have been recorded by many observers, and the remarkable traits these insects possess form one of the most interesting topics in entomology.

One species (Fig. 377) deserves particular attention because of its singular ways. It is a large wasp often called the cicada killer (*Sphecius speciosus* Drury), its body being over an inch long, its abdomen black with yellow marks. It is found over a large portion of the United States and appears during the dog days in summer. It makes its nests in the ground and provisions them with adult dog-day cicadas (Homoptera), larger and heavier than itself, which it catches in the trees. The prey cannot be carried to the nest by flight but the wasp starts from the point of capture with its paralyzed prey and flies as far as possible before strik-

FIG. 377.—Cicada killer (*Sphecius speciosus* Drury), about natural size.

FIG. 378.—Tarantula killer (*Pepsis marginata* Fab.); somewhat reduced.

ing ground. It has been claimed that in some cases the wasp drags the cicada up trees or bushes several times en route, in order to gain elevation for a fresh start toward its nest. The nests themselves may branch underground several times, each having a terminal chamber for the reception of one or two cicadas and an egg of the wasp.

Another species known as the tarantula killer (Fig. 378) digs nests which it stores with tarantulas, the large hairy spiders of the south and southwest where this insect is found. It is a large and powerful wasp, about two inches long, but in its battles with the tarantula it is not always the victor.

Taking the wasps as a whole, we find an interesting progressive development in the different groups. As regards their habitations, we may perhaps regard the holes dug in the ground as being the simplest, followed by excavations of the pith of woody stems, the construction of mud nests and finally along this line the formation of artistically shaped urns, as progressive steps in architectural ability. The construction of hexagonal cells of paper pulp, first in a single layer, then in several layers surrounded by a paper wrapping and finally much more substantially built to resist exposure to the weather above ground may be regarded as continued progress in this line, the nest of the hornet marking the climax of the series.

Somewhat parallel to this is the nature of the food. The nests in the ground, in plant stems and in mud cells are provisioned with insects stored as food for the young of the forms constructing them; in other words these wasps are parasitic insects. With the appearance of cells of paper pulp, the food changes to a mixture of insects killed and partly chewed up and of plant materials such as pollen. At this same point, also, a change from a solitary to a colonial life begins and as the colony becomes larger the nest increases in size and strength.

There is therefore a progressive development in the insects of these superfamilies, illustrated in nest structure, food and the advance from solitary life to that of a large colony.

*Superfamily* **APOIDEA** (the bees).—The bees familiar to everybody are the bumblebees and the honeybee, but these form a very small part of the insects belonging in this superfamily. Many of the bees are solitary in their habits and are rather small insects and little attention is paid to them. They are important insects, however, valuable to man, as they visit flowers and cross-pollinate the blossoms.

The bees have the first segment of the hind tarsus somewhat enlarged and flattened, and, in those which carry pollen there, hairs are present to aid in this. In addition, the hairs on the thorax are branched or plumose, while in the other Hymenoptera they are simple.

Some of the bees are solitary (Fig. 379) and dig holes in the ground, generally with side pockets in which pollen or pollen and honey are placed as food for the young. An egg is then laid in each pocket. Others lay their eggs in the nests of other bees and are parasites upon them, or inquilines in some cases, consuming the food provided for the rightful inhabitant and starving it. Some construct mud nests; others cut off pieces of leaves or sometimes flower petals, with which they line cavities they excavate in wood, for their nests; and still others tunnel in wood but use no leafy lining. The colonial forms establish their homes in various places and build combs of wax in which to store the pollen and nectar which is their food and that of their young.

Though many of the bees are solitary, there is in some species a tendency to make their holes in groups, forming what are frequently called bee villages. In a number of species this goes still farther, several bees uniting in the excavation of a central burrow but each making lateral passages from this to cells which are her own and in which her own young are produced. If the former could fairly be called villages, it would seem that these last could with equal propriety be described as apartment houses, as has been done. Some of the bee villages include several thousand nests within a few square feet and might even be termed bee cities.

Fig. 379.—Solitary bee; about twice natural size.

Some bees have a rather short hinder lip and are known as the short-tongued bees, but in the majority of these insects the central portion is long and slender, enabling such forms to reach the nectar in long-tubed flowers that would otherwise be inaccessible to them.

The leaf-cutter bees are usually rather small. Their nests are not often noticed, being made in holes (frequently in wood) sometimes dug by the bees themselves, but the leaves which they cut are familiar objects, as the cut is frequently a very true circle or double circle, the piece removed in the latter case being rather oblong with rounded ends. These leaves are used to line the nests.

The large carpenter bees (*Xylocopa*) are about the size of bumblebees but in most cases are easily distinguished from them by the smooth and glossy upper surface of the abdomen. These insects tunnel in wood, often to quite a distance. The tunnels are divided into cells by partitions of wood chips, a partition being built across after each cell has been provided with a mixture of pollen and nectar and an egg.

**Bumblebees** (*Bombus*, etc., of many species).—There are many kinds of bumblebees widely distributed over the globe but none is found native in Australia. They live in colonies during the summer but only the queens (females) survive the winter. In spring the queen (Fig. 380) seeks some suitable place for a nest, generally a hole in the ground; frequently the deserted nest of a field mouse is chosen for the purpose. Here she places a mass of pollen on which she lays some eggs. The larvae that hatch feed upon the pollen and, when full-grown, pupate in silken cocoons from which workers emerge. These are undeveloped females, smaller than the queen, and they now take up the work of the colony, strengthening the cocoons with wax and using them to store honey in. The colony increases in numbers and late in the season males (drones) and females (queens) are also produced and live together until the approach of cold weather, when all but the young queens die, these going to protected places to pass the winter.

FIG. 380.—Queen bumblebee (*Bombus pennsylvanicus* DeG.); natural size.

The value of the bumblebees to man is apparently based upon the fact that in these insects the middle part of the hinder lip (tongue) is longer than in most of the other bees; therefore they visit and cross-pollinate flowers having a nectary so long that the nectar in it, from which honey is made, cannot be reached by the other species, which accordingly do not visit such flowers. One such plant is the common red clover which in the United States is enabled to produce seed chiefly as a result of the visits of bumble-bees. In this way these insects are important aids to those who raise clover seed.

Insects so closely resembling bumblebees that it has incorrectly been said that the latter cannot distinguish them from themselves are often found in bumblebee nests, living there as inquilines. The females of these inquilines (genus *Psithyrus*), however, have no structures on their hind tarsi for carrying pollen. In these inquilines there is no worker caste. The eggs are laid in the bumblebee cells and on hatching the young are fed by the bumblebee workers like their own, and the adults go in and out of the nest without molestation. Whether they have some function beneficial to the insects with which they live and which provide for them is as yet unknown.

**The honeybee** (*Apis mellifera* L.).—There are a number of species of honeybees in the Orient, but only *Apis mellifera*, often called the hive bee, has been introduced into the United States. Of this species there are several races, the first to reach this country being the black or German bee which has a black abdomen. This race spread rapidly, many colonies becoming wild. It has a bad temper, is a rather poor honey gatherer and is less able to protect itself from such insect enemies as the wax moth, which has led to the introduction of the Italian race which is better in these regards and which is now the chief race in this country. It has interbred with the black bee until the latter is now rare in its pure strain.

A colony consists of a queen or fully developed female, workers which are partly developed females and, for a part of the year, drones or males

(Fig. 381). A strong colony will consist of thousands of bees, sometimes over 50,000. The chief purpose of the queen is to lay eggs; the workers care for the developing young, gather food for themselves and the young bees, keep the nest in good condition, build the honeycomb and do all the work necessary for the colony; the drones exist solely to fertilize new queens, taking no part in the work of the colony but feeding upon the food brought in.

The queen bee after beginning to lay eggs has a body about three-quarters of an inch long; the drone has a shorter but stouter body; and the workers are about half an inch long. On the outer surface of the hind tibia in the workers is a "pollen basket," a slightly hollowed area surrounded by a fringe of hairs. Various brush- and comb-like structures on the tibiae and tarsi are used in the process of pollen collection.

Fig. 381.—Honeybee (*Apis mellifera* L.): *a*, drone; *b*, queen; *c*, worker; slightly enlarged. (*From Minn. Agr. Exp. Sta.*)

The life of the queen may be several years. Ordinarily the workers live only a month or two, but those developed in the fall live through the winter and long enough in the spring to care for the young produced at that time. The drones are fewer in number and are driven out and killed by the workers when their usefulness has ended.

Although methods of managing bees have been modified to make bee-keeping practices more efficient the bees themselves follow the same routine of life whether they live in an apiary or in a hollow tree deep in the forest. In an apiary where honey production is the main object the beekeeper furnishes honeycombs already partly formed so his bees can use more of their time gathering nectar. The bees, however, lose none of their ability to produce wax when it may be needed.

Swarming is for the double purpose of relieving colonies that would otherwise become overcrowded and for the establishment of new ones. Many of the details of this process may vary under different conditions. but the usual procedure is about as follows.

When a swarm of bees leaves its former home it consists of the old queen and a large number of workers. In its new home, such as an unoccupied hive box or a hollow tree, the workers clean up the place and make the comb for storage of food supplies and the production of young bees. Some of them gather propolis with which to stop up cracks in the nest. Propolis is a dark-colored sticky material which the bees gather from the buds of trees, particularly poplars, and carry to the nest in their pollen baskets.

At the same time that this work is being done, some of the younger workers begin the production of wax. They feed freely and hang to the walls without working. After about twenty-four hours tiny scales of wax formed in glands on the underside of the abdomen are produced; these are removed and molded by means of the mandibles into honey-combs which are attached at the top of the hive and hang downward more or less parallel to each other.

Each sheet of honeycomb consists of two sets of six-sided cells opening on opposite sides of the comb. The long axis of each cell is tipped slightly upward from the plane in which the comb itself hangs. The base, or inner end, of a cell on one side forms one third of the bases of three cells on the opposite side of the comb. The partition at the inner end of each cell slopes so that the center is its deepest point (Fig. 382). This form

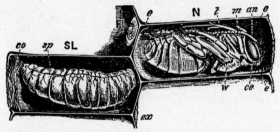

Fig. 382.—Section of comb of honeybee: *FL*, feeding larva in the bottom of its cell; *SL*, larva ready to pupate, spinning its cocoon; *N*, pupa; *an*, antenna; *ce*, compound eye; *co*, cocoon; *e*, excrement; *ex*, exuvium; *m*, mandible; *sp*, spiracle; *t*, tongue; *w*, wing. (*After Cheshire.*)

and arrangement of the cells is such that the greatest amount of storage space is obtained with the least expenditure of wax.

As soon as comb is available, the storage of food and the production of "brood" (young stages of the bee) are begun. In a general manner honey is located toward the top of a comb; next is pollen; and below these is the brood, but this order may be modified according to the needs of the bees.

Worker bees gather pollen in their pollen baskets and bring it to the nest. They also collect nectar from the flowers and carry it in the honey stomach as the crop of the bee is commonly called (Fig. 25, *hs*). At the nest this nectar is expelled into a cell. Here by natural evaporation it becomes more concentrated and, by the action of glandular secretions added by the workers at the time of collection and possibly also during subsequent drawing up of the nectar and expelling it back into the cell, the nectar passes through a ripening process and becomes honey.

The queen lays one egg in the bottom of each empty brood cell, the number apparently depending upon the rate at which nectar is brought in. The eggs hatch in about three days and the stout, white, maggot-like larvae (Fig. 382SL) are fed by young worker bees which secrete a white, paste-like larval food, usually with pollen grains added. "Bee-bread" is pollen stored by the bees and used by newly emerged workers for the development of their bodies and for the production of the larval food. When the worker larvae are nearly full-grown about five days after hatching, the worker bees close their cells with porous wax caps and the larvae within spin silk linings in their cells and pupate. Ten days later they emerge as adults and chew their way out of their cells.

Eggs destined to become drones are unfertilized and are laid in cells of a slightly greater diameter than those in which workers are produced. There are different theories as to the way in which the queen controls fertilization of the eggs she lays. From fertilized eggs both queens and workers are produced.

Queens are developed usually during the late spring and summer months when swarming is most frequent. Special queen cells are constructed, much larger than ordinary cells and often hanging along the lower edge of a comb. When the egg in a queen cell hatches the larva is fed more abundantly than the worker larvae, thus stimulating the growth of the structures typical of the queen. There are often a number of queen cells of different ages in a nest at one time.

The time required to produce a queen from egg to adult is about 15½ days; for a worker, 21 days; and for a drone, 24 days.

When swarming is desirable during late spring or summer, drone and queen cells are constructed and eggs laid in them. When a new queen is about to appear a peculiar sound is heard in the nest, called a piping sound, which is generally believed to be made by the young queen as she gnaws her way out. This seems to be a signal that a swarm must prepare to start and the old queen often tries to locate the queen cell to kill the young queen before she escapes. If for any reason swarming at that time (*e.g.*, a heavy shower coming) is not desirable, it is said that the workers do not prevent this action by the queen; if swarming conditions are satisfactory the workers keep her from stinging the queen cell and shortly the old queen and many workers leave the nest together and generally settle on some tree or other object for a time before flying to their new home. How this is located is not apparently positively known but it is generally thought that scout bees have been sent out to find a place and the swarm waits for their return.

The part of the colony remaining in the old nest consists of a virgin queen—possibly several of them—workers and drones. When the first new queen emerges she usually explores the brood cells searching for other queens which have not yet escaped, and if she finds them, stings them to assure her supremacy. If other queens have also escaped it is usually the case that they fight until all but one are killed, though occasionally nests with more than one queen are found. A few days later the queen leaves the nest some good day for a flight during which she mates, after which she returns to take up her duties as queen of the colony.

If this new queen happens to be killed while on her mating flight, or if in her struggle with other young queens in the nest all are killed, the nest is without a queen unless younger queen cells are present. If not, the workers search for an egg or a worker brood cell containing a larva two and one-half to three days old. If such are present, the cell walls are torn down and a queen cell is built around it and its food is changed to the more nutritious material fed to queen bee larvae and in this way a queen is produced. If no egg or worker larva young enough can be found, however, the colony cannot hope to obtain a queen and it breaks up.

The greatest value of the honeybee to man is in the pollination of blossoms to produce crops of seeds and fruit. The direct financial returns from the production of honey and wax amount to many millions of dollars each year. The annual honey crop in the United States is from 150 to 200 million pounds. Beeswax amounts to several millions of pounds.

# CHAPTER XXXIV

## ANIMALS OTHER THAN INSECTS

The entomologist is expected to recommend control measures for a number of common pests that are not insects. Although most of these animals are Arthropoda, principally mites and ticks, other phyla are represented.

### PHYLUM MOLLUSCA

Various **snails and slugs** belonging to the phylum Mollusca are injurious to garden and greenhouse crops. The snails bear coil-like shells upon their backs, and the slugs although much like the snails are without shells. They are soft, slimy animals, mottled gray, brown or almost black, and varying in length from less than an inch to several inches. They have no legs but travel in a slimy secretion which dries behind them as a shiny trail. Feeding is largely at night on succulent leaves, mushrooms and fruit. The eggs which are laid in soft, jelly-like masses, generally under boards or rubbish, hatch in the spring and the young animals may take a year or more to reach full growth.

*Control.*—The snails and slugs may be collected at night where they feed or during the daytime where they hide under piles of weeds, boards or other objects resting on the ground. Lime, if it will not come in contact with growing plants, may be applied to the surface of the soil or it may be placed in a band around seedbeds. The band is effective, however, only as long as it remains dry and dusty. Poisoned bran baits or cooked potatoes dusted with white arsenic or Paris green, a potato for about two square feet of treated area, are effective. Solutions of corrosive sublimate may be applied to the soil as directed for the control of earthworms.

### PHYLUM NEMATHELMINTHES

**Nematodes, or eelworms,** belong to the phylum Nemathelminthes. They are mostly small, even microscopic, whitish, unsegmented worms. The eggs are laid in the soil and the young worms penetrate tender roots where their activities lead to the formation of root galls. Severe infestations may affect the host plants seriously.

*Control.*—Infested greenhouse soil is most effectively treated by steam sterilization. In the field nematodes are controlled chiefly by crop rota-

371

tion and summer fallowing, although soil fumigation with such chemicals as chloropicrin is sometimes recommended.

## PHYLUM ANNELLIDA

The earthworms, common representatives of the phylum Annellida, are familiar to everyone. Although they are generally considered beneficial as earth builders because they loosen and renovate the soil, their work is not appreciated so much when their castings are found in abundance on lawns and golf greens.

*Control.*—The best treatment is to sprinkle the surface of the ground with a solution of two ounces of mercuric chloride (corrosive sublimate or bichloride of mercury) in fifty gallons of water, which is then washed into the soil with liberal applications of water. As soon as the worms are reached by the solution they will come to the surface and die. It is important to remember that this chemical is highly poisonous and care should be taken in handling it. Because the solution corrodes metal containers, the sprinkling cans and other utensils used in its preparation and application should be rinsed thoroughly after use.

## PHYLUM ARTHROPODA

In this group (see Chap. I) are numerous animals of economic importance in addition to the insects. They are found in those major divisions (called classes) Crustacea, Diplopoda and Arachnida.

Sowbugs (class Crustacea).—These little animals (Fig. 2), sometimes also known as pill bugs or wood lice, are commonly found on damp ground under stones, boards or dead leaves, or in damp basements. Outdoors they attack small plants, especially the roots, and are often pests of mushrooms. In basements they seldom do much damage unless vegetables are stored there, but their mere presence is undesirable.

*Control.*—As sowbugs feed at night it is sometimes possible on a small scale to pick them by hand with the aid of a light. Where large numbers are congregated under boards or other objects they may be destroyed with hot water or a contact spray. Basements should be made tight around the windows and doors, well ventilated on dry days and closed in wet weather. Boxes and other stored articles should be raised from the floor and set out from the walls to allow for air circulation to eliminate surface dampness. Raw potatoes cut in pieces and smeared with Paris green or sodium fluoride and placed where the sowbugs feed are usually a good control. A poison bran bait like that recommended for cutworms (page 276), placed in small amounts near where the animals are found, is generally effective.

Millipedes (class Diplopoda).—These creatures, sometimes spoken of wrongly as wireworms, are often called thousand-leggers. The common kinds, much smaller than the one shown in Fig. 3, average from one to one and one-half inches in length when full-grown. They are generally cylindrical, dark brown in color, and with two pairs of short legs to each of the numerous body segments. Most of them coil up, something like a coil spring, when disturbed. Their food is chiefly decaying vegetable matter, including manure, at or just below the surface of the ground, although they occasionally eat small roots and seeds, and bores holes in larger roots, tubers and bulbs as well as fruits that lie upon the ground.

*Control.*—The same baits that are recommended for the control of sowbugs and also the mercuric chloride soil treatment used against earthworms are often effective against millipedes. Frequent cultivation of the ground and allowing it to lie fallow for a time are helpful, as nothing is left for the animals to feed upon.

**Spiders, ticks, and mites** (class Arachnida) are the best known or the most important economically of the various types of animals included in the class Arachnida. The spiders belong to the order Araneida, and the ticks and mites to the order Acarina. The principal characteristics of Arachnida have already been pointed out in the first chapter.

**Spiders** have an unwarranted reputation for being generally poisonous and harmful. They are, on the contrary, decidedly beneficial because of the numbers of destructive insects that they consume. Those spiders which are most feared in the United States, the southern

Fig. 383.—Female black widow spider (*Latrodectus mactans* Fab.): enlarged about one half; seen from below, showing the hour-glass shaped red spot. (*After Baerg, Ark. Agr. Exp. Sta.*)

tarantulas (belonging to the superfamily Avicularioidea) and the black widow (*Latrodectus mactans* F.), bite only under considerable provocation (Fig. 383). The black widow appears to be the most dangerous of all North American spiders. Although fatalities occur due to its bite, relatively few persons are bitten and most of these recover. The adult spider is small, nearly black in color, with rather long legs and smooth body. On the underside of the body is an orange-red marking of variable shape but usually like an hourglass.

In the spiders the head and body are distinct, but in the ticks and mites they are not clearly separated. Furthermore, in the order Acarina the newly hatched young have only six legs whereas the older nymphs and the adults have eight. The ticks are much larger than the mites.

*Family* IXODIDÆ.—A number of species in this family of ticks are highly important because they transmit certain diseases of animals and man (see Figs. 7 and 8).

**The cattle tick** (*Boophilus annulatus* Say).—This species has been a serious pest of cattle in the southern states. The eggs are laid on the ground and the young "seed ticks" climb up on plants and from there get on to cattle. Here they feed on the blood until full-grown, when the females are about half an inch long. Then they drop to the ground and lay eggs for another generation. In infected ticks there are microscopic Protozoa, and during feeding on the blood these tiny parasites enter the cattle and feed within the red blood cells, producing "Texas fever." Cattle thus infected develop a fever which affects their health so seriously that many die; others become emaciated, the milk production falls off and the value of the hides is much reduced. The disease was within recent years present in all the states from Virginia south and west to Texas inclusive, and also in southern California. In 1906 the Bureau of Animal Industry, conjointly with the states concerned, took up eradication work and at the end of 1941 only small areas in Florida and Texas remained infested. This elimination of the ticks has been accomplished either by dipping the cattle in arsenical and other washes or by pasture rotation.

**The Rocky Mountain spotted-fever tick** (*Dermacentor andersoni* Stiles).—This tick occurs in the northern Rocky Mountain region in the United States and northward into Canada. It is the most important carrier of Rocky Mountain spotted fever in this area, and also disseminates tularemia. It is frequently responsible for tick paralysis.

The unfed adults pass the winter on the ground in grass and leaves. During the spring months they attach themselves to passing cattle, horses, man or other large animals, and feed upon blood from these hosts. After mating, the full-fed females drop to the ground where they lay several thousand eggs, usually during June or July. In a few weeks the eggs hatch and the young six-legged "larvae" or seed ticks feed on the blood of mice and other rodents. After molting to the eight-legged nymphal stage they overwinter. In the second year they must find another host such as a rabbit or mouse, obtain more blood, again drop to the ground, and finally molt the last time. Two years is the common period for the development of one generation, but three or four years may be required.

Rocky Mountain spotted fever is a rodent disease highly fatal to man in the Bitterroot Valley of western Montana and dangerous elsewhere, including eastern localities where it is carried by the American dog tick. Tularemia is another rodent disease transmitted by various kinds of insects and ticks among wild and domestic animals as well as man.

*Control.*—Great care should be exercised not to allow the ticks to fasten themselves to the body. In areas where the ticks are highly infected with spotted fever it may be advisable to be vaccinated against that disease. When ticks become fastened to the skin they should be removed in such a manner that the mouth parts are not left behind in the skin, either by a steady pull or by the application of gasoline or turpentine to the tick. Domestic animals may be dipped as for the cattle tick during the spring months through June, the only time when either the spotted-fever tick or the American dog tick feeds upon the larger animals and man.

**The American dog tick** (*Dermacentor variabilis* Say).—This species is common throughout the central and eastern United States, and is known frequently as the wood tick. It carries both spotted fever and tularemia. The life history and control on animals are similar to those for the spotted-fever tick. Derris dusts and washes may be used to free dogs of tick infestations.

*Family* **TROMBIDIIDÆ** (the harvest mites and chigger mites).—The young stages of these mites are parasitic, mostly on arthropods and vertebrates.

**Chiggers** (*Eutrombicula alfredugesi* Oud., formerly known as *Leptus irritans* Riley).—These mites, often also known as jiggers or red bugs, occur east of the Rocky Mountains as far north as Massachusetts, Ohio and southern Minnesota but are much more abundant southward. Another species occurs in the west. Chiggers in their early stages live normally on land turtles, snakes, rabbits and other animals, but they do bite man, causing much irritation from the poison they introduce during feeding. A place around each bite the size of a dime or larger becomes reddened, accompanied by intense itching.

Chiggers lay their eggs in the spring. The young six-legged "larvae," the only stage that is parasitic, get on to animals and man from grass and underbrush. After becoming full fed they drop to the ground, molt and pass the quiescent nymphal stage in the soil. In the late fall they change to adults and spend the winter in the ground. The adults are scavengers and feed on decaying wood.

*Control.*—Sulfur dusted freely into the clothing before going out in infested localities is quite effective as a protection against the attacks of chiggers. Bathing in strong soapsuds within three or four hours after exposure is nearly always effective. If the presence of chiggers is not suspected until the irritation has begun, little can be done except to kill the mites and relieve the irritation by application of household ammonia. To avoid scratching and subsequent infection of the bites the itching should be relieved with soothing ointments or lotions.

*Family* **TETRANYCHIDÆ** (spider mites or spinning mites).—These mites usually spin silk where they feed on tender plant tissues.  Many of them are called red spiders although some are not red.

**The common red spiders** (*Tetranychus* species).—The so-called red spiders are very common and important pests of world-wide distribution.  They are usually not red but pale yellowish or greenish.  Tiny light spots on the leaves are produced by their sucking mouth parts which are inserted into the under surface.  This species is common outdoors on many plants but also thrives particularly well under the hot, dry conditions that frequently prevail in greenhouses.  Under average conditions a generation requires a month or less.  Frequent forceful watering of greenhouse plants is effective when it is not a harmful practice from the standpoint of the plants.  The nature and effectiveness of control measures depends largely upon the kind of plant that is involved.  Fine dusting sulfur and sprays of derris or the newer synthetic contact insecticides are used commonly in red spider control.  Summer strength lime-sulfur or oil emulsions (1 or 2 per cent oil) are often used outdoors.  It is important to reach the undersides of the leaves with a spray delivered under high pressure.

A recent discovery that a 2 per cent phthalic glyceryl alkyd resin in water spray kills all stages of the red spiders without injury to the plants, though still needing further tests, promises to be a good treatment for this pest.

**The cyclamen mite** (*Tarsonemus pallidus* Banks) is an imported species now common in greenhouses everywhere in the United States.  Although cyclamen is the most injured the mite occurs on a variety of ornamental greenhouse plants. **The European red mite** (*Paratetranychus pilosus* Canestr. and Fanz.) is an imported pest of deciduous fruit and shade trees that is now important in northeastern North America and in the Pacific northwest.  Dormant sprays, usually with oil emulsions containing at least 2.5 per cent oil and applied to the overwintering egg stage on twigs, are the best control for this species. **The clover mite** (*Bryobia prœtiosa* Koch) injures the leaves of various trees and of clover and many other plants.  The minute, spherical red eggs are often found in large numbers on the twigs of fruit trees in winter.  In fall, the reddish adults seeking places in which to hibernate often enter near-by houses in large numbers; such infestations may be eradicated with a kerosene spray.

*Family* **PARASITIDÆ** (the gamasid mites).—These species, often given the family name Dermanyssidae, are mostly parasitic on animals although some are free living.

**The chicken mite** (*Dermanyssus gallinœ* DeG.).—This species feeds mainly at night on the blood of fowls, and hides during the day in cracks around roosts, nests and elsewhere in poultry houses.  The mites frequently become numerous enough to reduce the egg production of the hens and to affect seriously the health of the poultry. They may be controlled by cleanliness, elimination of hiding places and the repeated treatment of floors, walls, roosts and nests with kerosene or preferably with two parts crankcase oil or similar material thinned with one part kerosene. Creosote sprays are often used effectively.

*Family* **TYROGLYPHIDÆ.**—These mites are not parasitic but live on dried or decaying organic substances. *Tyroglyphus farinæ* DeG. is a common species known, with a few related species, as the flour mite, the grain mite or the cheese mite, according to the food consumed by it. Frequently serious injury to various products is caused by these mites. The bulb mite (*Rhizoglyphus hyacinthi* Bdv.) is a whitish introduced species which hides and feeds among the bud scales of such common flowering bulbs as crocus, lily, amaryllis and others. Its attacks result in rotten bulbs which fail to produce any healthy growth. It is controlled frequently by submerging dormant bulbs for three hours in water heated carefully to 110 to 111.5°F.

*Family* **SARCOPTIDÆ.**—These mites cause various types of itch and mange in the skin of mammals and some birds.

**The itch mite** (*Sarcoptes scabiei* DeG.).—One strain of the itch mite infests man and other strains cause "sarcoptic mange," a dry scabby condition, in horses, dogs, hogs and other animals. The female mites burrow beneath the skin and lay their eggs there. The itch mites differ from mites of other families in that they spend their entire life cycle on the animal host. Cleanliness and the use of sulfur ointments (one part sulfur to eight parts lard; and other recipes) serve to control the itch mite on man. Lime-sulfur dips are effective in controlling mange on those animals for which it is suitable. Sulfur ointments may be used also in the control of mange of horses, dogs and cats.

**The scab mite** (*Psoroptes communis* Feurst.).—This species, besides occurring on some other animals, is a serious pest of sheep and causes the trouble known as sheep scab or scabies ("psoroptic mange" in contrast to the "sarcoptic mange" discussed previously). The scab mite feeds on the surface of the skin instead of beneath the surface. Both lime-sulfur and creosote dips are used for control of this pest.

*Family* **ERIOPHYIDÆ** (gall mites).—These mites feed on plant juices, causing galls and other plant deformities by their feeding activities. Each gall has an opening, thus differing from the galls of Hymenoptera and Diptera. These mites are more elongate in general than those of other families. An example is **the citrus rust mite** (*Phyllocoptes oleivorus* Ashm.), one of the three most important citrus pests of the Gulf states. It causes a russeting of citrus fruit. Control is with sulfur dusts and sprays.

# INDEX

379

## L

## M